AF571822

ALLE · ZEIT · WACH
1842

11 Progress in Molecular and Subcellular Biology

Edited by
P. Jeanteur, Y. Kuchino,
W.E.G. Müller (Managing Editor),
P.L. Paine

With 13 Figures

Springer-Verlag Berlin Heidelberg New York
London Paris Tokyo Hong Kong

Prof. Dr. Werner E. G. Müller
Physiologisch-Chemisches Institut
Abt. Angewandte Molekularbiologie
Duesbergweg 6
6500 Mainz, FRG

Dr. Yoshiyuki Kuchino
National Cancer Center
Research Institute
Tsukiji 5-chome
Chuo-ku, Tokyo 104, Japan

Prof. Dr. Philippe Jeanteur
UA CNRS 1191
Laboratoire de Biologie Moléculaire
Université des Sciences et Technique
du Languedoc
34060 Montpellier Cedex, France

Prof. Dr. Philip L. Paine
Department of
Biological Sciences
St. John's University
Grand Central & Utopia Parkways
Jamaica, New York 11439, USA

ISBN 3-540-51832-0 Springer-Verlag Berlin Heidelberg New York
ISBN 0-387-51832-0 Springer-Verlag New York Berlin Heidelberg

The Library of Congress has catalogued this serial publication as follows:
Library of Congress Catalog Card Number 75-79748

Typesetting: Thomson Press India Ltd., New Delhi, India
Printing and bookbinding: Konrad Triltsch, Graphischer Betrieb, Würzburg
2131/3145-543210 – Printed on acid-free paper

Contents

L. PHI-VAN and W.H. STRÄTLING: Association of DNA with Nuclear Matrix

D.D. NEWMEYER: Nuclear Import in Vitro

Contributors

You will find the addresses at the beginning of the respective contribution.

Association of DNA with Nuclear Matrix

L. PHI-VAN[1,2] and W. H. STRÄTLING[1]

A. Introduction

There is increasing evidence that chromosomal DNA is attached to a nuclear skeleton or matrix. The composition and morphology of the matrix appears to be highly complex in keeping with the long list of known and postulated functions, which seems to include nearly all important processes of the nucleus, such as transcription, RNA processing and transport, replication, and the organization of interphase chromatin. A significant problem is, however, that nuclear matrices are operationally defined structures and that results obtained by use of different methods are not comparable. Depending on various reports, the matrix contains a more-or-less wide spectrum of nonhistone proteins but few of these (mostly enzymes) have been identified (Razin et al. 1981; Smith and Berezney 1983; Staufenbiel and Deppert 1983; Berrios et al. 1985; Jackson and Cook 1986; Lehner et al. 1986; Pieck et al. 1987; Tubo et al. 1987; Tubo and Berezney 1987a, b, c; Fey and Penman 1988). A class of major structural proteins such as the histones in chromatin or the lamins in the nuclear lamina has not yet been found in nuclear matrix preparations. The matrix, when prepared with 2 M NaCl and DNase I digestion (Berezney and Coffey 1974), further contains less than 1% of the nuclear DNA. Several laboratories have studied the distribution of nuclear DNA in matrices. Repeatedly, actively transcribed genes and their flanking sequences were found to be enriched in nuclear matrices (Jackson et al. 1981; Robinson et al. 1982; Ciejek et al. 1983; Hentzen et al. 1984; Jost and Seldran 1984; Rose and Garrard 1984; Strätling et al. 1986; Strätling 1987). An enrichment of repeated DNA sequences in nuclear matrix preparations was also reported (Goldberg et al. 1983; Chimera and Musich 1985).

B. MAR Elements and Their Properties

The structure in metaphase chromosomes thought to be homologous to the skeleton in interphase nuclei is called the scaffold. Both structures are believed to

[1] Institut für Physiologische Chemie, Universitäts-Krankenhaus Eppendorf, Martinistr. 52, 2000 Hamburg 20, FRG

[2] Present address: Kernforschungszentrum Karlsruhe, Institut für Genetik und Toxikologie, Postfach 3640, 7500 Karlsruhe, FRG

organize chromosomal DNA into domains or loops. While general evidence for this model has been gathered by biochemical and electron microscopic studies in the late 1970s and early 1980s (Benyajati and Worcel 1976; Cook and Brazell 1976; Paulson and Laemmli 1977; Igo-Kemenes and Zachau 1978; Lebkowski and Laemmli 1982), the relationship of the loop organization of chromatin to specific sequences has become apparent since 1984. In 1984, Mirkovitch et al. reported that the tandemly repeated histone genes of *Drosophila melanogaster* are attached in histone-depleted nuclei to the matrix (= scaffold) via specific sites located within a defined fragment of the H1-H3 spacer. Secondly, in two hsp70 heat shock gene loci they found attachment sites upstream of the promoter regions and of regulatory elements. Since this first report, the matrix attachment regions (= MARs = SARs = MAR elements) of four other genes and within a 320 kb region around the rosy and Ace loci of *Drosophila* have been mapped by Laemmli and co-workers (Gasser and Laemmli 1986b; Mirkovitch et al. 1986; Mirkovitch et al. 1988) (see Table 1). In *Drosophila*, MAR elements occur in the nontranscribed flanking regions and are found in most, but not all, cases in one, occasionally two, copies upstream as well as downstream of the gene. MAR elements can bracket one or several transcription units. A surprise was the

Table 1. List of MAR elements

Drosophila melanogaster	Reference
Histone-gene repeat	
hsp70 (87A7 locus)	Mirkovitch et al. (1984)
hsp70 (87C1 locus)	
Alcohol dehydrogenase	
Sgs-4	Gasser and Laemmli (1986b)
Fushi tarazu	
Region of rosy and Ace loci	Mirkovitch et al. (1986)
Actin 5C	Mirkovitch et al. (1988)
Yeast	
ARS elements: ARS1, HO ARS,	
Histone H4 ARS, HMR-E ARS, 2 μm	Amati and Gasser (1988)
Plasmid ARS	
Centromer elements: CENIII, CENIV, CENXI	
Chicken	
Lysozyme	Phi-Van and Strätling (1988)
Mouse	
Immunoglobulin κ light chain	Cockerill and Garrard (1986)
Immunoglobulin heavy chain locus	Cockerill et al. (1987)
Chinese hamster	
Dihydrofolate reductase	Käs and Chasin (1987)
Human	
ß-Interferon	Bode and Maaß (1988)
ß-globin gene locus	Jarman and Higgs (1988)
Plants	
Soybean leghemoglobin	Izaurralde et al. (1988)

detection of a MAR element within the immunoglobin κ light chain gene of the mouse adjacent to the enhancer (Cockerill and Garrard 1986a) and of two MAR elements immediately upstream and downstream, respectively, of the enhancer in the immunoglobulin heavy chain locus of the mouse (Cockerill et al. 1987). Intragenic MAR elements were further found in the fourth intron region of the Chinese hamster dihydrofolate reductase gene (Käs and Chasin 1987) and in the second intron of the human ß-globin gene (Jarman and Higgs 1988). On the other hand, the MAR elements of the chicken lysozyme gene were localized to sequences 8.86 and 1.3 kb upstream and downstream, respectively, of the gene and were found to comap with the boundaries of the "active" chromatin domain of the gene (Phi-Van and Strätling 1988). The flanking regions of the human ß-interferon gene contain three very large MAR elements encompassing together approximately 15 kb (Bode and Maaß 1988). Eight MAR elements were found within 90 kb of the human ß-globin gene complex (Jarman and Higgs 1988). Two are located near the boundaries of the regulatory domain and two others are close to known enhancer elements of the ß-globin gene. In contrast, no MAR element could be detected in the same study within 140 kb of the human α-globin gene complex. Finally, MAR elements were also found near plant genes such as the soybean leghemoglobin gene (Izaurralde et al. 1988).

Two methods are presently available to detect MAR elements. In the first one, isolated nuclei are treated with the detergent lithium 3,5-diiodosalicylate (LIS) to remove histones and other nuclear constituents (Mirkovitch et al. 1984). The protruding DNA loops that form halos around the nuclei are then digested with appropriate restriction endonucleases. The resulting samples are centrifuged to separate the released DNA fragments from the associated ones. The purified DNA samples are displayed by agarose gel electrophoresis and transferred to filters for hybridization with cloned probes. In the second one (Cockerill and Garrard 1986a), radiolabeled, cloned restriction fragments are incubated in the presence of prokaryotic competitor DNA with matrices prepared by the method of Berezney and Coffey (1974). The matrix-associated fragments are purified, electrophoretically resolved, and visualized by autoradiography. At a first glimpse, the LIS technique seems to analyze the in vivo situation, while the matrix-incubation method is clearly an in vitro assay. However, fragments containing MAR elements bind specifically to LIS-extracted nuclei during or after digestion with restriction endonucleases (Mirkovitch et al. 1984). This raises the possibility that at least some fragments containing MAR elements bind to matrices after extraction and restriction endonuclease cleavage. In fact, the LIS technique was recently modified by Izaurralde et al. (1988) by incubating labeled fragments with extracted or digested halos. Thus the LIS technique and the method described by Cockerill and Garrard (1986a) have several features in common.

When looking at the properties of the MAR elements listed in Table 1, it is difficult to find features which are common to all MAR elements reported up to now. MAR elements were found in flanking regions as well as in coding sequences, indicating that their function is independent of their relative position.

MARs located in the flanking regions of a particular gene normally map relatively close to that gene. Further, most MAR elements were detected in single-copy sequences, when analyzed by Southern hybridization to whole genomic DNA (possible exception: ß-interferon MAR elements). Some sequence MAR elements exhibit a relatively high A-T content (Cockerill and Garrard 1986a; Cockerill et al. 1987; Phi-Van and Strätling 1988), but A-T richness per se is not sufficient to define matrix attachment regions, since regions flanking the 5′-MAR element of the immunoglobulin heavy chain locus and the lysozyme gene are as A-T rich as the MAR elements themselves (Cockerill et al. 1987; Phi-Van and Strätling 1988). Similarly, some MAR elements contain A-rich and T-rich stretches (so-called A-boxes and T-boxes) but again these are not sufficient to define matrix attachment regions, since flanking sequences also contain such stretches (Cockerill et al. 1987; Phi-Van and Strätling 1988). Nevertheless, as demonstrated by the competition experiments between MAR elements from different genes and species (see below), MAR elements are expected to contain either very similar (probably short) sequences or (probably short) sequences with very similar structures. It is conceivable that the recognition of MAR elements by the matrix is not determined by a specific sequence but by a specific structure fulfilled by several different sequences. A precedent for this may be the α-protein, a high mobility group protein recognizing a configuration of the minor groove in the α-satellite DNA (Solomon et al. 1986). In some MAR elements, such as the MAR elements of the *Drosophila* histone-gene repeat, alcohol dehydrogenase gene, Sgs-4 gene, hsp70 heat shock gene at the locus 87A7 and the mouse immunoglobulin κ light chain gene, sequences similar to the consensus sequence of the topoisomerase II cleavage site are clustered (Cockerill and Garrard 1986a; Gasser and Laemmli 1986b; Gasser and Laemmli 1987). In other cases such sequences are not clustered in MAR elements (Cockerill et al. 1987; Phi-Van and Strätling 1988). The possibility remains that topoisomerase II cleavage sites in MAR elements play a role in determining the superhelical density of looped domains (Cockerill and Garrard 1986a), but it may be noted that such sites are expected to localize within loops and not necessarily in MAR elements. Although significant attachment-relevant similarities between the sequences of different MAR elements can thus not be detected, they must exist, since it has been shown in many cases that matrix binding of a given MAR element is competed for by other MAR elements (Cockerill and Garrard 1986a; Izaurralde et al. 1988; Phi-Van and Strätling 1988). For example, the *Drosophila* histone MAR element is an effective competitor for the binding of the mouse immunoglobulin κ light chain MAR element to matrices from mouse plasmacytome nuclei (Cockerill and Garrard 1986a). As a second example, binding of the chicken lysozyme 5′ MAR element to chicken oviduct matrices is effectively competed by MAR elements from *Drosophila* and mouse genes (Phi-Van and Strätling 1988). Computational analysis of the MAR elements in the mouse and rabbit immunoglobin κ light chain genes, the mouse immunoglobulin heavy chain locus, and the *Drosophila* hsp70 heat shock locus 87A7 had revealed periodically repeated sequence elements known to generate an intrinsic curvature of the DNA (Anderson 1986).

The best-characterized MAR element is located in the non-transcribed H1-H3 spacer of the *Drosophila* histone-gene repeat (Mirkovitch et al. 1984). Exonuclease III digestion studies showed that it consists of two matrix-binding domains, each encompassing approximately 200 bp (Gasser and Laemmli 1986a). The MAR elements of the immunoglobulin heavy chain locus flanking the enhancer were delimited by the matrix-DNA-binding assay to 406 bp and 350 bp fragments, respectively (Cockerill et al. 1987). Other MAR elements are much larger and contain multiple matrix binding sites (Gasser and Laemmli 1986b; Phi-Van and Strätling 1988, Bode and Maaß 1988). It appears that the binding sites within some of these MAR elements are redundant with respect to in vitro matrix attachment.

Very little is known about the matrix structure, to which MAR elements are attached. Chicken oviduct matrices recognize the chicken lysozyme MAR elements as specifically as a *Drosophila* or a mouse MAR element (Phi-Van and Strätling 1988). Similarly a mouse MAR element is specifically bound by yeast nuclear matrices (Cockerill and Garrard 1986b). Further, several *Drosophila* MAR elements bind with similar specificity to matrices derived from rat liver, HeLa, and *Drosophila* nuclei (Izaurralde et al. 1988). The interchangeability between yeast, *Drosophila* and vertebrate matrix structures, as well as *Drosophila* and vertebrate MAR elements, suggests an evolutionary conservation of the basic mechanism of MAR element attachment. The molecule or molecules within the matrix (probably proteins) determining the attachment are not known. Topoisomerase II, although a major structural protein in matrices (Berrios et al. 1985), is unlikely to fulfill this function, since topoisomerase II levels within a particular cell are rather a reflection of the proliferative state of that cell (Heck and Earnshaw, 1986). Further, the remnants of the matrices derived from hen erythrocytes, which lack any topoisomerase II (Heck and Earnshaw 1986), specifically bind MAR elements, although with a slightly reduced affinity relative to matrices from oviduct nuclei (Phi-Van and Strätling 1988).

Although not explicitly said, the loop model evolved by Laemmli and coworkers (Paulson and Laemmli 1977; Lebkowski and Laemmli 1982) assumes a direct alignment of loops without intervening regions. Yunis and Bahr (1979), however, reported in an electron microscopic study an alternating arrangement of loops and extended fiber segments in human interphase chromatin. This shows that the organization of loops in general as well as of particular loops at the chromosomal level is not at all yet clear.

C. Roles of MAR Elements in DNA Packaging and DNA Replication

To fold a meter of DNA into a 10-μm-diameter mammalian cell nucleus is surely a difficult task. DNA packaging is achieved at a basal level by winding of the DNA into nucleosomes and at a second level by folding of the nucleofilament into 30-nm fibers (Brasch 1976; Klug et al. 1980). Condensation of chromatin by formation of loops operates independently of these two levels of packaging. Thus loops in transcribed regions may contain disrupted nucleosomes, while loops in inactive regions and in chromosomes contain 30-nm or even thicker fibers (Tanaka and Iino 1973).

In the last few years it has become increasingly accepted that the sites of DNA synthesis and the origins of DNA replication are associated with the nuclear matrix. While the origins of DNA replication are known in some viral molecules, our information on these sites around cellular genes comes mostly from yeast. In yeast, autonomous replicating sequences (ARSs) have been defined, which confer on plasmids the ability to be maintained autonomously as minichromosomes. For one of these, ARSI, it has been shown to serve as an origin of replication (Brewer and Fangman 1987). In addition, the ARS element on the yeast 2 μm circle plasmid serves as an origin of replication (Brewer and Fangman 1987). Fragments containing these two elements have now been demonstrated to be attached to yeast matrices prepared with LIS (Amati and Gasser 1988). Very similar results were obtained with the histone H4 ARS, the HO ARS and the HMR-E ARS. In addition, the centromer regions from yeast chromosomes III, IV, and XI were found to be matrix-attached (Amati and Gasser 1988). Competition experiments with ARS1 and CENIII showed that both elements share one common binding site. In the amplified dihydrofolate reductase gene domain in CHO cells, the earliest replicating portion was localized to a 4.3 kb fragment that maps 14 kb downstream from the gene (Burhans et al. 1986). Two MAR elements were, however, localized to the fourth intron region (Käs and Chasin 1987). To test a role of the matrix in the putative function of an origin of replication 3′ to the dihydrofolate reductase gene, it will be necessary to analyze the matrix attachment of the 4.3 kb fragment.

D. A Likely Function of MAR Elements in Gene Expression

As mentioned above, many but not all described MAR elements contain clustered sequences similar to the consensus of the 15 bp topoisomerase II cleavage site [GTN(A/T)A(T/C) ATTNATNN(G/A)]. Udvardy et al. (1985) have shown that the MAR element of the *Drosophila* histone-gene repeat and the hsp70 heat shock genes are preferred sites for topoisomerase II cleavage in vitro. In vivo, topoisomerase II cleaved at multiple specific sites at the 5′ and 3′ ends of the hsp70 genes, but not in the 5′ MAR elements, unless the cells were heat-shocked (Rowe et al. 1986). The topoisomerase II cleavage sites in MAR elements may thus represent sites used to modulate gene expression (Gasser and Laemmli 1987).

The position of a universally found sequence element with respect to the coding region or to regulatory elements can be highly indicative for its function. MAR elements have been mapped to coding sequences as well as to flanking regions. Interestingly, many MAR elements in both positions are located close to cis-acting elements required for high levels of transcription and its developmental and tissue-specific regulation. The 5′ MAR elements of the *Drosophila* Sgs-4 and *fushi tarazu* genes were mapped to restriction fragments which contain upstream regulatory sequences of these genes (Gasser and Laemmli 1986). (This does not exclude the possibility that more refined mapping experiments might separate both types of elements). For the mouse immunoglobulin κ light chain gene and heavy chain locus, the MAR elements were found adjacent to the respective enhancer elements (Cockerill and Garrard 1986 and 1987). In the case of the chicken lysozyme gene, the 5′ MAR element is separated from the nearest putative regulatory element (hypersensitive site) by at least 1.05 kb (Phi-Van and Strätling 1988). Although MAR elements thus do not always map adjacent to transcriptional control elements, it may be noted that a distance of 1.05 kb is small compared to the 6.1-kb distance of the major lysozyme enhancer from the start site of transcription. Further, compared to the mostly large distances between genes and gene families in higher encaryotes, MAR elements map rather close to the respective genes and apparently within the functional units. Finally it is interesting that the feature of MAR elements to exert their function in a manner relatively independent of distance and position with respect to the coding region is highly reminiscent of the transcriptional enhancer elements.

It has been pointed out previously (Gasser and Laemmli 1987) that some MAR elements comap with the boundaries of "active" chromatin domains. The best example for this situation is the chicken lysozyme gene (Phi-Van and Strätling 1988). In the oviduct, where this gene is expressed, the nucleosomal organization of the domain bracketed by the MAR elements is disrupted, while the chromatin structure 5′ and 3′ of the domain exhibits a normal nucleosome repeat (Strätling et al. 1986). Other examples are the human ß-interferon gene and the *Drosophila* H1-H3 spacer region, in which two MAR elements coincide with micrococcal nuclease-protected, nucleosome-size regions (Samal et al. 1982).

In electron microscope pictures of interphase chromatin, using the routine "Miller" spreading technique, a nuclear matrix is not visible. Apparently, the conditions to spread chromatin by this technique are such that the nuclear matrix is disassembled. Thus transcription on the extrachromosomal amplified rRNA transcriptional units of *Xenopus laevis* and other species is normally seen as tandemly repeated regions with lateral fibrils of gradually increasing length. However, in one report on transcription of rDNA in oocytes of *Acheta domesticus* (house cricket) these units were observed to occur also as looped structures often further coiled into snail-shell-like aggregates (Trendelenburg et al. 1973). In those genes, which contain intragenic MAR elements (immunoglobulin κ light chain, immunoglobulin heavy chain, dihydrofolate reductase, ß-globin), the DNA matrix complex apparently does not impede transcription (Lorch et al. 1987).

The chicken lysozyme domain bracketed by 5′ and 3′ MAR elements contains the gene and all known regulatory elements required for tissue and stage specific expression of the gene (Fritton et al. 1984; Phi-Van and Strätling 1988). Other examples might be the *Drosophila* histone-gene cluster, Sgs-4 gene, and *fushi tarazu* gene (Mirkovitch et al. 1984; Gasser and Laemmli 1986b). This suggests that some MAR elements might define positionally independent, functional units (Gasser and Laemmli 1987). Unless P-elements contain MAR elements, previous P-element transformation experiments using constructs, which contain either the *fushi tarazu* gene and both its 5′ MAR element and a 1.3-kb segment of its 3′ MAR element or only the gene and the 5′ MAR element, may lend support to this suggestion (Hiromi et al. 1985). When both MAR elements were present in the transforming plasmid, all transformants showed high levels of expression, but when just the 5′ one was present, only three of seven transformants showed high expression levels. A function of MAR elements in gene expression is also shown in studies generating stable transfectants of a chicken macrophage cell line by use of constructs, which contain the chloramphenicol-acetyl-transferase gene either fused to the lysozyme promoter, or to the lysozyme promoter and the lysozyme −6.1-kb enhancer. When the transcription units contained in both constructs are flanked on both sides by lysozyme 5′ MAR elements, gene expression is enhanced by a factor of about ten relative to transfectants, which contain the constructs lacking MAR elements (Stief et al. 1989). Notably, an effect on gene expression is only observed in stable transfectants, but not in transiently transfected cells. The MAR elements in the integrated copies of the constructs are attached to LIS-extracted, digested nuclei (Phi-Van, unpublished). Similarly, in transfectants containing multiple copies of the dihydrofolate reductase gene the integrated MAR elements are attached to LIS-extracted, digested nuclei (Käs and Chasin 1987).

The MAR elements in the flanking regions of the *Drosophila* hsp70 heat shock, *fushi tarazu*, alcohol dehydrogenase, and Sgs-4 genes and of the histone-gene repeat bind to scaffolds of *Drosophila* metaphase chromosomes (Mirkovitch et al. 1988). On the other hand, the intragenic MAR elements of the dihydrofolate reductase gene are not attached to scaffolds prepared from metaphase chromosomes, but attachment is regained within 2 h after mitosis (Käs and Chasin 1987). This difference may be either due to technical problems in the procedure, or may be indicative for the division of the MAR elements into two subgroups, i.e., intragenic ones not attached and flanking ones attached to metaphase chromosomes. Another puzzling observation is that the distribution of MAR elements over 320 kb around the *Drosophila* rosy and Ace loci does not correlate with the distribution of chromomeres in this region (Mirkovitch et al. 1986). Thus it is possible that two general classes of loops occur in nuclei. One class of loops is relevant for the structural organization of interphase chromatin and chromosomes (Yunis and Bahr 1979), while the other class is required for specific functions of the nucleus, such as efficient transcription or replication.

References

Amati BB, Gasser SM (1988) Chromosomal ARS and CEN elements bind specifically to the yeast nuclear scaffold. Cell 54:967–978

Anderson JN (1986) Detection, sequence patterns and function of unusual DNA structures. Nucleic Acids Res 14:8513–8533

Benyajati C, Worcel A (1976) Isolation, characterization, and structure of the folded interphase genome of *Drosophila melanogaster*. Cell 9:393–407

Berezney R, Coffey D (1974) Identification of a nuclear protein matrix. Biochem Biophys Res Commun 60:1410–1419

Berrios M, Osheroff N, Fisher PA (1985) In situ localization of DNA topoisomerase II, a major polypeptide component of the *Drosophila* nuclear matrix fraction. Proc Natl Acad Sci USA 82:4142–4146

Bode J, Maass K (1988) Chromatin domain surrounding the human interferon-ß gene as defined by scaffold-attached regions. Biochemistry 27:4706–4711

Brasch K (1976) Studies on the role of histones H1 (f1) and H5 (f2c) in chromatin structure. Exp Cell Res 101:396–410

Brewer BJ, Fangman WL (1987) The localization of replication origins origins on ARS plasmids in *S. cerevisiae*. Cell 51:463–471

Burhans WC, Selegue JE, Heintz NH (1986) Isolation of the origin of replication associated with the amplified Chinese hamster dihydrofolate reductase domain. Proc Natl Acad Sci USA 83:7790–7794

Chimera JA, Musich PR (1985) The association of the interspersed repetitive KpnI sequences with the nuclear matrix. J Biol Chem 260:9373–9379

Ciejek EM, Tsai M-J, O'Malley BW (1983) Actively transcribed genes are associated with the nuclear matrix. Nature 306:607–609

Cockerill PN, Garrard WT (1986a) Chromosomal loop anchorage of the kappa immunoglobulin gene occurs next to the enhancer in a region containing topoisomerase II sites. Cell 44:273–282

Cockerill PN, Garrard WT (1986b) Chromosomal loop anchorage sites appear to be evolutionarily conserved. FEBS Lett 204:5–7

Cockerill PN, Yuen M-H, Garrard WT (1987) The enhancer of the immunoglobulin heavy chain locus is flanked by presumptive chromosomal loop anchorage elements. J Biol Chem 262:5394–5397

Cook PR, Brazell IA (1978) Spectrofluorometric measurement of the binding of ethidium to superhelical DNA from cell nuclei. Eur J Biochem 84:465–477

Fey EG, Penman S (1988) Tumor promoters induce a specific morphological signature in the nuclear matrix-intermediate filament scaffold of Madin-Darby canine kidney (MDCK) cell colonies. Proc Natl Acad Sci USA 85:121–125

Fritton HP, Igo-Komenes T, Nowock J, Strech-Jurk U, Theisen M, Sippel AE (1984) Alternative sets of DNase I-hypersensitive sites characterize the various functional states of the chicken lysozyme gene. Nature 311:163–165

Gasser SM, Laemmli UK (1986a) The organization of chromatin loops: characterization of a scaffold attachment site. EMBO J 5:511–518

Gasser SM, Laemmli UK (1986b) Cohabitation of scaffold binding regions with upstream/enhancer elements of three developmentally regulated genes of *D. melanogaster*. Cell 46:521–530

Gasser SM, Laemmli UK (1987) A glimpse at chromosomal order. Trends Genet 3:16–22

Goldberg GI, Collier I, Cassel A (1983) Specific DNA sequences associated with the nuclear matrix in synchronized mouse 3T3 cells. Proc Natl Acad Sci USA 80:6887–6891

Heck MMS, Earnshaw WC (1986) Topoisomerase II: a specific marker for cell proliferation. J Cell Biol 103:2569–2581

Hentzen PC, Rho JH, Bekhor I (1984) Nuclear matrix DNA from chicken erythrocytes contains ß-globin gene sequences. Proc Natl Acad Sci USA 81:304–307

Hiromi Y, Kuroiwa A, Gehring WJ (1985) Control elements of the *Drosophila* segmentation gene fushi tarazu. Cell 43:603–613

Igo-Kemenes T, Zachau J (1978) Domains in chromatin structure. Cold Spring Harbor Symp Quant Biol 42:109–118

Izaurralde E, Mirkovitch J, Laemmli UK (1988) Interaction of DNA with nuclear scaffolds in vitro. J Mol Biol 200:111–125

Jackson DA, Cook PR (1986) Different populations of DNA polymerase α in Hela cells. J Mol Biol 192:77–86

Jackson DA, McCready SJ, Cook PR (1981) RNA is synthesized at the nuclear cage. Nature 292:552–555

Jarman AP, Higgs DR (1988) Nuclear scaffold attachment sites in the human globin gene complexes. EMBO J 7:3337–3344
Jost J-P, Seldran M (1984) Association of transcriptionally active vitellogenin II gene with the nuclear matrix of chicken liver. EMBO J 3:2005–2008
Käs E, Chasin LA (1987) Anchorage of the Chinese hamster dihydrofolate reductase gene to the nuclear scaffold occurs in an intragenic region. J Mol Biol 198:677–692
Klug A, Rhodes D, Smith J, Finch JT, Thomas JO (1980) A low resolution structure for the histone core of the nucleosome. Nature 287:509–516
Lebkowski JS, Laemmli UK (1982) Evidence for two levels of DNA folding in histone-depleted Hela interphase nuclei. J Mol Biol 156:309–324
Lehner CF, Eppenberger HM, Fakan S, Nigg EA (1986) Nuclear substructure antigens. Monoclonal antibodies against components of nuclear matrix preparations. Exp Cell Res 162:205–219
Lorch Y, LaPointe JW, Kornberg RD (1987) Nucleosomes inhibit the initiation of transcription but allow chain elongation with the displacement of histones. Cell 49:203–210
Mirkovitch J, Mirault M-E, Laemmli UK (1984) Organization of the higher-order chromatin loop: specific DNA attachment sites on nuclear scaffold. Cell 39:223–232
Mirkovitch J, Spierer P, Laemmli UK (1986) Genes and loops in 320,000 base-pairs of the *Drosophila melanogaster* chromosome. J Mol Biol 190:255–258
Mirkovitch J, Gasser SM, Laemmli UK (1988) Scaffold attachment of DNA loops in metaphase chromosomes. J Mol Biol 200:101–109
Paulson JR, Laemmli UK (1977) The structure of histone-depleted metaphase chromosomes. Cell 12:817–828
Phi-Van L, Strätling WH (1988) The matrix attachment regions of the chicken lysozyme gene co-map with the boundaries of the chromatin domain. EMBO J 7:655–664
Pieck ACM, Rijken AAM, Wanka F (1987) Nuclear matrix and chromosome scaffold preparations of in vitro cultured bovine liver cells have two proteins in common. FEBS Lett 212:276–280
Razin SV, Chernokhvostov VV, Roodyn AV, Zbarsky IB, Georgiev GP (1981) Proteins tightly bound to DNA in the regions of DNA attachment to the skeletal structures of interphase nuclei and metaphase chromosomes. Cell 27:65–73
Robinson SI, Nelkin BD, Vogelstein B (1982) The ovalbumin gene is associated with the nuclear matrix of chicken oviduct cells. Cell 28:99–106
Rose SM, Garrard WT (1984) Differentiation-dependent chromatin alterations precede and accompany transcription of immunoglobulin light chain genes. J Biol Chem 259:8534–8544
Rowe TC, Wang JC, Liu LF (1986) In vivo localization of DNA topoisomerase II cleavage sites on *Drosophila* heat shock chromatin. Mol Cell Biol 6:985–992
Samal B, Worcel A, Louis C, Schedl P (1982) Chromatin structure of the histone genes of *D. melanogaster*. Cell 23:401–409
Smith HC, Berezney R (1983) Dynamic domains of DNA polymerase α in regenerating rat liver. Biochemistry 22:3042–3046
Solomon MJ, Strauss F, Varshavsky A (1986) A mammalian high mobility group protein recognizes any stretch of six AT base pairs in duplex DNA. Proc Natl Acad Sci USA 83:1276–1280
Staufenbiel M, Deppert W (1983) Different structural systems of the nucleus are targets for SV40 large T antigen. Cell 33:173–181
Stief A, Winter DM, Strätling WH, Sippel AE (1989) A nuclear DNA attachment element mediates elevated and position-independent gene activity. Nature 341:343–345
Strätling WH (1987) Gene-specific differences in the supranucleosomal organization of rat liver chromatin. Biochemistry 26:7893–7899
Strätling WH, Dölle A, Sippel AE (1986) Chromatin structure of the chicken lysozyme gene domain as determined by chromatin fractionation and micrococcal nucleus digestion. Biochemistry 25:495–502
Tanaka K, Iino (1973) Demonstration of fibrous components in hepatic interphase nuclei by high resolution scanning electron microscopy. Exp Cell Res 81:40–46
Trendelenburg MF, Scheer U, Franke WW (1973) Structural organization of the transcription of ribosomal DNA in oocytes of the house cricket. Nature New Biol 245:167–170

Tubo RA, Berezney R (1987a) Pre-replicative association of multiple replicative enzyme activities with the nuclear matrix during rat liver regeneration. J Biol Chem 262:1148–1154
Tubo RA, Berezney R (1987b) Identification of 100 and 150 S DNA polymerase α-primase megacomplexes solubilized from the nuclear matrix of regenerating rat liver. J Biol Chem 262:5857–5865
Tubo RA, Berezney R (1987c) Nuclear matrix-bound DNA primase. Elucidation of an RNA priming system in nuclear matrix isolated from regenerating rat liver. J Biol Chem 262:6637–6642.
Tubo RA, Martelli AM, Berezney R (1987) Enhanced processivity of nuclear matrix bound DNA polymerase α from regenerating rat liver. Biochemistry 26:5710–5718
Udvardy A, Schedl P, Sander M, Hsieh T (1985) Novel partitioning of DNA cleavage sites for *Drosophila* topoisomerase II. Cell 40:933–941
Yunis JJ, Bahr GF (1979) Chromatin fiber organization of human interphase and prophase chromosomes. Exp Cell Res 122:63–72

Nuclear Import in Vitro

D. D. Newmeyer[1]

A. Overview of Nuclear Import

The eukaryotic cell, divided into several compartments, is faced with the problem of how to put macromolecules where they should be. For example, an mRNA molecule transcribed in the nucleus must move to the cytoplasm to be translated. Its protein product can either remain soluble in the cytoplasm or it can enter one of several different organelles or the cytoskeleton. The processes by which proteins and RNAs reach their final destinations are of great interest to cell biologists. In this review we will concentrate on one route of intracellular traffic, the import of macromolecules into the cell nucleus, with specific emphasis on. certain in vitro systems recently devised for studing nuclear import. Before discussing these in vitro systems, we will summarize some of what is known about nuclear import in vivo. The reader may also wish to refer to other reviews on nuclear import (Bonner 1978; Paine and Horowitz 1980; De Robertis 1983; Dingwall 1985; Dingwall and Laskey 1986; Newport and Forbes 1987; Silver and Hall 1987).

I. Nuclear Import Occurs Through the Nuclear Pore

Biologists have long known that the nuclear boundary is unusual (Bahr and Beerman 1954; Gall 1954; Watson 1955). Whereas many organelles are enclosed by a single membrane, the nuclear envelope is surrounded by *two* lipid bilayers. The outer nuclear membrane is studded with ribosomes, much like the rough endoplasmic reticulum, and is sometimes seen to be connected to the ER (Watson 1955). Furthersome, there are many proteins in common between nuclear and ER membranes (Fahl et al. 1978; Richardson and Maddy 1980; Matsuura et al. 1981; Gerace et al. 1982), and the nuclear membrane performs many of the biosynthetic functions of the ER (Franke et al. 1981; Smith and Wells 1983; Puddington et al. 1985). In fact, some have argued that the nuclear membrane may be a "generator"

---

[1] La Jolla Cancer Research Foundation, 10901 North Torrey Pines Road, La Jolla, California 92037, USA

of the ER membrane (Kessel et al. 1986; Pathak et al. 1986). This might suggest that the nuclear membrane is little more than a specialized ER cisterna. One might also imagine that macromolecules could enter the nucleus and the ER by analogous mechanisms.

However, the nuclear membrane is decidedly different from the ER, in at least two respects: (1) the nuclear membrane appears in the electron microscope to be "perforated" at many places. The sites of fenestration, called nuclear pores, are in fact large macromolecular assemblies with a regular structure (Franke 1974; Maul 1977; Franke et al. 1981; Unwin and Milligan 1982; Milligan 1986). (2) The nucleoplasmic face of the inner nuclear membrane is lined with a network of protein filaments known as the nuclear lamina (Gerace and Blobel 1980; Franke et al. 1981, Krohne and Benavente 1986; Aebi et al. 1986; Newport and Forbes 1987). We refer to the outer and inner membranes, nuclear pores, and nuclear lamina collectively as the nuclear envelope.

These morphological distinctions hint that the nuclear envelope is also different from the ER in function. In particular, import of macromolecules into the nuclear interior porbably occurs by a pathway much different from transport into the ER. Even if nuclear proteins were to enter the lumen of the nuclear envelope (the region between the outer and inner membranes, sometimes called the perinuclear space) by means similar to those used by proteins to enter the ER, they would still need to cross the inner nuclear membrane and the nuclear lamina to reach the nuclear interior. Certain viruses employ this route to enter or leave the nucleus. For example, herpes simplex virus is known to move from the nucleus to the cytoplasm by budding through the nuclear membrane (Darlington and Moss 1968; Poliquin et al. 1985), acquiring a double envelope coat in the process. SV40 may enter the nucleus through both the outer and inner membranes, losing its envelope along the way (Hummeler et al. 1970). Another possible path into the nucleus is suggested by work of Torrisi et al. (1987), which shows that the two nuclear membranes are connected: proteins can diffuse freely between the inner and outer membranes. In theory, proteins could bind to the outer membrane, diffuse laterally along the membrane, and then pass through the membranous region at the periphery of the nuclear pore, finally reaching the inner nuclear membrane (see Fig. 2 for a diagram illustrating the topology of the nuclear membrane in the pore.) From the inner membrane, proteins could be released into the nuclear interior by proteolysis or some other mechanism. It is also conceivable that proteins could be imported through both membranes simultaneously at a place where the membranes contact one another, as is thought to occur for import into chloroplasts (Pain et al. 1988) and mitochondria (Schleyer and Neupert 1985); such membrane contact sites in the nuclear envelope are not usually seen, however.

Despite these possibilities, the central channel of the nuclear pore is nevertheless the major port of entry into the nucleus. That the pores can permit the passage of large macromolecules was first shown by Stevens and Swift (1966), who observed in the electron microscope certain large messenger RNP particles of *Chironomus* salivary glands in the central channels of nuclear pores en route to the cytoplasm. Early ultrastructural studies also showed that certain viruses discharge their macromolecular contents through the nuclear pore into the nucleus (Summers 1971; Morgan et al. 1969). However, these studies did not determine the molecular weights of the macromolecules traversing the pores. The first clear demonstration that large nuclear proteins can be imported into the nucleus via the nuclear pore came only recently. Feldherr et al. (1984) coated collodial gold particles with the nuclear protein nucleoplasmin and injected them into *Xenopus* oocytes. In the electron microscope, the nucleoplasmin-coated gold paricles were seen to enter the nucleus through the nuclear pores. Particles as large as 20 nm in diameter were seen in the pores, demonstrating that the pore can transport large rigid objects. This result also implies that macromolecules need not be unfolded in order to pass through the nuclear pore, a fact further distinguishing nuclear import from systems in which proteins must cross a lipid bilayer (Eilers and Schatz 1988). Newmeyer and Forbes (1988) and Dworetzky et al. (1987) found that the nuclear import signal of SV40 T-antigen (discussed in Sect. A.IV) also directs transport through the nuclear pores. It is likely, then, that the nuclear pore is the site of nuclear entry for most, if not all, nuclear proteins, if we accept that nucleoplasmin and SV40 T-antigen are typical of proteins accumulating in the nucleus. Nevertheless, it remains possible that some proteins enter the nucleus by passing through the nuclear membrane.

II. The Structure and Composition of the Nuclear Pore

The nuclear pore is unlike molecular pores found in single membranes: it is an eightfold symmetric macromolecular complex, ca. 100 nm in diameter, that spans and joins two separate lipid bilayers. Electron microscopy and image reconstruction techniques (Figs. 1, 2) reveal an elaborate structure (Unwin and Milligan 1982; Milligan 1986). The pore complex is composed of two stacked rings or annuli, each in contact with a lipid membrane. Eight particles can be seen attached to the ring at the cytoplasmic face of the pore. In the plane midway between the rings, there are eight connections, called “spokes”, radiating between the circumference and center of the pore. In isolated nuclear envelopes, fibers can sometimes be seen extending from the rings outward into the cytoplasm and inward towards the nucleoplasm (Franke et al. 1981; Richardson et al. 1988). (In Sect. C. we will discuss a hypothetical role of these fibers in the mechanism of nuclear import.) Some pores contain a central plug, a large granule that may be a ribonucleoprotein particle in transit through the central channel (Unwin and Milligan 1982; Milligan 1986).

Because the pore has been difficult to isolate cleanly away from other components of the nuclear envelope, its protein composition is ill-defined. Until recently only one pore-associated protein, gp190, had been identified (Gerace et al. 1982). Gp190 is not part of the pore per se but is probably present in both the nuclear membrane and nuclear lamina near the pore and may help anchor the pore in the nuclear envelope. Work in several laboratories has now identified a

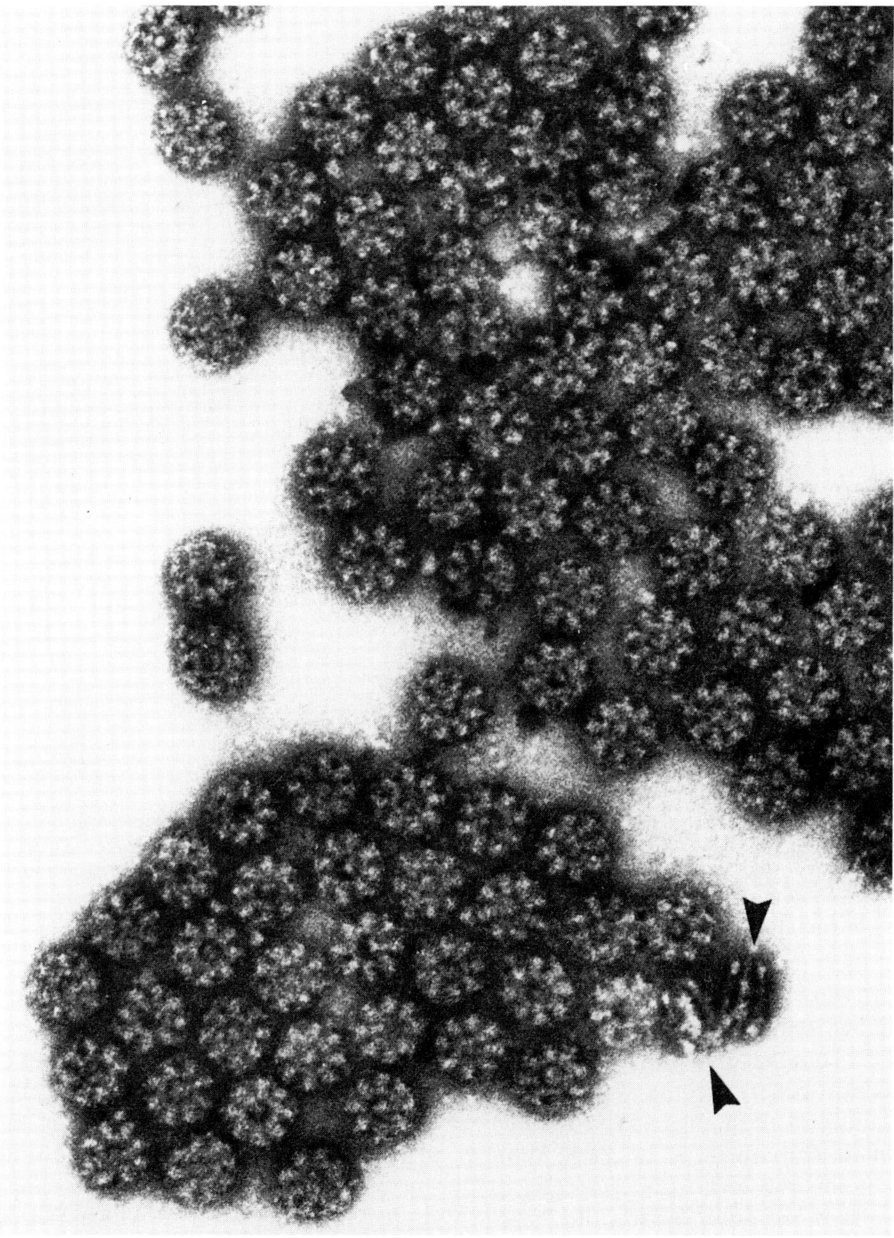

Fig. 1. A cluster of pore complexes released from the nuclear envelope or annulate lamellae by incubation in 0.1% Triton X-100. Two pores shown edge-on are indicated by *arrows*; the rest are *en face*. Detail of a figure from Milligan (1986)

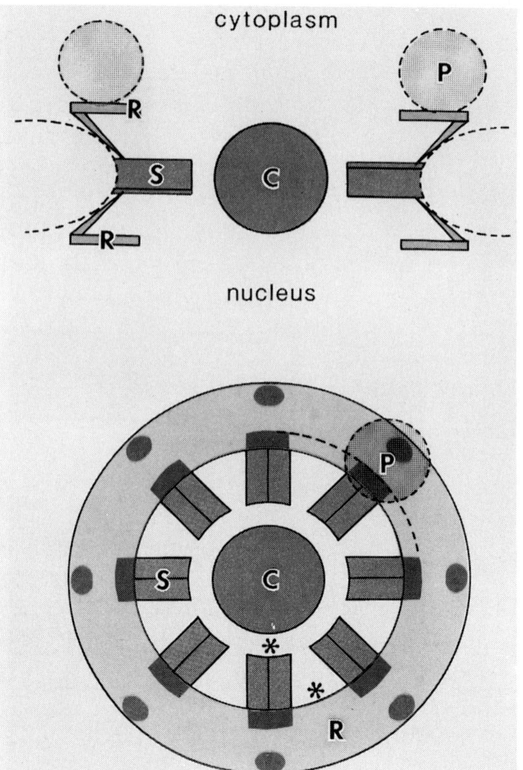

Fig. 2. Schematic representation of the nuclear pore complex in central cross-section (*top*) and in projection down the octad axis (*bottom*). Several features are indicated: spokes (*S*), each composed of two domains or subunits, rings (*R*), and a central plug (*C*). *Dashed lines* mark additional features seen in pore complexes in the nuclear envelope: the nuclear membrane border and large particles (*P*) resembling ribosomes. These particles are easily detached and not always present (Milligan 1986)

new class of nuclear envelope glycoproteins (Holt and Hart 1986; Davis and Blobel 1986; Finlay et al. 1987; Holt et al. 1987; Schindler et al. 1987; Snow et al. 1987; Hanover et al. 1987; Park et al. 1987), at least some of which are found in the pore proper. The lectin, wheat germ agglutinin (WGA), inhibits nuclear import by binding to these proteins in the nuclear pore (Finlay et al. 1987; Yoneda et al. 1987b; Dabauvalle et al. 1988; Wolff et al. 1988). Some of these WGA-binding proteins may participate directly in the process of macromolecular transport through the pore. In Sect. B.I.4 we will discuss possible ways in which WGA might inhibit nuclear import.

III. Functional Properties of the Nuclear Pore

The passive permeability properties of the nuclear envelope have been well characterized (see reviews by Bonner 1978; Paine and Horowitz 1980; Peters

1986). The nuclear envelope is permeable to small solutes, biologically inactive molecules such as dextran polymers below a certain size (Paine et al. 1975; Lang and Peters 1984; Peters et al. 1986; Lang et al. 1986; Schulz and Peters 1987), and certain proteins that enter but do not become concentrated in the nucleus (Gurdon 1970; Bonner 1975a, De Robertis et al. 1978; Dabauvalle and Franke, 1984, 1986; Stacey and Allfrey 1984). Because dextrans are not likely to pass through two lipid membranes and the nuclear lamina, their entry into the intact nuclei of living cells almost certainly reflects the permeability properties of the nuclear pore. Indeed, as Feldherr has shown using electron microscopy, the pore does have a central channel through which particles can diffuse. Polyvinylpyrrolidone (PVP)-coated gold particles up to 4.5–14.5 nm diameter can be seen in these central channels (Feldherr 1962, 1965, 1966; there is some variation between species in the limiting size of PVP-coated gold particles that can enter the pore). The rates of influx of fluorescent dextrans have been used to calculate the effective diameter of the pore channel, yielding values between 9 and 11 nm (reviewed by Paine and Horowitz 1980; Peters 1986). The diffusion channel of the pore is therefore much smaller than the total width of the pore complex, ca. 100 nm. The general conclusion reached by these studies is that the nuclear pore is a molecular sieve. Dextrans below about 20 kDa, and globular proteins below about 70 kDa in molecular mass can equilibrate between nucleus and cytoplasm by diffusion through the pores. [Myosin, a large protein, also equilibrates between nucleus and cytoplasm (Stacey and Allfrey 1984) presumably because it is rod-shaped and can pass through the pore lengthwise.]

The nuclear pore functions more subtly than a simple molecular sieve, however. Many proteins and RNP particles much larger than 70 kDa not only enter the nucleus, but accumulate there rapidly (Bonner 1975a, b; De Robertis et al. 1978; De Robertis et al. 1982; Lanford et al. 1986; Yoneda et al. 1987a; and many other reports). As mentioned is Section A.I., electron microscope studies show that the pore can allow the passage of large macromolecular complexes and protein-coated particles (Stevens and Swift 1966; Feldherr et al. 1984; Dworetzky and Feldherr 1988). Moreover, while the pore is permeable to small macromolecules indiscriminately, it allows entry only to certain large macromolecules, those destined for the nucleus. Hypothetical mechanisms of pore function therefore need to account for both the nonselective diffusion of small macromolecules and the selective transport of larger ones.

Are all pores alike? Although it is possible that some pores are specialized, the evidence so far indicates that at least most of the pores are functionally homogeneous. The studies of Feldherr et al. (1984) suggest that most, if not all, pores in the *Xenopus* oocyte can import nucleoplasmin. Newmeyer and Forbes (1988) found the same result using an *in vitro* system based on extracts of *Xenopus* eggs (see section B): both nucleoplasmin and the SV40 T-antigen signal sequence (signal sequence will be discussed in the next section) are recognized by nearly all pores. Dworetzky and Feldherr (1988) extended this question to ask whether a given pore can engage in both the import of proteins and the export of RNA. These authors labeled tRNA with small (5 nm) gold particles and nucleoplasmin with larger ones (20 nm). They then injected the tRNA-gold into the oocyte nucleus and nucleoplasmin-gold into the cytoplasm. The tRNA-gold particles were seen to be exported from the nucleus into the cytoplasm through the nuclear pores, while nucleoplasmin-gold particles, as expected, entered the nucleus through the pores. Many pores had both small (RNA-coated) and large (nucleoplasmin-coated) gold particles passing through them. Thus many, and probably all, pores are capable of bidirectional transport.

IV. Signals for Nuclear Accumulation

Is there a property of nuclear macromolecules that allows them to enter and accumulate in the nucleus, despite being too large to pass through the nuclear pore by simple diffusion? Studies of Bonner (1975a, b) and De Robertis et al. (1978) showed that many soluble nuclear proteins reaccumulate in the *Xenopus* oocyte nucleus after microinjection into the cytoplasm. Thus the ability to accumulate in the nucleus is a property of the mature protein and therefore does not involve cleavage of a signal sequence, as usually occurs when protein precursors enter mitochondria (reviewed by Douglas et al. 1986; Hurt and Van Loon 1986) and the endoplasmic reticulum (reviewed by Walter et al. 1984; Garoff 1985; Shekman 1985; Rapoport 1986; Rothman 1987; Pfeffer and Rothman 1987). Dabauvalle and Franke (1982) found that nuclear proteins translated in vitro and later microinjected in the cytoplasm of oocytes were able to accumulate in the nucleus. Proteins are therefore not required to enter the nucleus co-translationally. It makes sense that mature nuclear proteins retain their nuclear targeting signals, considering that nuclear proteins are often dispersed throughout the cytoplasm during mitosis and must reenter the daughter nuclei afterwards (e.g., the lamin proteins, Gerace and Blobel 1980).

Dabauvalle and Franke (1982) coined the adjective “karyophilic” to describe proteins that become concentrated in the nucleus. As shown by Bonner (1975a, b) and De Robertis et al. (1978), there are also proteins that equilibrate between nucleus and cytoplasm, presumably because they are small enough to diffuse through the nuclear pore. Furthermore, some proteins are strictly cytoplasmic. Certain of these proteins might be excluded from the nucleus, either because they are simply too large to diffuse through the pore, or because they are complexed with other large proteins or macromolecular assemblies. However, Dabauvalle and Franke (1984, 1986) found an interesting class of nonnuclear proteins (called “karyophobic”) that stay in the cytoplasm, despite being small enough to diffuse through the nuclear pore. These karyophobic proteins exist in the cell in a mobile, low-molecular-weight (perhaps monomeric) state, since they can diffuse into small-pore gel filtration beads implanted in the cytoplasm of *Xenopus* oocytes. How the nucleus excludes these proteins is still unknown.

In a classic experiment, Dingwall et al. (1982) pursued the nuclear localization signal of the *Xenopus* oocyte protein nucleoplasmin. The accumulation of nucleoplasmin in the nucleus was found to depend on a protease-sensitive domain called the "tail"; the protease-resistant "core" of nucleoplasmin fails to accumulate in the nucleus. Nucleoplasmin is a pentamer of identical 20 kDa subunits, and partial proteolysis yields a mixture of molecules having between zero and five tails. The tailless core pentamer is excluded from the nucleus, but pentamers with one to five tails (and also the tail itself) accumulate in the nucleus. The rate of accumulation increases as more tails are present per molecule.

This experiment identified the nucleoplasmin tail as a signal domain specifying nuclear accumulation of the nucleoplasmin molecule. Later, molecular genetic studies showed that nuclear localization signals consist of very short stretches in the primary amino acid sequences of nuclear proteins. Hall et al. (1984) made systematic deletions in the coding sequence for yeast MATα2 (a nuclear protein), fused genetically to the *E. Coli* gene for β-galactosidase. A short (13-amino acid) sequence at the N-terminus of MATα2 was sufficient to cause the fusion protein to be associated with the nucleus. (However, this is not the whole story: see section A.V.) Lanford and Butel (1984) and Kalderon et al. (1984b) studied mutations in the large T-antigen of SV40 that caused this protein to lose its nuclear accumulation capacity, and Kalderon et al. (1984a) identified regions of the T-antigen coding sequence that targeted T-antigen/pyruvate kinase or T-antigen/β-galactosidase fusion proteins to the nucleus. What emerged is that a seven-amino-acid sequence (pro-lys-lys$_{128}$-lys-arg-lys-val) within T-antigen is necessary and sufficient for its nuclear accumulation. Point mutations at lys$_{128}$ and (to a lesser extent) lys$_{129}$ and other surrounding residues (Kalderon et al. 1984b; Smith et al. 1985; Lanford et al. 1988) result in a defect in nuclear targeting. Signal sequences or domains have been identified for several other nuclear proteins, including polyoma T-antigen (Richardson et al. 1986), nucleoplasmin (Bürglin and De Robertis 1987; Dingwall et al. 1987) and others (Silver et al. 1984; Munro and Pelham 1984; Davey et al. 1985; Moreland et al. 1985, 1986, 1987; Krippl et al. 1985; Richter et al. 1985; Gritz et al. 1985; Wychowski et al. 1986). The presence in nuclear proteins of signals for nuclear accumulation argues for the existence of a molecule recognizing these signals that is involved in the nuclear import process. In Sections A.VII. and B.I.4., we will cite other evidence for the existence of such a signal-sequence receptor.

No consensus sequence for nuclear targeting has emerged from these studies, although many of the signals have a preponderance of the basic amino acid residues lysine and arginine. However, it appears that overall charge is not the determining characteristic, but rather how the charges are positioned spatially (Lanford et al. 1988). The SV40 T-antigen signal sequence seems to function as an autonomous entity, since its function is largely insensitive to location in the primary sequence of the protein (Roberts et al. 1987). Indeed, recent work has shown that this nuclear targeting signal peptide can also function when covalently attached to a non-nuclear protein. Goldfarb et al. (1986) and Lanford et al. (1986, 1988) coupled synthetic peptides corresponding to the SV40 T-antigen nuclear signal sequence to proteins of various sizes that would normally be excluded from the nucleus. Conjugates of proteins to the wild-type signal accumulated in the nucleus, even for proteins as large as ferritin (465 kDa). On the other hand, conjugates of these proteins with mutant peptides known to be transport-defective in native T-antigen were not transported into the nucleus.

V. The Effect of Multiple Nuclear Targeting Signals in a Protein

These studies and those of Dingwall et al. (1982), Richardson et al. (1986) and Roberts et al. (1987), found that the rate and extent of nuclear accumulation of a protein are increased when it contains multiple signal sequences. In particular, Roberts et al. (1987) found that the presence of two or three copies of a transport signal could compensate for a partial defect in that signal. This may explain why some proteins have more than one nuclear import signal (Richardson et al. 1986; Hall and Fried 1987; Kleinschmidt and Seiter 1988; Silver and Hall 1988). The *Xenopus* oocyte protein N1, for example, has two nuclear targeting signals, neither of which is sufficient for nuclear accumulation by itself (Kleinschmidt and Seiter 1988).

A possible role for multiple signal sequences was suggested by Hall and Fried (1987) and Silver and Hall (1988), who speculated that the presence of multiple signals may mean that each signal participates in a different step in the import process. Their hypothesis is motivated by the observation that the yeast MATα2 protein appears to have two signals: one in the middle of the protein and one at the N-terminus (Hall et al. 1984). The internal signal by itself is sufficient for accumulation of MAT*α2 inside* the nucleus. However, the N-terminal signal is not sufficient: Hall and Fried (1987) state that in the absence of the internal signal, the N-terminal signal causes the associated fusion protein to bind to the nuclear envelope in a punctate manner, suggesting association with the nuclear pores (M.N. Hall, C. Craik, G. Mullenback, and Y. Hiraoka, unpubl. data). Hall and colleagues propose that one signal may be required for binding to the pore, the second for translocation into the nucleus. Alternatively, Silver and Hall (1988) proposed that the two signals could act together in a signal step.

The idea that nuclear import is a multi-step process now has direct experimental support. Results of Newmeyer and Forbes (1988) and Richardson et al. (1988) demonstrate that nuclear import can indeed be separated into two steps: binding to the pore and translocation through the pore (See Sect. B.I.4.). However, the model of Hall and colleagues (two signals, one for each step) is difficult to reconcile with what is known about the nuclear import signal of SV40 T-antigen: this seven-amino-acid signal by itself is perfectly adequate for nuclear accumulation (Kalderon et al. 1984a; Goldfarb et al. 1986; Lanford et al. 1986; Yoneda et al. 1987a). Moreover, Newmeyer and Forbes (1988) showed explicitly that the SV40 T-antigen signal (present in multiple copies attached covalently to a nonnuclear protein) was able to mediate both pore binding and translocation through the pore.

On the other hand, this same T-antigen signal sequence, when present in a different β-galactosidase fusion protein, was found by Bonnerot et al. (1987) not to cause intranuclear accumulation, but instead to produce punctate binding at the nuclear envelope (again, perhaps reflecting association of the signal sequence with the nuclear pores). Richardson et al. (1988) found that the nucleoplasmin tail domain, when tagged with colloidal gold, could bind to the nuclear pore but was not translocated into the nucleus, even though the tail domain by itself is capable of accumulating in the nucleus (Dingwall et al. 1982). The reason for lack of translocation through the pore in these two instances is obscure. Nevertheless, the observations suggest that a nuclear import signal can have different effects in different molecular environments.

Roberts et al. (1987) have made a more methodical study of the effect of protein context on the nuclear targeting activity of the SV-40 T-antigen signal. These authors made five different constructs, in each of which the nuclear import signal was inserted in a different place in the coding sequence for chicken pyruvate kinase. In four of these positions the signal lead to nuclear accumulation, whereas in the fifth position the signal was inactive. Mapping the insertion sites in the known crystal structure of cat muscle pyruvate kinase led to the idea that the signal is active when exposed on the surface of the protein but not when buried in a hydrophobic domain. One implication of these results is that when a protein contains an amino acid sequence similar to a known nuclear transport signal, one cannot necessarily conclude that the sequence functions as an import signal in *that* protein. These results also suggest a possible mechanism for regulating nuclear import: masking and unmasking of a signal sequence. Masking could occur through a conformational change in the protein itself or by binding to a second protein.

VI. Is There a Role for Intranuclear Binding in Nuclear Import?

Because the nuclear pore behaves as a channel for diffusion of molecules smaller than 60 kDa, one might hypothesize that larger molecules also pass through the pore by "facilitated" diffusion. If that were so, we would need to invoke another mechanism to account for the *accumulation* of proteins inside the nucleus against a concentration gradient. Some careful experiments have been interpreted to mean that intranuclear binding of nuclear proteins and RNPs may play some role in their nuclear accumulation (Feldherr and Ogburn 1980; Feldherr and Pomerantz 1978; De Robertis 1983 and personal communication; Paine 1987). In these experiments, it was found that puncture or removal of the nuclear envelope of *Xenopus* oocyte nuclei did not prevent retention, or even accumulation, of certain nuclear proteins and snRNPs.

However, a recent study (Zimmer et al. 1988) reexamined this question. In one experiment, they found that when the nucleus of a *Xenopus* oocyte was punctured, nucleoplasmin leaked out into the cytoplasm. Nucleoplasmin retention is therefore not due to intranuclear binding, but rather to an inability to cross the nuclear envelope once inside the nucleus. In a second experiment, the authors isolated a nucleus, under oil, from one *Xenopus* oocyte and removed its nuclear envelope completely. They then reimplanted this nucleus in a second oocyte (which still contained its endogenous nucleus). Finally, they asked whether the nuclear protein N1 was retained in the demembranated donor nucleus. The authors found that N1 diffused almost immediately out of the donor nucleus and later became concentrated in the intact host nucleus. When the host nucleus was punctured 30 times, it accumulated N1, but more slowly than when intact. The authors interpret this result to mean that import through the intact remnants of the nuclear envelope can partially counteract outward leakage through the wounds. The conclusion of these experiments is that intranuclear binding cannot account for the accumulation of nucleoplasmin or protein N1 in the nucleus. Instead, the nuclear envelope (i.e., the nuclear pore) must play a primary role in transporting nucleoplasmin and N1 into the nucleus against a concentration gradient.

These conclusions are supported also by direct measurements of the diffusibility of nucleoplasmin in the nucleus (Schulz and Peters 1987; Dabauvalle et al. 1988). These studies, using the fluorescence microphotolysis method, have shown that nucleoplasmin is freely diffusible after transport into cultured cell nuclei. This again argues against a nuclear import mechanism requiring intranuclear binding. Thus, although it may be true that some proteins bind to components inside the nucleus, intranuclear binding cannot be responsible for nuclear import of nucleoplasmin.

VII. Nuclear Import is an Active Process. Evidence for a Signal Sequence Receptor

Substantial evidence has now established that nuclear import, rather than being a passive diffusional process, is actively mediated by the nuclear pore. Dingwall et al. (1982) found that the protease-resistant nucleoplasmin core pentamer, while unable to enter the nucleus from the cytoplasm, remains in the nucleus if injected there. These authors concluded that discrimination between nucleoplasmin core and tail occurs at the point of entry into the nucleus rather than inside the nucleus. Nuclear import in vivo of bulk nuclear proteins (Wu and Warner 1971) and nucleoplasmin (Dingwall et al. 1982; Schulz and Peters 1987) is temperature dependent. Since diffusion should not display a temperature variation as strong as that observed for nuclear import, this suggests (but does not prove) that nuclear accumulation is an enzymatic process.

Feldherr et al. (1983) contended that diffusion alone could not account for the rate of uptake of the nuclear proteins N1 and N2 in the *Xenopus* oocyte, an argument also advanced by Dingwall et al. (1986) for nucleoplasmin import. A need for rapid uptake into the nucleus (Gurdon 1970; Wu and Warner 1971; Warner 1979) may also explain why small proteins such as ribosomal proteins and histones have nuclear import signal sequences (Dingwall and Allan 1984; Moreland et al. 1985, 1986, 1987), suggesting that they are imported into the nucleus actively, like larger proteins.

Newmeyer et al. (1986a, b) showed that nuclear import, both in vivo (in *Xenopus* oocytes) and in an in vitro system based on *Xenopus* egg extracts (discussed in Sect. B.I.) requires the presence of ATP. In fact, import appears to require ATP hydrolysis, since the nonhydrolyzable analogs AMP-PCP and AMP-PNP cannot substitute for ATP (Newmeyer, unpublished observations). Furthermore, nuclear accumulation of nucleoplasmin in the in vitro system occurs only when the nuclear envelope is intact. It was concluded that nucleoplasmin import in this system is not a consequence of intranuclear binding, but rather of energy-dependent transport through the nuclear envelope (Newmeyer et al. 1986b).

Further evidence that proteins enter the nucleus by a receptor-mediated mechanism was provided by Goldfarb et al. (1986), who found that nuclear import in the *Xenopus* oocyte is a saturable process. A synthetic peptide containing the nuclear targeting signal for SV40 T-antigen, when covalently coupled to bovine serum albumin (BSA), conferred on BSA the capacity to accumulate in the nucleus. BSA conjugated with a mutant nuclear targeting signal (corresponding to the point mutation at lys_{128} discussed in Sect. A.IV., which leads to a defect in nuclear accumulation of native SV40 T-antigen) was imported about sixfold less efficiently by the oocyte nucleus. Nuclear import of the wild-type signal-BSA conjugate displayed saturable kinetics. Furthermore, the extent of accumulation in a 40-min interval was lowered twofold by coinjection of free wild-type signal peptide and to a lesser extent by the mutant peptide. These results argue that import is mediated by specific binding of the signal sequence to a receptor.

The existence of both a signal-sequence recognition site and an active translocation motor in the nuclear pore were directly demonstrated by Newmeyer and Forbes (1988), using an in vitro system, and by Richardson et al. (1988), using microinjected cells. (These results are discussed in more detail in Sect. B.I.4.).

The results of Newmeyer and Forbes (1988) and Richardson et al. (1988) predict the presence of an ATPase in the nuclear pore that participates in the translocation event. There are several reports of ATPase or NTPase activity in the nuclear envelope, based on histochemical (Yasuzumi and Tsubo 1966; Scheer and Franke 1969; Chardonnet and Dales 1972; Vorbrodt and Maul 1972) or biochemical (Berrios et al. 1983; Berrios and Fisher 1986; Kondor-Koch et al. 1982; Schröder et al. 1986; Smith and Wells 1984) data. As yet there is no direct evidence that any of these enzymes is involved in transport through the pore.

In summary, nuclear import is a process of energy-dependent, carrier-mediated translocation through the nuclear pore. The selectivity of the import process is likely to be the result of specific binding to a signal sequence receptor. This receptor might be a permanent component of the nuclear pore, or it might originate in the cytoplasm. A soluble cytoplasmic signal sequence receptor might serve as a "carrier", conveying karyophilic proteins to the nuclear pore. The data of Newmeyer and Forbes (1988) and Richardson et al. (1988) do not discriminate between these two possibilities; however, they imply that such a carrier, if it exists, does not require ATP for bringing proteins to the pore.

Recent studies have identified polypeptides that may function as receptors for nuclear localization signals. Adam et al. (1989) observed that two polypeptides, 60 and 70 kDa in size, could be cross-linked in vitro to a synthetic peptide containing the SV40 T-antigen nuclear localization signal. These proteins were found in both nuclear and cytosolic fractions. Yoneda et al. (1988) identified candidate receptor proteins using an independent approach. Supposing that charge interactions might be important for recognition of the nuclear targeting signal, they raised antisera against oligopeptides that might be considered electrostatically complementary to the SV40 signal. The antiserum to one peptide, DDDED, was found to recognize two polypeptides, 59 and 69 kDa in size, in rat liver nuclei. When the antibody was used as a probe for immunofluorescence microscopy, a punctate perinuclear pattern of staining was seen, suggestive of nuclear pore localization. Moreover, the antiserum was found to inhibit nuclear import of nucleoplasmin. In contrast to the results of Adam et al., Yoneda et al. did not detect the proteins in cytosolic fractions. Most recently, Yamasaki et al. (1989) identified four signal-binding proteins with a cross-linking assay. Two of these (140 and 55 kDa) were found to be loosely associated with rat liver nuclei, and two (100 and 70 kDa) were found in cytosol from BRL (Buffalo rat liver) cells.

These intriguing results suggest that there may indeed be cytoplasmic carrier molecules that escort signal-bearing proteins to the pore. However, conclusive evidence that any of the candidate receptor proteins indeed function as signal receptors in vivo is still awaited. On the other hand, there is functional evidence that cytosolic factors are required for nuclear protein import. Newmeyer and Forbes (Cell Biol, in press) have found that at least one cytosolic factor (called nuclear import factor, or NIF) is required for the ATP-independent association of signal-bearing proteins with the nuclear pore. NIF was identified by its ability to restore nuclear import activity to in vitro transport extracts inactivated with the sulfhydryl reagent N-ethylmaleimide. NIF could be a cytosolic signal receptor, or it could promote the pore-binding step by stimulating the interaction of nuclear localization signals with a distinct signal receptor. Whether NIF is identical to one of the signal-binding proteins identified by cross-linking studies remains to be determined.

VIII. Is the Signal Sequence Receptor Heterogeneous?

The diversity of nuclear targeting sequences poses a question: are all signal sequences recognized by the same receptor? Signals for the import of proteins into mitochondria (Roise and Schatz 1988) and the ER (Watson 1984) are also heterogeneous; one might suppose, then, that the important features of a transport signal are its shape and charge, rather than the amino acid sequence *per se*. On the other hand, there may be a family of signal sequence receptors in the nuclear pore, each receptor recognizing a class of nuclear targeting signals. The "one receptor" hypothesis predicts that all karyophilic proteins would compete for binding to the receptor and hence for import into the nucleus, while the "multiple receptor" model predicts that some proteins would not compete with each other. So far, data concerning competition are few. Bonner (1975a) found that different histone species competed with one another for import into the *Xenopus* oocyte nucleus. Newmeyer and Forbes (unpublished data) found that the signals of nucleoplasmin and SV40 T-antigen competed for nuclear import in an in vitro system (Newmeyer et al. 1986a, b; Newmeyer and Forbes 1988). Likewise, Dworetzky et al. (1987) showed using the electron microscope that nucleoplasmin and SV40 T-antigen signals are imported by the same pores. How interesting these results are depends on whether the import signals for nucleoplasmin and T-antigen are different. The nuclear targeting signal of nucleoplasmin was at first not conclusively identified. One candidate, denoted "box B" (ala-lys-lys-lys-lys), closely resembles the signal for SV40 T-antigen (Bürglin and De Robertis 1987; Dingwall et al. 1987). Deletion of this sequence from nucleoplasmin-β-galactosidase fusion proteins results in loss of nuclear accumulation. However, fused by itself to β-galactosidase, it does not confer nuclear acumulation. Thus box B is required, but not sufficient, for nucleoplasmin import ((Bürglin and De Robertis 1987).

More recently, Dingwall et al. (1988) found that a longer sequence, containing box B and flanking sequences, is necessary for nuclear import of nucleoplasmin. The length of the minimal nucleoplasmin signal compared with that of the T-antigen signal may suggest that the binding interactions between signal and receptor are more complicated for nucleoplasmin than for T-antigen. On the other hand, Rihs and Peters (1989) obtained evidence that the SV40 T-antigen signal is longer than originally believed. These investigators examined the kinetics of nuclear transport of fusion proteins containing various domains of SV40 T-antigen, after microinjection into living cells. They found that the previously identified signal, consisting of residues 126–132, did direct nuclear transport, but only very slowly: after 90 min the protein was accumulated only 1.7-fold over cytoplasmic concentrations. In contrast, a fusion protein containing a larger domain of T-antigen, residues 111–135, was rapidly accumulated in the nucleus, becoming 15-fold concentrated there within 20 min. Since this longer sequence contains known phosphorylation sites in native T-antigen, the authors speculated that phosphorylation may play some role in nuclear protein transport. Regardless of whether this hypothesis is correct, these results caution us that our understanding of nuclear localization signals is still incomplete.

Evidence of a different sort implies that the signal for SV-40 T-antigen is related structurally to domains found in other nuclear proteins. Goldfarb et al. (1986) prepared a polyclonal antiserum against the T-antigen signal peptide. On western blots, this antiserum was found to react with several other proteins, all nuclear. The antiserum may react with epitopes on these proteins which also serve as nuclear import signals.

IX. Regulation of Nuclear Import

Nucleocytoplasmic localization might be a way for the cell to modulate the functions of macromolecules by controlling their access to other molecules. A kinase, for example, confined to the cytoplasm would be unable to phosphorylate nuclear substrates. We now know of several macromolecules that move between nucleus and cytoplasm in response to changes in the state of the cell.

1. Changes in Nuclear/Cytoplasmic Localization During Embryogenesis
One example of shifts in nuclear/cytoplasmic localization during embryonic development was provided by Dreyer and colleagues (Dreyer et al. 1982; Dreyer and Hausen 1983; Dreyer et al. 1986; Dreyer 1987.) These authors used immunolocalization with monoclonal antibodies to study the nuclear accumulation of several *Xenopus* oocyte nuclear proteins during embryogenesis. Although some of these proteins reenter the zygotic nuclei immediately after fertilization, there is a class of nuclear proteins (the "late-shifting antigens") that enter embryonic nuclei only at various times later in development. Proteins that behave similarly have been found in embryos of the newt *Pleurodeles* (Abbadie et al. 1987) and *Drosophila* (Dequin et al. 1984; Frasch et al. 1986).

The mechanism for delaying nuclear accumulation of these proteins is still unknown. According to one hypothesis examined by Dreyer (1988), "late" migration to the nucleus may simply reflect a low rate of accumulation. Since nuclear disassembly occurs every 30 min in the early *Xenopus* embryo, there may be insufficient time for accumulation of slowly imported proteins in the nucleus. Later in development, the cell cycle lengthens, and these proteins would presumably have enough time to accumulate in the nucleus. However, Dreyer (1988) provided evidence that this mechanism may not be correct. Artificial lengthening of the cell cycle by treatment with cycloheximide or aphidicolin did not result in the expected nuclear accumulation of the late-shifting antigens. Furthermore, in somatic cell cultures derived from tadpoles, there was no difference between early- and late-shifting antigens in their kinetics of nuclear accumulation. Thus the nuclear import of these proteins may be regulated more subtly. Perhaps (like the snRNP proteins, discussed in the next section) the late-shifting proteins are transported only when they complex with other molecules not synthesized until late in development; or perhaps the composition of the import machinery itself is modified during embryogenesis. In vitro nuclear import systems (discussed in Sect. B.) may be the best way of attacking this problem.

2. Nuclear Import of snRNP Particles
Another example of developmental shifts in nuclear/cytoplasmic localization is that of snRNA-associated proteins. As De Robertis et al. (1982) showed, snRNAs accumulate in the nucleus after injection into the *Xenopus* oocyte cytoplasm. Later studies (Zeller et al. 1983; Fritz et al. 1984) found that the protein components normally associated with snRNAs (in snRNP particles) were located

in the cytoplasm of early *Xenopus* embryonic cells and entered embryonic nuclei only after gastrulation. This is because the protein components of snRNPs are stockpiled in excess over snRNA in the *Xenopus* oocyte cytoplasm during oogenesis. The snRNP proteins remain cytoplasmic (probably in a 6S RNA-free particle, Fisher et al. 1985) in the early embryo. At gastrulation, however, snRNA accumulates (Forbes et al. 1983) to a level stoichiometric with the pre-existing pool of snRNA-binding protein (Zeller et al. 1983; Fritz et al. 1985). The proteins are thus quantitatively assembled into mature snRNP particles which are transported into the nucleus. Cytoplasmic pools of RNA-free snRNP proteins are also found in mammalian cultured cells, where, as in *Xenopus* embryos, the normal path of biogenesis of snRNPs involves export of snRNAs from the nucleus to the cytoplasm, cytoplasmic assembly of the mature snRNP, and finally, import into the nucleus (Zieve et al. 1988).

snRNA-protein complexes have the capacity to accumulate in the nucleus, whereas the protein components of these particles remain in the cytoplasm if not complexed with RNA. This suggests that the signal for nuclear accumulation either resides in the RNA moiety, is a combination of RNA and protein, or is present in a masked form in the proteins until the RNA binds. To begin to identify the signal, Mattaj and De Robertis (1985) asked whether specific sequences in the U2 snRNA were required for nuclear accumulation of U2 snRNP. By systematic deletions, they showed that one particular oligoribonucleotide domain is responsible for binding of the "Sm antigens" (a set of snRNP proteins defined immunologically) and for nuclear accumulation. Since the RNA domain required for nuclear localization is associated with protein, it is unlikely that the RNA itself is the nuclear localization signal. Instead, the nuclear localization signal appears either to reside in the amino-acid sequence of the snRNP proteins and to be unmasked by a conformational change brought about by RNA binding, or to consist of a combination of RNA and protein. Now that the genes encoding some of the snRNP proteins have been isolated (Wieben et al. 1985; Theissen et al. 1986; Habets et al. 1987; Sillekens et al. 1987), it may be possible to determine whether snRNP proteins bear the signals for nuclear localization of the snRNP particle. This should be possible by in vitro reconstitution of snRNP particles (Wieben et al. 1983; Fisher et al. 1983; Hamm et al. 1987) using individually omitted or mutated snRNP proteins.

3. Nuclear Exclusion of Transcription and Replication Factors: A Regulatory Mechanism?

Mattaj et al. (1983) reported that the nuclear protein TFIIIA, a factor required for transcription of 5S rRNA, is excluded from the nucleus of immature *Xenopus* oocytes when it is present in a 7S complex with 5S rRNA. Mattaj and colleagues proposed that nuclear exclusion of TFIIIA might be a mechanism for regulating 5S gene transcription. Alternatively, one might imagine that the 7S particle may be simply a form of long-term stockpiling for TFIIIA and 5S RNA.

Nuclear exclusion of a transcription factor may also be a means of regulating immuoglobulin gene expression, as recent work by Baeuerle and Baltimore

(1988a, b) has shown. The immunoglobulin κ light chain genes contain an enhancer which is the recognition site for a DNA-binding protein, NF-κB. In cells not expressing κ light chain genes, NF-κB is nevertheless present, although in an inactive form. Treatment of pre-B cells with the phorbol ester, TPA, causes inactive NF-κB to be converted to the DNA-binding form and stimulates Igκ transcription concomitantly. This conversion occurs in the absence of protein synthesis. The inactive factor is present in cytosolic fractions and can be converted in vitro into an active, sequence-specific DNA-binding form by denaturation and renaturation. The authors have shown that, in cells not expressing Igκ genes, NF-κB is bound to an inhibitor and that this binding is released in vivo by treatment with phorbol ester and in vitro by agents that dissociate protein complexes. They propose that activation of NF-κB by TPA (presumably mediated by protein kinase C) unmasks a signal for its transport into the nucleus.

Recent work of Blow and Laskey (1988) has suggested that exclusion of a protein from the nucleus can regulate DNA replication. Using an in vitro system for nuclear assembly and DNA replication based on extracts of *Xenopus* eggs, these authors studied the mechanism by which DNA replication is limited to one round per division cycle. They found that permeabilization of the nuclear membrane was sufficient to allow DNA to rereplicate even when the extract is maintained in an interphase state. This led the authors to a simple model in which a cytoplasmic factor (termed "licensing factor"), that permits replication to initiate on a DNA template, is excluded from the nucleus during interphase. When the nuclear envelope disassembles in mitosis, the factor would gain access to the DNA, "licensing" it for another round of replication.

4. *Reversible Nucleocytoplasmic Movement*

Macromolecules usually cross the nuclear pore in only one direction: nucleus-to-cytoplasm, for ribosomes, newly transcribed snRNA and mRNPs; or cytoplasm-to-nucleus, for mature snRNP particles and most nuclear proteins. There are, however, cases in which the nuclear localization of a protein is reversible. The *Drosophila* heat-shock protein, hsp70, moves from the cytoplasm to the nucleus upon heat shock. When the temperature returns to normal, hsp70 moves back to the cytoplasm (Velasquez and Lindquist 1984). The mechanism of regulated nucleocytoplasmic targeting for hsp70 is unknown. There are at least two possibilities: (1) diffusion through the pore followed by temperature-dependent binding to nuclear or cytoplasmic molecules, or (2) temperature-dependent unmasking of nuclear import and export signals. The finding by Munro and Pelham (1984) that hsp70 has two nuclear targeting domains suggests that the latter mechanism may apply.

Certain protein kinases are intimately involved in intracellular responses to external signals; often these responses involve changes in transcriptional activity. Nuclear accumulation of protein kinases may be an important step in communicating extracellular signals to the transcriptional machinery. Nigg et al. (1985) reported that the regulatory subunit of cAMP-dependent protein kinase type II was always located near the Golgi region of the cell. The catalytic subunit, however, moved from the Golgi region to the nucleus upon elevation of cAMP levels and returned to the Golgi when cAMP levels dropped. Since the catalytic subunit of cAMP-dependent protein kinase is small (40 kDa), it may be able to diffuse through the pore. If so, a diffusion/binding mechanism similar to that proposed above for hsp70 might apply. Another regulatory enzyme, protein kinase C, rapidly and reversibly moves to a "detergent-resistant compartment" of the cell nucleus after B lymphocytes are given stimuli that elevate cAMP (Cambier et al. 1987).

Madsen et al. (1986) found evidence that one particular pair of proteins, called IEF 8Z30 and IEF 8Z31, can "shuttle" reversibly between nucleus and cytoplasm and cross the pore by a signal-dependent mechanism rather than by simple diffusion. Their argument is based on the finding that a monoclonal antibody to this protein, when injected into the cytoplasm of cultured cells, accumulates in the nucleus. Normally, IgG molecules are excluded from the nucleus (Einck and Bustin 1984). However, anti-nucleoplasmin (Sugawa et al. 1985) and anti-HMG I (Tsuneoka et al. 1986) IgG molecules accumulate in the nucleus when complexed with their respective antigens. This illustrates that a multimeric complex can enter the nucleus if at least one of the subunits has a nuclear targeting signal. (For other examples of this, see Dingwall et al. 1982; and Moreland et al. 1987.) Thus the monoclonal antibody to IEF 8Z30/31 presumably enters the nucleus because it binds to the antigen in the cytoplasm and is carried with it into the nucleus.

The chromatin protein HMG1 provides another illustration of a "shuttling" protein. HMG1, when introduced into cultured cells by the technique of red blood cell-mediated microinjection (Rechsteiner and Kuehl 1979), accumulates in the cell nuclei. However, in heterokaryons (fused cells containing more than one nucleus), radiolabeled HMG1 can leave one nucleus and enter another. Since HMG1 is a small protein, it may be able to diffuse through the nuclear pore. If so, its accumulation in the nucleus may perhaps be accounted for simply through binding to replicating chromatin. Bonne-Andrea et al. (1986) reported that, while some HMG1 was always present in the cytoplasm, HMG1 accumulated in the nucleus only in cells active in DNA replication (cells either actively dividing or infected with SV40.) Moreover, HMG1 was seen to accumulate at sites of active viral DNA replication.

A 350 kDa microtubule-associated protein (MAP) was found by Sato et al. (1986a, b) to be cytoplasmic in growth-arrested cells but nuclear in dividing cells (during mitosis it becomes spindle-associated.) Because of its large size, it presumably enters by a signal-sequence-mediated active import mechanism. Newmeyer and Ohlsson-Wilhelm (1985) described a similar, possibly identical, protein.

5. *Nuclear Import of Hormone Receptors: Hormone-Dependent?*

There are a number of nuclear hormone receptors whose intracellular location may be hormone-dependent. Although this has been a controversial issue, it appears that some hormone receptors are transported constitutively into the nucleus (King and Greene 1984; Welshons et al. 1984, 1985; Perrot-Applanat et al. 1986; Sap et al. 1986) whereas others, like the glucocorticoid receptor (Govindan 1980; Papamichail et al. 1980; Antakly and Eisen 1984; Picard and Yamamoto 1987) accumulate in the nucleus in a hormone-dependent manner. In *Dictyostelium*, a cAMP receptor was found to change its localization from the cytoplasm to the nucleus during development (Kay et al. 1987), although it was not explicitly shown that cAMP binding is the reason for the shift in intracellular localization.

The glucocorticoid receptor is intriguing in that it has two nuclear targeting signals. One (called NL1) is constitutive, and the other (NL2) is hormone-dependent (Picard and Yamamoto 1987). NL1, however, is active only in the absence of both the hormone-regulated signal and a third domain that seems to inhibit nuclear import mediated by NL1; NL1 may therefore be a cryptic nuclear targeting signal not used in the native protein. NL1, contained in a 28-amino-acid region, is somewhat similar to the SV40 T-antigen signal. NL2, on the other hand, is a 256-amino-acid domain also responsible for hormone binding; it contains no sequences similar to known nuclear targeting signals. Picard and Yamamoto suggest, because of their inability to obtain nuclear accumulation with smaller polypeptides within the 256-amino-acid region, that NL2 may be "assembled" from noncontiguous amino acid residues, as a result of a conformational change induced by hormone binding. NL2 could also mediate binding to an immobile cytoplasmic molecule in the absence of hormone. In fact, an interaction has been demonstrated between the glucocorticoid receptor and a 90-kDa heat shock protein that may be anchored to the cytoskeleton (e.g., Howard and Distelhorst 1988).

B. In Vitro Systems for Studying Nuclear Import

The study of nuclear import in vivo has helped us understand the properties of nuclear signal sequences and, to a lesser extent, the mechanisms of transport. In vitro systems are, however, much more amenable to experimental manipulation and open the possibility of reconstituting the entire nuclear import system from purified components. There have been two approaches to in vitro systems for nuclear import. The first makes use of extracts from amphibian eggs. This system seeks to mimic, as far as possible, the intracellular milieu and to maintain normal nuclear functions such as nuclear membrane growth, DNA replication, and, of course, protein import. The other strategy, aiming for simplicity, begins with isolated nuclei in a defined buffer, in the hope that these isolated nuclei contain all the components of the transport machinery.

For an in vitro system to be trustworthy, it must behave like its counterpart in vivo. For example, authentic nuclear import in vitro must discriminate between proteins that have signal sequences and those that do not. Nuclei must be shown to be intact, otherwise accumulation of a protein in nuclei could be attributed to diffusion of proteins through holes in the nuclear envelope and binding to nondiffusible substances inside the nucleus. Since nuclear import in vivo is temperature- and ATP-dependent and inhibited by WGA, these properties should be displayed in vitro as well. (It should be noted that ATP-dependence and WGA inhibition were first discovered in the *Xenopus* egg extract in vitro system and later verified in vivo). Finally, the most compelling proof that transport is functioning normally is to show, using the electron microscope, that protein-coated colloidal gold particles pass through the nuclear pores. We will apply these criteria in evaluating several reports of in vitro nuclear import systems.

I. In Vitro Systems Based on Xenopus Egg Extracts

1. Rationale for the Use of Egg Extracts

The first signs that amphibian egg extracts might be a medium in which nuclear functions are maintained in vitro came from work of Lohka and Masui (1983) and Forbes et al. (1983a). Lohka and Masui (1983) observed that extracts of *Rana pipiens* eggs contained the activities needed to assemble nuclei from added sperm chromatin, mimicking normal events following fertilization. Sperm pronuclei assembled in vitro were active in DNA synthesis and, in time, underwent the mitotic processes of chromatin condensation and nuclear envelope breakdown. Forbes et al. (1983a) found that pure bacteriophage λ DNA, microinjected into *Xenopus laevis* eggs, was assembled into structures much like native nuclei. These "synthetic" nuclei had normal nuclear envelope morphology: double membranes, pore complexes, and nuclear lamina. Furthermore, synthetic nuclei formed in microinjected eggs underwent chromosome condensation and nuclear envelope breakdown in response to subsequent microinjection of MPF (mitosis-promoting factor). Later reports showed that extracts from *Xenopus* eggs have the capacity to form synthetic nuclei from bacteriophage DNA in vitro (Newport and Forbes 1985; Newmeyer et al. 1986a; Blow and Laskey 1986; Newport 1987). Thus *Xenopus* eggs, and extracts made from them, contain all the ingredients needed to make a nucleus except DNA. These observations illustrate one aspect of the developmental strategy of some amphibians: the stockpiling of materials other than DNA in the egg for use in later development (Laskey et al. 1979).

The frog egg, moreover, is arrested in metaphase of meiosis II and is therefore a ready source of cytoplasm having a defined cell-cycle state. If egg cytoplasmic extracts are prepared in a buffer containing EGTA and phosphatase inhibitors, the extracts are stabilized in a mitotic state. Nuclei placed in such "mitotic" extracts undergo chromosome condensation and nuclear envelope disassembly, events normally accompanying mitosis (Lohka and Masui 1984b; Lohka and Maller 1985; Miake-Lye and Kirschner 1985; Newport and Spann 1987; Lohka and Maller 1987). On the other hand, if no attempt is made to remove calcium ions and inhibit phosphatases, or if the eggs are "activated" (meaning that the cell cycle is made to resume by one of several different treatments), the extract is in a nonmitotic, or an interphase state. (To preserve the interphase state, cycloheximide must be included in the buffer to block the eventual protein-synthesis-dependent appearance of endogenous mitotic factors [Newport 1987].) "Interphase" extracts cause chromosomes to decondense and have the ability to assemble, rather than break down, the nuclear envelope (Lohka and Masui 1983, 1984a; Newport and Forbes 1985; Stick and Hausen 1985; Newmeyer et al. 1986a; Newport 1987; Dreyer 1987). Egg extracts thus offer a means to study the assembly and disassembly of the nucleus and the regulation of cell cycle events.

How functional are the nuclei assembled in egg extracts? We have already mentioned their responsiveness to mitotic factors. Although there are no reports so far on transcriptional activity and RNA export, there is good evidence that nuclei assembled in egg extracts are competent in DNA replication (Lohka and Masui 1983; Blow and Laskey 1986; Newport 1987; Blow and Watson 1987; Hutchison et al. 1987; Sheehan et al. 1988; Blow and Laskey 1988). Most relevant for this discussion, nuclei assembled in vitro in egg extracts can import nuclear proteins (Newmeyer et al. 1986a, b; Peters et al. 1986; Dreyer 1987). Native nuclei isolated from heterologous sources (i.e., from rat liver) also function in nuclear import and nuclear membrane growth when placed in egg extracts (Newmeyer et al. 1986b; Finlay et al. 1987; Newmeyer and Forbes 1988). (Burke and Gerace [1986] and Suprynowicz and Gerace [1986] have developed similar systems for nuclear assembly and disassembly using extracts of cultured mammalian cells synchronized in mitosis. However, nuclei assembled in mammalian cell extracts have not yet been tested for nuclear import activity.)

2. Nuclear Import Activity in Egg Extracts is Authentic

There is now good evidence that nuclear import in egg extracts is faithful to the properties of nuclear import in vivo. First, import in the *Xenopus* in vitro system shows the same specificity seen in vivo. For nucleoplasmin, import required the protease-sensitive signal domain both in vitro (Newmeyer et al. 1986b; Peters et al. 1986), and in vivo (Dingwall et al. 1982.) Newmeyer and Forbes (1988) found that the nuclear import signal SV40 T-antigen, when coupled covalently to human serum albumin (HSA), was accumulated by nuclei in vitro, while a point-mutant signal (the equivalent of lys_{128} replaced by thr) was not. Thus the in vitro system, like import in vivo, can discriminate between the wild-type and mutant T-antigen signal sequences. Further, Dreyer et al. (1986) found that the import of early- and late-shifting embryonic proteins (discussed in Sect. A.I.1.) in a similar in vitro system based on a *Xenopus* egg extract showed the same specificity seen in early *Xenopus* embryos. That is, the early-shifting proteins were accumulated by nuclei in vitro whereas the late-shifting proteins were not.

Second, nuclear import in the in vitro system is mediated by the nuclear pores. Colloidal gold particles coated with nucleoplasmin or HSA-signal peptide conjugates were seen in the electron microscope to pass through the nuclear pores in vitro (Newmeyer and Forbes 1988), as Feldherr et al. (1984) had shown for nucleoplasmin earlier in vivo. This, and the observation that nucleoplasmin accumulation occurs only in sealed nuclei (Newmeyer et al. 1986b), shows that nuclear accumulation of proteins in the *Xenopus* egg extract is not a matter of diffusion through holes in the nuclear envelope followed by binding inside the nucleus. Instead, it reflects authentic nuclear import through the nuclear pores. The results of Zimmer et al. (1988), discussed earlier in Sect. 1A.VI., show that nucleoplasmin import in vivo also requires an intact nuclear envelope and cannot be mediated by intranuclear binding alone.

Third, nucleoplasmin import in vitro is temperature-dependent (Newmeyer et al. 1986b) and requires ATP (Newmeyer et al. 1986a, b). ATP- (Newmeyer et al. 1986a; Schulz and Peters 1987) and temperature dependence (Wu and Warner 1971; Dingwall et al. 1982; Newmeyer et al. 1986b; Schulz and Peters 1987) are displayed in vivo as well. Furthermore, the efficiency of accumulation seen for nucleoplasmin in vitro is comparable to that in vivo, in *Xenopus* oocytes (Newmeyer et al. 1986b; Zimmer et al. 1988).

Nuclear import in the *Xenopus* egg extract, then, is authentic in all respects so far tested. Because of the speed and ease of experimental manipulation it affords, this in vitro system has a considerable advantage over in vivo systems for studying nuclear protein import.

3. Nuclear Import is Inhibited by the Lectin, Wheat Germ Agglutinin. Are Nuclear Pore Glycoproteins Involved in the Transport Mechanism?

Finlay et al. (1986) discovered that nuclear import of nucleoplasmin in the egg extract system is inhibited by the lectin wheat germ agglutinin (WGA), a finding later reproduced in vivo, both in microinjected oocytes (Dabauvalle et al. 1988; Forbes, unpublished data) and in microinjected cultured somatic cells (Yoneda et al. 1987b; Dabauvalle et al. 1988; Wolff et al. 1988). Finlay et al. (1987) showed that inhibition is the result of WGA binding to proteins in the nuclear pore. Independent investigations in several laboratories have identified a family of about eight WGA-binding glycoproteins in the nuclear envelope (Davis and Blobel 1986; Finlay et al. 1987; Holt and Hart 1986; Holt et al. 1987; Schindler et al. 1987; Snow et al. 1987; Hanover et al. 1987; Park et al. 1987). These proteins are glycosylated in a novel pathway in which multiple N-acetylglucosamine residues are O-linked to serine and possibly threonine (Holt and Hart 1986; Holt et al. 1987). Monoclonal antibodies that bind to members of this family of nuclear envelope proteins usually react with epitopes present on more than one protein (Snow et al. 1987; Park et al. 1987). One antibody, however, obtained by Snow et al. (1987) recognizes an epitope unique to a 180-kDa polypeptide. Immunolocalization at the electron microscopic level shows that the epitopes recognized by all the antibodies are found at the nuclear pore; thus at least some, and probably all, of the proteins are located in the pore. These nuclear pore glycoproteins may participate in the mechanism of protein translocation through the pore (see also next section).

4. Nuclear Import is Separable Experimentally into Two Steps: Signal-Mediated Binding and ATP-Dependent Translocation

The discovery of ways to inhibit protein uptake by the nucleus allows us to analyze the mechanism of nuclear import. Newmeyer and Forbes (1988) asked whether removal of ATP or treatment with WGA would arrest the import machinery at some intermediate step. The authors prepared conjugates of HSA with the nuclear import signal peptide of SV40 T-antigen and showed that these conjugates were imported by nuclei in the *Xenopus* egg extract in vitro system. Import involved specific recognition of the signal, since a mutant signal peptide was defective in the in vitro system, as it is in vivo. Using the electron microscopic method of Feldherr et al. (1984) for visualizing transport through individual nuclear pores, they showed that the nuclear import mechanism can be dissociated into at least two steps. The first step, binding to the cytoplasmic face of the nuclear pore, involves the specific recognition of a nuclear import signal sequence. This binding step does not require ATP. Furthermore, nuclear pore binding of the signal sequence is not inhibited by prior binding of WGA to the pore. The second step, translocation through the central channel of the pore, is ATP-dependent and WGA-sensitive. Richardson et al. (1988) obtained complementary results in vivo: when nucleoplasmin is microinjected into cultured cells, it first binds to the nuclear envelope and is then translocated through the pores into the nucleus. At low temperatures or under conditions of metabolic inhibition (incubation with sodium fluoride and 2-deoxyglucose), translocation, but not pore binding, is inhibited.

The results demonstrate, first, that a signal sequence receptor resides in the nuclear pore. Second, translocation through the pore is an ATP-driven event; one would predict the existence of a "motor" responsible for the translocation. Finally, the results bear on the mechanism of transport inhibition by WGA. According to the data of Newmeyer and Forbes (1988), WGA does not inhibit the nuclear pore binding step, but instead arrests the translocation event. Since WGA binding has no effect on the diffusion of 20 kDa dextran molecules into the nucleus (Finlay et al. 1987; Dabauvalle et al. 1988; Yoneda et al. 1987), it appears that WGA does not act simply by obstructing the central channel of the pore. Rather, by binding to pore proteins, WGA apparently disables the translocation motor.

The precise roles of the nuclear pore glycoproteins in nuclear import are an important topic of study. The *Xenopus* egg extract system will be especially useful for this problem, and indeed for determining the role of any protein in nuclear import. Because the extract has the ability to assemble nuclei de novo, one can in principle reconstitute "mutant" nuclei lacking a given protein, i.e., a pore protein, and observe the effect on transport function.

II. In Vitro Systems Based on Isolated Nuclei in Buffers

An important question, so far unanswered, is whether nuclei contain all the components of the nuclei import system, or whether cytoplasmic factors are also required. If cytoplasmic factors are *not* required, that is, if the nuclear pore is a self-contained motor, it should be possible to devise an in vitro system for nuclear import consisting purely of isolated nuclei, buffer components, and a protein substrate. This goal has motivated recent reports from several laboratories (Cox 1982; Riedel and Fasold 1987a, b; Riedel et al. 1987; Markland et al. 1987; Imamoto-Sonobe et al. 1988). The conditions employed in these studies are summarized in Table 1.

1. Heparin-Extracted Nuclei

Arguing that whole isolated nuclei are themselves too complicated, Riedel, Fasold and colleagues have developed a system based on heparin-extracted nuclear ghosts (Riedel and Fasold 1987a, b; Riedel et al. 1987). These preparations retain the normal nuclear envelope morphology: nuclear pores and membranes appear in the electron microscope much the same as in whole nuclei. However, the nuclear contents are extracted to some extent: residual DNA is present at 1–1.5% of the content of unextracted nuclei (the proportion of residual protein was unreported). An important concern not addressed conclusively by these authors is whether these heparin ghosts are sealed. A result arguing that they are not was obtained by Lang and Peters (1984), who found that the permeability of heparin ghosts to 40-kDa dextrans was vastly greater than that of whole isolated nuclei. Riedel et al. (1987) showed that histones, nucleoplasmin, and polylysine became associated with the heparin ghosts, while myoglobin, cytochrome C, and IgG did not. The maximum levels of association were reached in 3–5 min. Since the results of Riedel et al. (1987) are not expressed in terms of accumulation ratios, it is impossible to compare the degree of nuclear protein association obtained by these authors with the accumulation seen in vivo or in vitro in other reports.

The authors found that there was no effect of adding ATP on the rate or extent of protein association with heparin vesicles. Instead they observed a small (30%) increase in the initial rate of nuclear association of radiolabeled histones in the presence of 5 mM GTP. This effect, as these authors show, seems to reflect a GTP-induced decrease in the rate of exchange of histones. In other words, in the absence of GTP, labeled histone molecules associated with the heparin ghosts are exchanged with unlabeled histone molecules from the surrounding buffer; exchange is slower in the presence of GTP. These results suggest that the association of histones with heparin ghosts reflects reversible binding to nuclear components. This binding may be to the nuclear pores (Newmeyer and Forbes 1988; Richardson et al. 1988) or to intranuclear material.

2. Systems Involving Whole Isolated Nuclei in Defined Buffers

Other laboratories (Cox 1982; Markland et al. 1987; Imamoto-Sonobe et al. 1988) have developed in vitro systems in which whole isolated nuclei are placed in defined buffers, in the absence of cytosol, and a protein transport substrate added. After an incubation period, the nuclei are, for example, recovered by centrifugation and the amount of protein associated with the nuclear pellet is determined either as total radioactivity or by polyacrylamide gel electrophoresis and fluorography. In two of these reports, association of proteins with nuclei was shown to be dependent on the presence of a signal

Table 1. Studies of nuclear protein association with isolated nuclei in defined buffers

Reference	Nuclei	Buffer	Substrates	Assay	Remarks
Cox (1982)	HeLa 0.3% Triton-washed) fresh or frozen	0.32 M sucrose 1 mM $Mg(SO_4)_2$ 5 mM Tris-HCl (pH 7.4)	Mixed cytosolic proteins Nuclear extract Actin BSA Histones (radiolabeled)	Total radioactivity in nuclear pellet[a]	Temperature-dependent pH optimum at 5.0 Not ATP-dependent Stimulated by NEM, Mg^{2+} cytosol Association not abolished by washing nuclei with detergent
Riedel and Fasold (1987a, b) Riedel et al. (1987)	Rat liver, heparin-extracted	50 mM Tris-HCl (pH 7.2) 25 mM KCl 2.5 mM $MgCl_2$	Histones HMG proteins Polylysine Myoglobin IgG Cytochrome c Nucleoplasmin (radiolabeled)	Total radioactivity in nuclear pellet[a]	Not ATP-dependent (see text)
Markland et al. (1987)	Rat liver (fresh)	50 mM Tris-HCl (pH 7.4) 25 nM KCl 2.5 mM $MgCl_2$ 3.3 mM $CaCl_2$ 5 mM Na_2HPO_4 5 mM spermidine	Wild-type, d10 mutant of SV40 T-antigen T-antigen/pyruvate kinase fusion protein (radiolabeled) T-antigen, BSA (fluorescently labeled)	SDS-PAGE and fluorography of nuclear pellet[a] Fluorescence microscopy (washed nuclei)[a,c]	Not ATP-dependent[b] Inhibited irreversibly by apyrase TRITC-BSA not shown to be excluded

Imamoto-Sonobe et al. (1988)	Rat liver	10 mM Hepes (pH 7.8) 60 mM KCl 2 mM $CaCl_2$ 3 mM $KHCO_3$ 0.4 mM ATP 1mg ml^{-1} BSA	Nucleoplasmin Nucleoplasmin core HMG1, BSA, IgG (radiolabeled)	Preincubate nuclei 2 h in ATP-free buffer, add ATP, ^{125}I-protein, incubate, count radioactivity in nuclear pellet	AMP-PCP substitutes for ATP Temperature-dependent Requires HCO_3^-, Ca^{2+} Association abolished by 1% Triton X-100
			Nucleoplasmin--phycoerythrin conjugate	Fluorescence microscopy (qualitative)	Association occurs with sonicated nuclei also BSA-SV40 T-antigen signal peptide conjugate does not associate with nuclei

[a]No competing protein added to block nonspecific binding of substrate to nuclei.
[b]Exogenously added ATP not required.
[c]Fluorescence microscope examination of *washed* nuclei does not measure the accumulation of proteins in nuclei relative to concentrations in the external medium.

domain: that of wild-type SV40 T-antigen, in the work of Markland et al. (1987), or that present in the nucleoplasmin tail, in the study by Imamoto-Sonobe et al. (1988). Remarkably, in this latter system the SV40 T-antigen signal peptide does not lead to nuclear association of BSA-signal peptide conjugates.

Although signal specificity is an important prerequisite for credibility, these systems need satisfy the additional criteria defined above to be judged authentic. In particular, it is important to demonstrate that nuclei are intact, i.e., that they exclude large nonnuclear proteins. Cox (1982) found that detergent treatment did not impair the ability of isolated HeLa cell nuclei to take up proteins, implying that the nuclei used in that study were leaky, and that the association of proteins with the isolated nuclei was probably due to binding rather than true pore-mediated transport. Interestingly, Imamoto-Sonobe et al. (1988) report that nucleoplasmin associates not only with whole nuclei but also with mildly sonicated nuclei in an ATP-dependent manner. Thus their system appears not to reflect true nuclear import through the nuclear pores, but instead binding either to the nuclear pores or to intranuclear material.

Markland et al. (1987) observed a signal-sequence-dependent association of SV40 large T-antigen with isolated nuclei. Nuclei were placed in a physiological buffer and incubated with radiolabeled wild-type T-antigen or the d10 mutant of T-antigen, which contains a point mutation at residue 128 leading to a transport defect in vivo. After various times of incubation, the nuclei were recovered and the nuclear contents analyzed by gel electrophoresis. It was found that wild-type T-antigen, but not the d10 mutant, associated in a time-dependent manner with the nuclei. In this study, nuclei for were assayed for intactness in several ways. First, fluorochrome-labeled concanavalin A (con A), which binds to oligosaccharide moieties in the cisternal space between the outer and inner nuclear membranes (Newmeyer et al. 1986b; Finlay et al. 1987), was bound by only 5% of the nuclei (note, however, that these authors used a concentration of con A ten times lower than that found by Newmeyer et al. [1986b] and Finlay et al. [1987] to be required for detecting damaged nuclei). Second, radiolabeled proteins lacking a nuclear targeting signal did not associate strongly with the isolated nuclei. This, however, is not evidence that nonnuclear proteins were *excluded* from the isolated nuclei, since one can easily imagine that proteins could diffuse into leaky nuclei during incubations and then out again during reisolation of the nuclei.

Markland and colleagues also address the question of whether the association of SV40 T-antigen is a trivial consequence of binding to the nuclear exterior or instead reflects internalization in the nuclei. They found that nucleus-associated T-antigen is resistant to proteolysis by Sepharose-bound trypsin but not free trypsin which can diffuse through the nuclear pores. They conclude that T-antigen cannot be on the nuclear exterior, and therefore must be internalized by the nuclei. However, the authors did not show that under the same conditions proteins in the nuclear pore are trypsin-sensitive. Thus, these results could mean that T-antigen is bound to the nuclear pore in a location inaccessible to immobilized trypsin. A second possibility is that the nuclei are leaky and allow T-antigen to diffuse in and bind inside the nuclei, while the much larger trypsin-coated beads are excluded. The assertion that T-antigen is imported into these nuclei by a true pore-mediated process must therefore be greeted cautiously.

These groups have obtained conflicting results on the nucleotide requirements for protein association with isolated nuclei in buffer. Cox (1982) found that ATP inhibited uptake. Markland et al. (1987) found no effect of added nucleotides, while, on the other hand, depletion of ATP with the enzyme apyrase abolished association of T-antigen with nuclei. However, this effect was not reversed upon subsequent addition of ATP, perhaps because the enzyme could not be washed out completely. In contrast, Newmeyer et al. (1986b) found that when nucleoplasmin transport in the *Xenopus* egg extract system was blocked by ATP depletion using the enzyme hexokinase (supplemented with glucose), the inhibition could later be reversed by the addition of an ATP-regenerating system. Imamoto-Sonobe et al. (1988) observed that association of nucleoplasmin and HMG1 with nuclei in their system required ATP. However, ATP hydrolysis was not required for the interactions they observed, since AMP-PCP, a nonhydrolyzable analog of ATP, had the same effect as ATP. This is unlike what is observed in the *Xenopus* egg extract system, where AMP-PCP cannot substitute for ATP (Newmeyer and Forbes, unpublished data.)

So far none of the systems using isolated nuclei or nuclear ghosts in defined buffers has met all the criteria needed to establish authenticity. In particular, these systems have not shown satisfactorily that the nuclei under study were intact. Most importantly, there has been no demonstration in any of these reports that colloidal-gold-labeled proteins are translocated through the pores. Since there has been no conclusive evidence that nuclear import can occur in the absence of soluble factors, we cannot conclude that the nucleus contains all the macromolecular components required for nuclear protein import. However, recent results using the *Xenopus* egg extract system indicate that authentic nuclear import requires at least one soluble factor not contained in isolated nuclei (Newmeyer and Forbes, Cell Biol, in press).

III. Passive Influx into Isolated Nuclei

The fluorescence photobleaching approach was exploited by Peters and colleagues to study diffusion of dextrans into the nuclei of microinjected living cells (Lang and Peters 1984; Lang et al. 1986; Peters 1986; Peters et al. 1986). This technique has also been adopted for examining dextran influx into isolated nuclei (Jiang and Schindler 1986; Schindler and Jiang 1986; Schindler and Jiang 1987; Jiang and Schindler 1987). These authors have measured effects on the rate of nuclear influx of 60 kDa dextrans produced by the following substances: nucleotides, phosphoinositides, RNA, lectins (Jiang and Schindler 1986), insulin, epidermal growth factor (Jiang and Schindler 1986; Schindler and Jiang 1987), anti-actin antibodies, phalloidin and cytochalasin D (Schindler and Jiang 1986). The effects in each case are small, less than about threefold. Although the authors refer to dextran influx as "transport", clearly the phenomenon being studied is passive diffusion.

Does passive dextran influx in isolated nuclei occur through the nuclear pores or through holes in the nuclear membrane? Schindler and Jiang found that 60 kDa dextrans are excluded from nuclei in vivo, while they diffuse readily into isolated nuclei (Jiang and Schindler 1988). While it could be that, as the authors suggest, the pore complexes of isolated nuclei are larger than those in cultured cells, the most likely explanation is that the nuclear membranes are leaky, especially since the authors found that extracting the nuclear membranes with 1% Triton X-100 has no significant effect on the measured influx rate (Schindler and Jiang 1986).

Nevertheless, Jiang and Schindler have recently shown that the rate of nuclear influx of 20 kDa dextrans can be modulated in living cells, where the nuclear membrane is most likely intact: insulin and epidermal growth factor produced a threefold increase in the influx rate into 3T3 fibroblast nuclei. This result is intriguing in suggesting that the apparent diameter of the pore channel accessible to diffusing molecules can be modulated. We do not yet know if changes in the rate of passive diffusion through the pore have any relationship to the process of active signal-mediated nuclear import of large proteins.

C. Conclusion

In vitro systems, if authentic, promise to help us understand how the process of nuclear import works and identify the molecules involved. Already the *Xenopus* egg extract system has proven its utility in demonstrating the energy-dependence, inhibition by WGA, and multi-step character of nuclear import. The egg extract is nevertheless a complex mixture, since it contains all the activities needed for nuclear membrane assembly and growth, DNA replication, and possibly transcription. Simpler systems have not yet given clear evidence of active transport, and so have yet to define the minimal requirements for nuclear import. Therefore one of the major goals of research on nuclear import will be to determine whether the nucleus contains all the components involved in the transport machinery, or whether cytoplasmic components must be added.

If cytoplasmic factors are needed, they might participate in either the nuclear pore binding step or in translocation through the nuclear pore, or both (Newmeyer and Forbes 1988; Richardson et al. 1988). For example, there might be a factor in the cytoplasm that recognizes proteins bearing nuclear targeting signals and carries the proteins to, and perhaps through, the pore. Richardson et al. (1988) observed fibers (3–4 nm in diameter) emanating from the nuclear pores of isolated nuclear envelopes to which nucleoplasmin-coated gold particles were bound. While Newmeyer and Forbes (1988) did not observe nuclear-pore-associated fibrils in their in vitro system, they nevertheless found that the signal-sequence binding sites lie considerably distant from the center of the pore. These results may suggest the participation of fibers in the transport mechanism. If the translocation motor does involve fibers and is analogous to one of the known fiber-motility systems in the cytoplasm, e.g., the kinesin/microtubule (Vale 1987) or actin/myosin (Warrick and Spudich 1987) systems, then one would predict that there is a recycling component of the translocation motor: either the fiber monomer or a molecule moving along the fiber. The question of whether cytoplasmic factors are required for nuclear import therefore has implications for the translocation mechanism.

A powerful advantage that the *Xenopus* egg extract system has over simpler systems is its ability to assemble nuclei de novo. It should therefore be possible to determine not only how nuclear import works but also how nuclear pores are assembled. In principle, one can remove from the extract any given protein for which a specific antibody is available and ask (1) if nuclear membrane assembly occurs; (2) if nuclear pores are assembled; and (3) whether the pores are competent for transport. This approach may succeed in determining the functions of the nuclear pore glycoproteins (see Sect. B.I.3.) The egg extract also lends itself also to biochemical fractionation, another approach that may help identify factors, both nuclear and cytoplasmic, required for nuclear import.

Acknowledgements. The author thanks C. Dreyer, C. Feldherr, M. Hall, J. Hanover, J. Kleinschmidt. R. E. Lanford, and T. Uchida for communicating their results prior to publication. He is also indebted to Douglass Forbes and Kathy Wilson for advice on the manuscript, and to Ron Milligan for graciously providing Figs. 1 and 2. The author's work in the laboratory of Dr. Douglass J. Forbes was supported by an N.I.H. postdoctoral fellowship (to D.D.N.) and by a Pew Foundation scholarship awarded to Dr. Forbes.

References

Abbadie C, Boucher D, Charlemagne J, Lacroix JC (1987) Immunolocalization of three oocyte nuclear proteins during oogenesis and embryogenesis in *Pleurodeles*. Development 101:715–728

Adam SA, Lobl TJ, Mitchell MA, Gerace L (1989) Identification of specific binding proteins for a nuclear location sequence. Nature 337:276–279

Aebi U, Cohn J, Buhle L, Gerace L (1986) The nuclear lamina is a meshwork of intermediate-type filaments. Nature 323:560–564

Antakly T, Eisen HJ (1984) Immunocytochemical localization of glucocorticoid receptor in target cells. Endocrinology 115:1984–1989

Baeuerle PA, Baltimore D (1988a) Activation of DNA-binding activity in an apparently cytoplasmic precursor of the NF-κB transcription factor. Cell 53:211–217

Baeuerle PA, Baltimore D (1988b) IκB: a specific inhibitor of the NF-κB transcription factor. Science 242:540–546

Bahr GF, Beerman W (1954) The fine structure of the nuclear membrane in the larval salivary gland and midgut of *Chironomus*. Exp Cell Res 6:519–522

Berrios M, Fisher P (1986) A myosin heavy chain-like polypeptide is associated with the nuclear envelope in higher eukaryotic cells. J Cell Biol 103:711–724

Berrios M, Blobel G, Fisher PA (1983) Characterization of an ATPase/dATPase activity

associated with the *Drosophila* nuclear matrix-pore complex-lamina fraction. J Biol Chem 258:4548–4555
Blow JJ, Laskey RA (1986) Initiation of DNA replication in nuclei and purified DNA by a cell-free extract of *Xenopus* eggs. Cell 47: 577–587
Blow JJ, Laskey RA (1988) A role for the nuclear envelope in controlling DNA replication within the cell cycle. Nature 332:546–548
Blow JJ, Watson JV (1987) Nuclei act as independent and integrated units of replication in a *Xenopus* cell-free DNA replication system. EMBO J 6:1997–2002
Bonne-Andrea C, Harper F, Puvion E, Delpech M, De Recondo A-M (1986) Nuclear accumulation of HMG1 protection is correlated to DNA synthesis. Biol Cell 58:185–194
Bonner WM (1975a) Protein migration into nuclei. I. Frog oocyte nuclei in vivo accumulate microinjected histones, allow entry to small proteins, and exclude large proteins. J Cell Biol 64:421–430
Bonner WM (1975b) Protein migration into nuclei. II. Frog oocyte nuclei accumulate a class of microinjected oocyte nuclear proteins and exclude a class of microinjected oocyte cytoplasmic proteins. J Cell Biol 64:431–437
Bonner WM (1978) Protein migration and accumulation in nuclei. In: Busch H (ed) The Cell Nucleus. Academic Press, New York *6, part C*, pp 97–148
Bonnerot C, Rocancourt D, Briand P, Grimber G, Nicolas J-F (1987) A β-galactosidase hybrid protein targeted to nuclei as a marker for developmental studies. Proc Natl Acad Sci USA 84:6795–6799
Bürglin TR, De Robertis EM (1987) The nuclear migration signal of *Xenopus laevis* nucleoplasmin. EMBO J 6:2617–2625
Burke B, Gerace L (1986) A cell free system to study reassembly of the nuclear envelope at the end of mitosis. Cell 44:639–652
Cambier JC, Newell MK, Justement LB, McGuire JC, Leach KL, Chen ZZ (1987) Ia binding ligands and cAMP stimulate nuclear translocation of PKC in B lymphocytes. Nature 327:629–632
Chardonnet Y, Dales S (1972) Early events in the interaction of adenoviruses with HeLa cells. III. Relationship between an ATPase activity in nuclear envelopes and transfer of core material: a hypothesis. Virology 48:342–359
Cox GS (1982) Discrimination in the uptake of soluble proteins by isolated nuclei. J Cell Sci 58:363–384
Dabauvalle M-C, Franke WW (1982) Karyophilic proteins: polypeptides synthesized in vitro accumulate in the nucleus on microinjection into the cytoplasm of amphibian oocytes. Proc Natl Acad Sci USA 79:5302–5306
Dabauvalle M-C, Franke WW (1984) Karyophobic proteins. A category of abundant soluble proteins which accumulate in the cytoplasm. Exp Cell Res 153:308–326
Dabauvalle M-C, Franke WW (1986) Determination of the intracellular state of soluble macromolecules by gel filtration in vivo in the cytoplasm of amphibian oocytes. J Cell Biol 102:2006–2014
Dabauvalle M-C, Schulz B, Scheer U, Peters R (1988) Inhibition of nuclear accumulation of karyophilic proteins in living cells by microinjection of the lectin wheat germ agglutinin. Exp Cell Res 174:291–296
Darlington RW, Moss LH (1968) Herpesvirus envelopment. J Virol 2:48–55
Davey J, Dimmock NJ, Colman A (1985) Identification of the sequence responsible for the nuclear accumulation of the influenza virus nucleoprotein in *Xenopus* oocytes. Cell 40:667–675
Davis LI, Blobel G (1986) Identification and characterization of a nuclear pore protein. Cell 45:699–709
Dequin R, Saumweber H, Sedat JW (1984) Proteins shifting from the cytoplasm into the nuclei during early embryogenesis of *Drosophila melanogaster*. Dev Biol 104:37–48
De Robertis EM (1983) Nucleocytoplasmic segregation of proteins and RNAs Cell 32:1021–1025
De Robertis EM, Longthorne RF, Gurdon JB (1978) Intracellular migration of nuclear proteins in *Xenopus* oocytes. Nature 272:254–256

De Robertis EM, Lienhard S, Parisot RF (1982) Intracellular transport of microinjected 5S and small nuclear RNAs. Nature 298: 572–577
Dingwall C (1985) The accumulation of proteins in the nucleus. Trends Biochem Sci 10:64–66
Dingwall C, Allan J (1984) Accumulation of the isolated carboxyl-terminal domain of histone H1 in the *Xenopus* oocyte nucleus. EMBO J 3:1933–1937
Dingwall C, Laskey RA (1986) Protein import into the cell nucleus. Annu Rev Cell Biol 2:365–388
Dingwall C, Sharnick SV, Laskey RA (1982) A polypeptide domain that specifies migration of nucleoplasmin into the nucleus. Cell 30:449–458
Dingwall C, Bürglin TR, Kearsey SE, Dilworth S, Laskey RA (1986) Sequence features of the nucleoplasmin tail region and evidence for a selective entry mechanism for transport into the cell nucleus. In: Peters R, Trendelenburg M (eds) Nucleocytoplasmic transport. Springer, Berlin Heidelberg New York, pp 159–169
Dingwall C, Dilworth SM, Black SJ, Kearsey SE, Cox LS, Laskey RA (1987) Nucleoplasmin cDNA sequence reveals polyglutamic acid tracts and a cluster of sequences homologous to putative nuclear localization signals. EMBO J 6:69–74
Dingwall C, Robbins J, Dilworth SM, Roberts B, Richardson WD, (1988) The nucleoplasmin nuclear location sequence is larger and more complex than that of SV-40 large T antigen. J Cell Biol 107:841–849
Douglas MG, McCammon MT, Vassarotti A (1986) Targeting proteins into mitochondria. Microbiol Rev 50:166–178
Dreyer C (1987) Differential accumulation of oocyte nuclear proteins by embryonic nuclei of *Xenopus*. Development 101:829–846
Dreyer C, Hausen P (1983) Two-dimensional gel analysis of the fate of oocyte nuclear proteins in the development of *Xenopus laevis*. Dev Biol 100:412–425
Dreyer C, Scholz E, Hausen P (1982) The fate of oocyte nuclear proteins during early development of *Xenopus laevis*. Wilhelm Roux's Arch 191:228–233
Dreyer C, Stick R, Hausen P (1986) Uptake of oocyte nuclear proteins by nuclei of *Xenopus* embryos. In: Peters R, Trendelenburg M (eds) Nucleocytoplasmic transport. Springer, Berlin Heidelberg New York Tokyo, pp 143–157
Dworetzky SI, Feldherr CM (1988) Translocation of RNA-coated gold particles through the nuclear pores of oocytes. J Cell Biol 106: 575–584
Dworetzky SI, Lanford RE, Feldherr CM (1987) Transport of a synthetic peptide homologous to SV 40 T antigen through the nuclear pores. J Cell Biol 105:73a
Eilers M, Schatz G (1988) Protein unfolding and the energetics of protein translocation across biological membranes. Cell 52:481–483
Einck L, Bustin M (1984) Functional histone antibody fragments traverse the nuclear envelope. J Cell Biol 98:205–213
Fahl WE, Jefcoate CR, Kasper CB (1978) Characteristics of Benzo(a)pyrene metabolism and cytochrome P-450 heterogeneity in rat liver nuclear envelope and comparison to microsomal membrane. J Biol Chem 253:3106–3113
Feldherr CM, (1962) The nuclear annuli as pathways for nucleo-cytoplasmic exchanges. J Cell Biol 14:65–72
Feldherr CM, (1965) The effect of the electron-opaque pore material on exchanges through the nuclear annuli. J Cell Biol 25:43–51
Feldherr CM, Ogburn JA (1980) Mechanism for the selection of nuclear polypeptides in *Xenopus* oocytes. II. Two-dimensional gel analysis. J Cell Biol 87:589–593
Feldherr CM, Pomerantz J (1978) Mechanism for the selection of nuclear polypeptides in *Xenopus* oocytes. J Cell Biol 78:168–175
Feldherr CM, Cohen RJ, Ogburn JA (1983) Evidence for mediated protein uptake by amphibian oocyte nuclei. J Cell Biol 96:1486–1490
Feldherr CM, Kallenbach E, Schultz N (1984) Movement of a karyophilic protein through the nuclear pores of oocytes. J Cell Biol 99:2216–2222
Finlay DR, Newmeyer DD, Price TM, Forbes DJ (1987) Inhibition of in vitro nuclear transport by a lectin that binds to nuclear pores. J Cell Biol 104:189–200
Fisher DE, Conner GE, Reeves WH, Blobel G, Kunkel HG (1983) Synthesis and assembly of

human small nuclear ribonucleoproteins generated by cell-free translation. Proc Natl Acad Sci USA 80:6356–6360

Fisher DE, Conner GE, Reeves WH, Wisniewolski R, Blobel G (1985) Small nuclear ribonucleoprotein particle assembly in vivo: demonstration of a 6S RNA-free core precursor and posttranslational modification. Cell 42:751–758

Forbes DJ, Kirschner MW, Newport JW (1983a) Spontaneous formation of nucleus-like structures around bacteriophage DNA microinjected into *Xenopus* eggs. Cell 34:13–23

Forbes DJ, Kornberg TB, Kirschner MW (1983b) Small nuclear RNA transcription and ribonucleoprotein assembly in early *Xenopus* development. J Cell Biol 97:62–72

Franke WW (1974) Structure, biochemistry, and functions of the nuclear envelope. Int Rev Cytol 4:71–236

Franke WW, Scheer U, Krohne G, Jarasch E-D (1981) The nuclear envelope and the architecture of the nuclear periphery. J Cell Biol 91:39s–50s

Frasch M, Glover DM, Saumweber H (1986) Nuclear antigens follow different pathways into daughter nuclei during mitosis in early *Drosophila* embryos. J Cell Sci 82:155–172

Fritz A, Parisot R, Newmeyer D, De Robertis EM (1984) Small nuclear U-ribonucleoproteins in *Xenopus laevis* development. J Mol Biol 178:273–285

Gall JG (1954) Observations on the nuclear membrane with the electron microscope. Exp Cell Res 7:197–200

Garoff H (1985) Using recombinant DNA techniques to study protein targeting in the eucaryotic cell. Annu Rev Cell Biol 1:403–445

Gerace L, Blobel G (1980) The nuclear envelope lamina is reversibly depolymerized during mitosis. Cell 9:277–287

Gerace L, Ottaviano Y, Kondor-Koch C (1982) Identification of a major polypeptide of the nuclear pore complex. J Cell Biol 95:826–837

Goldfarb DS, Garièpy J, Schoolnik G, Kornberg RD (1986) Synthetic peptides as nuclear localization signals. Nature 322:641–644

Govindan MV (1980) Immunofluorescence microscopy of the intracellular translocation of glucocorticoid receptor complexes in rat hepatoma (HTC) cells. Exp Cell Res 127:293–297

Gritz L, Abovich N, Teem JL, Rosbash M (1985) Posttranscriptional regulation and assembly into ribosomes of a *S. cerevisiae* ribosomal protein-β-galactosidase fusion. Mol Cell Biol 5:3436–3442

Gurdon JB (1970) Nuclear transplantation and the control of gene activity in animal development. Proc R Soc (Lond) B 176: 303–314

Habets WJ, Sillekens PTG, Hoet MH, Schalken JA, Roebroek AJM, Leunissen JAM, Van de Ven WJM, van Venrooij WJ (1987) Analysis of a cDNA clone expressing a human autoimmune antigen: full-length sequence of the U2 small nuclear RNA-associated B″ antigen. Proc Natl Acad Sci USA 84:2421–2425

Hall MN, Fried SR (1987) Is nuclear protein localization receptor-mediated? In: Fox CF (ed) Molecular biology of intracellular protein sorting and organelle assembly, UCLA symposia on molecular and cellular biology. Alan R. Liss, New York

Hall MN, Hereford L, Herskowitz I (1984) Targeting of *E. coli* beta-galactosidase to the nucleus in yeast. Cell 36:1057–1065

Hamm J, Kazmaier M, Mattaj IW (1987) In vitro assembly of U1 snRNPs. EMBO J 6:3479–3485

Hanover JA, Cohen CK, Willingham MC, Park MK (1987) O-linked N-acetylglucosamine is attached to proteins of the nuclear pore: evidence for cytoplasmic glycosylation. J Biol Chem 262:9887–9894

Holt GD, Hart GW (1986) The subcellular distribution of terminal N-acetylglucosamine moieties: localization of a novel protein-saccharide linkage, O-linked GlcNAc. J Biol Chem 261:8049–8057

Holt GD, Snow CM, Senior A, Haltiwanger RS, Gerace L, Hart GW (1987) Nuclear pore complex glycoproteins contain cytoplasmically disposed O-linked N-acetylglucosamine. J Cell Biol 104:1157–1164

Howard KJ, Distelhorst CW (1988) Evidence for intracellular association of the glucocorticoid receptor with the 90-kDa heat shock protein. J Biol Chem 263:3474–3481

Hummeler K, Tomassini N, Sokol F (1970) Morphological aspects of the uptake of simian virus 40 by permissive cells. J Virol 6:87–93
Hurt EC, Van Loon APGM (1986) How proteins find mitochondria and intramitochondrial compartments. Trends Biochem Sci 11:204–207
Hutchison CJ, Cox R, Drepaul RS, Gomperts M, Ford CC (1987) Periodic DNA synthesis in cell-free extracts of *Xenopus* eggs. EMBO J 6:2003–2010
Imamoto-Sonobe N, Yoneda Y, Iwamoto T, Sugawa H, Uchida T (1988) ATP-dependent association of nuclear proteins with isolated rat liver nuclei. Proc Natl Acad Sci USA 85:3426–3430
Jiang L-W, Schindler M (1986) Chemical factors that influence nucleocytoplasmic transport: a fluorescence photobleaching study. J Cell Biol 102:853–858
Jiang L-W, Schindler M (1987) Fluorescence photobleaching analysis of nuclear transport: dynamic evidence for auxiliary channels in detergent-treated nuclei. Biochemistry 26:1546–1551
Jiang L-W, Schindler M (1988) Nuclear transport in 3T3 fibroblasts: effects of growth factors, transformation, and cell shape. J Cell Biol 106:13–19
Kalderon D, Roberts BL, Richardson WD, Smith AE (1984a) A short amino acid sequence able to specify nuclear location. Cell 39:499–509
Kalderon D, Richardson WD, Markham AF, Smith AE (1984b) Sequence requirements for nuclear location of simian virus 40 large-T antigen. Nature 311:499–509
Kay CA, Noce T, Tsang AS (1987) Translocation of an unusual cAMP receptor to the nucleus during development of *Dictyostelium discoideum*. Proc Natl Acad Sci USA 84:2322–2326
Kessel RG, Tung HN, Beams HW, Lin JJ (1986) Is the nuclear envelope a 'generator' of membrane? Developmental sequences in cytomembrane elaboration. Cell Tissue Res 245:61–68
King WJ, Greene GL (1984) Monoclonal antibodies localize oestrogen receptor in the nuclei of target cells. Nature 307:747–749
Kleinschmidt JA, Seiter A (1988) Identification of domains involved in nuclear uptake and histone binding of protein N1 of *Xenopus laevis*. EMBO J 6:1605–1614
Kondor-Koch C, Riedel N, Valentin R, Fasold H, (1982) Characterization of an ATPase on the inside of rat-liver nuclear envelopes by affinity labeling. Eur J Biochem 127: 285–289
Krippl B, Ferguson B, Jones N, Rosenberg M, Westphal H (1985) Mapping of functional domains in adenovirus E1A proteins. Proc Natl Acad Sci USA 77:1034–1038
Krohne G, Benavente R (1986) The nuclear lamins: a multigene family of proteins in evolution and differentiation. Exp Cell Res 162:1–10
Lanford RE, Butel JS (1984) Construction and characterization of an SV40 mutant defective in nuclear transport of T antigen. Cell 37:801–813
Lanford RE, Kanda P, Kennedy RC (1986) Induction of nuclear transport with a synthetic peptide homologous to the SV40 T antigen transport signal. Cell 46: 575–582
Lanford RE, White RG, Dunham RG, Kanda P (1988) Effect of basic and nonbasic amino acid substitutions induced by SV40 T antigen synthetic peptide nuclear transport signals. Mol Cell Biol 8:2722–2729
Lang I, Peters R (1984) Nuclear envelope permeability: a sensitive indicator of pore complex integrity. In: Bolis CL, Heinrich EJM, Passow H (eds) Information and Energy Transduction in Biological Membranes. Alan R Liss, New York, pp 377–386
Lang I, Scholz M, Peters R (1986) Molecular mobility and nucleocytoplasmic flux in hepatoma cells. J Cell Biol 102:1183–1190
Laskey RA, Gurdon JB, Trendelenburg M (1979) Accumulation of materials involved in rapid chromosomal replication in early amphibian development. Br Soc Dev Biol Symp 4:65–80
Lohka MJ, Maller JL (1985) Induction of nuclear envelope breakdown, chromosome condensation, and spindle formation in cell-free extracts. J Cell Biol 101:518–523
Lohka MJ, Maller JL (1987) Regulation of nuclear formation and breakdown in cell-free extracts of amphibian eggs. In: Schlegel RA, Halleck MS, Rao PN (eds) Molecular regulation of nuclear events in mitosis and meiosis. Academic Press, Orlando, pp 67–109
Lohka MJ, Masui Y (1983) Formation in vitro of sperm pronuclei and mitotic chromosomes by amphibian ooplasmic components. Science 220:719–721

Lohka MJ, Masui Y (1984a) Roles of cytosol and cytoplasmic particles in nuclear envelope assembly and sperm pronuclear formation in cell- free preparations from amphibian eggs. J Cell Biol 98:1222–1230
Lohka MJ, Masui Y (1984b) Effects of Ca^{2+} ions on the formation of metaphase chromosomes and sperm pronuclei in cell-free preparations from unactivated *Rana pipiens* eggs. Dev Biol 103:434–442
Madsen P, Nielsen S, Celis JE (1986) Monoclonal antibody specific for human nuclear proteins IEF 8Z30 and 8Z31 accumulates in the nucleus a few hours after cytoplasmic microinjection of cells expressing these proteins. J Cell Biol 103:2083–2089
Markland W, Smith AE, Roberts BL (1987) Signal-dependent translocation of simian virus 40 Large-T antigen into rat liver nuclei in a cell-free system. Mol Cell Biol 7:4255–4265
Matsuura S, Masuda R, Omori I, Negishi M, Tashiro Y (1981) Distribution and Induction of cytochrome P-450 in rat liver nuclear envelope. J Cell Biol 91:212–220
Mattaj IW, De Robertis EM (1985) Nuclear segregation of U2 snRNA requires binding of specific snRNP proteins. Cell 40:111–118.
Mattaj IW, Lienhard S, Zeller R, De Robertis EM (1983) Nuclear exclusion of transcription factor IIIA and the 42S particle transfer RNA-binding protein in *Xenopus* oocytes: a possible mechanism for gene control? J Cell Biol 97:1261–1265
Maul GG (1977) The nuclear and cytoplasmic pore complex: structure, dynamics, distribution, and evolution. Int Rev Cytol Suppl 6:75–186
Miake-Lye R, Kirschner MW (1985) Induction of early mitotic events in a cell-free system. Cell 41:165–175
Milligan RA (1986) A structural model for the nuclear pore complex. In: Peters R, Trendelenburg M (eds) Nucleocytoplasmic Transport. Springer, Berlin Heidelberg New York Tokyo, pp 113–122
Moreland RB, Nam HG, Hereford LM, Fried HM (1985) Identification of a nuclear localization signal of a yeast ribosomal protein. Proc Natl Acad Sci USA 82:6561–6565
Moreland RB, Nam HG, Hereford LM, Fried HM (1986) Identification of a nuclear localization signal of yeast ribosomal protein L3. Yeast cell biology. Alan R Liss, Inc, New York, pp 379–393
Moreland RB, Langevin GL, Singer RH, Garcea RL Hereford LM (1987) Amino acid sequences that determine the nuclear localization of yeast histone 2B. Mol Cell Biol 7:4048–4057
Morgan C, Rosenkranz HS, Mednis B (1969) Structure and development of viruses as observed in the electron microscope. V. Entry and uncoating of adenovirus. J Virol 4:777–796
Munro S, Pelham HRB (1984) Use of peptide tagging to detect proteins expressed from cloned genes: deletion mapping functional domains of *Drosophila* hsp70. EMBO J 3:3087–3093
Newmeyer DD, Forbes DJ (1988) Nuclear import can be separated into distinct steps in vitro: nuclear pore binding and translocation. Cell 52:641–653
Newmeyer DD, Forbes DJ (1990) An N-ethylmaleimide-sensitive cytosolic factor necessary for nuclear protein import: requirement in signal-mediated binding to the nuclear pore. J Cell Biol (in press)
Newmeyer DD, Ohlsson-Wilhelm BM (1985) Monoclonal antibody to a protein of the nucleus and mitotic spindle of mammalian cells. Localization and synthesis throughout the cell cycle. Chromosoma 92:297–303
Newmeyer DD, Finlay DR, Forbes DJ (1986a) In vitro transport of a fluorescent nuclear protein and exclusion of non-nuclear proteins. J Cell Biol 103:2091–2102
Newmeyer DD, Lucocq JM, Bürglin TR, De Robertis EM (1986b) Assembly in vitro of nuclei active in nuclear protein transport: ATP is required for nucleoplasmin accumulation. EMBO J 5:501–510
Newport J (1987) Nuclear reconstitution in vitro: stages of assembly around protein-free DNA. Cell 48:205–217
Newport J, Forbes DJ (1985) Fate of DNA injected into *Xenopus* eggs and in egg extracts: assembly into nuclei. Banbury Rep 20:243–250
Newport J, Forbes DJ (1987) The nucleus: structure, function and dynamics. Annu Rev Biochem 56:535–565

Newport J, Spann T (1987) Disassembly of the nucleus in mitotic extracts: membrane vesicularization, lamin disassembly, and chromosome condensation are independent processes. Cell 48:219–230
Nigg EA, Hilz H, Eppenberger HM, Dutly F (1985) Rapid and reversible translocation of the catalytic subunit of cAMP-dependent protein kinase type II from the Golgi complex to the nucleus. EMBO J 4:2801–2806
Pain D, Kanwar YS, Blobel G (1988) Identification of a receptor for protein import into chloroplasts and its localization to envelope contact zones. Nature 331:232–236
Paine PL (1987) The in vivo cytomatrix: minimally-disturbed systems. Molecular mechanisms in the regulation of cell behavior. Alan R Liss Inc, pp 169–175
Paine PL, Horowitz SB (1980) The movement of material between nucleus and cytoplasm. In: Prescott DM, Goldstein L (eds.) Cell biology: a comprehensive treatise. Academic Press, New York, Vol 4, pp 299–338
Paine PL, Moore LC, Horowitz SB (1975) Nuclear envelope permeability. Nature 254:109–114
Papamichail M, Tsokos G, Tsawdaroglou N, Sekeris CE (1980) Immunocytochemical demonstration of glucocorticoid receptors in different cell types and their translocation from the cytoplasm to the cell nucleus in the presence of dexamethasone. Exp Cell Res 125:490–493
Park MK, D'Onofrio M, Willingham MC, Hanover JA (1987) A Monoclonal antibody against a family of nuclear pore proteins (nucleoporins) recognizes a shared determinant: O-linked N-acetylglucosamine. Proc Natl Acad Sci USA 84:6462–6466
Pathak RK, Luskey KL, Anderson RG (1986) Biogenesis of the crystalloid endoplasmic reticulum in UT-1 cells: evidence that newly formed endoplasmic reticulum emerges from the nuclear envelope. J Cell Biol 102:2158–2168
Perrot-Applanat M, Groyer-Picard MT, Logeat F, Milgrom E (1986) Ultrastructural localization of the progesterone receptor by an immunogold method: effect of hormone administration. J Cell Biol 102:1191–1199
Peters R (1986) Fluorescence microphotolysis to measure nucleocytoplasmic transport and intracellular mobility. Biochim Biophys Acta 864:305–359
Peters R, Lang I, Scholz M, Schulz B, Kayne F (1986) Fluorescence microphotolysis to measure nucleocytoplasmic transport in vivo et vitro. Biochem Soc Trans (Lond) 14:821–822
Pfeffer SR, Rothman JE (1987) Biosynthetic protein transport and sorting by the endoplasmic reticulum and Golgi. Annu Rev Biochem 56:829–852
Picard D, Yamamoto KR (1987) Two signals mediate hormone-dependent nuclear localization of the glucocorticoid receptor. EMBO J 6:3333–3340
Poliquin L, Levine G, Shore GC (1985) Involvement of Golgi apparatus and a restructured nuclear envelope during biogenesis and transport of herpes simplex virus glycoproteins. J Histochem Cytochem 33:875–883
Puddington L, Lively MO, Lyles DS (1985) Role of the nuclear envelope in synthesis, processing, and transport of membrane glycoproteins. J Biol Chem 260:5641–5647
Rapoport TA (1986) Protein translocation across and integration into membranes. CRC Crit Rev Biochem 20:73–137
Rechsteiner M, Kuehl L (1979) Microinjection of the nonhistone chromosomal protein HMG1 into bovine fibroblasts and HeLa cells. Cell 16:901–908
Richardson JC, Maddy AH (1980) The polypeptides of rat liver nuclear envelope. II. Comparison of rat liver nuclear membrane polypeptides to those of the rough endoplasmic reticulum. J Cell Sci 43:269–277
Richardson WD, Roberts BL, Smith AE (1986) Nuclear location signals in polyoma virus large-T. Cell 44:77–85
Richardson WD, Mills AD, Dilworth SM, Laskey RA, Dingwall C (1988) Nuclear protein migration involves two steps: rapid binding at the nuclear envelope followed by slower translocation through nuclear pores. Cell 52:665–664
Richter JD, Young P, Jones NC, Krippl B, Rosenberg M, Ferguson B (1985) A first exon-encoded domain of E1A sufficient for post-translational modification, nuclear-localization, and induction of adnovirus E3 promoter expression in *Xenopus* oocytes. Proc Natl Acad Sci USA 82:8434–8438

Riedel N, Fasold H (1987a) Preparation and characterization of nuclear-envelope vesicles from rat liver nuclei. Biochem J 241:203–212
Riedel N, Fasold H (1987b) Nuclear-envelope vesicles as a model system to study nucleo-cytoplasmic transport. Specific uptake of nuclear proteins. Biochem J 241:213–219
Riedel N, Bachmann M, Prochnow D, Richter H-P, Fasold H (1987) Permeability measurements with closed vesicles from rat liver nuclear envelopes. Proc Natl Acad Sci USA 84:3540–3544
Rihs H-P, Peters R (1989) Nuclear kinetics depend on phosphorylation-site-containing sequences flanking the karyphilic signal of the simian virus 40 T-antigen. EMBO J 8:1479–1484
Roberts BL, Richardson WD, Smith AE (1987) The effect of protein context on nuclear location signal function. Cell 50:465–475
Roise D, Schatz G (1988) Mitochondrial presequences. J Biol Chem 263:4509–4511
Rothman JE (1987) Protein sorting by selective retention in the endoplasmic reticulum and Golgi stack. Cell 50:521–522
Sap J, Muñoz A, Damm K, Goldberg Y, Ghysdael J, Leutz A, Beug H, Vennstroem B (1986) The c-erb-A protein is a high-affinity receptor for thyriod hormone. Nature 324:635–640
Sato C, Nishizawa K, Nakayama T, Nose K, Takasaki Y, Hirose S, Nakamura H (1986a) Intranuclear appearance of the phosphorylated form of cytoskeleton-associated 350-kDa proteins in U1-ribonucleoprotein regions after growth stimulation of fibroblasts. Proc Natl Acad Sci USA 83:7287–7291
Sato C, Nishizawa K, Nakayama T, Hirai R, Nakamura H (1986b) Phosphorylated 350-kDa protein in the nucleus as it is associated with cell transformation. Exp Cell Res 167:281–286
Scheer U, Franke WW (1969) Negative staining and adenosine triphosphatase activity of annulate lamellae of newt oocytes. J Cell Biol 42:519–533
Schindler M, Jiang L-W (1986) Nuclear actin and myosin as control elements in nucleocytoplasmic transport. J Cell Biol 102:859–862
Schindler M, Jiang L-W (1987) Epidermal growth factor and insulin stimulate nuclear pore-mediated macromolecular transport in isolated rat liver nuclei. J Cell Biol 104:849–853
Schindler M, Hogan M, Miller R, Gaetano D (1987) A nuclear specific glycoprotein representative of a unique pattern of glycosylation. J Biol Chem 262:1254–1260
Schleyer M, Neupert W (1985) Transport of proteins into mitochondria: translocational intermediates spanning contact sites between outer and inner membranes. Cell 43:339–350
Schröder HC, Rottman M, Bachmann M, Müller WEG (1986) Purification and characterization of the major nucleoside triphosphatase from rat liver nuclear envelopes. J Biol Chem 261:663–668
Schulz B, Peters R (1987) Nucleocytoplasmic protein traffic in single mammalian cells studied by fluorescence microphotolysis. Biochim Biophys Acta 930:419–431
Sheehan MA, Mills AD, Sleeman AM, Laskey RA, Blow JJ (1988) Steps in the assembly of replication-competent nuclei in a cell-free system. J Cell Biol 106:1–12
Shekman R (1985) Protein localization and membrane traffic in yeast. Annu Rev Cell Biol 1:115–143
Sillekens PTG, Habets WJ, Beijer RP, Vanrooij WJ (1987) cDNA cloning of the human U1 snRNA-associated A protein: extensive homology between U1 and U2 snRNP proteins. EMBO J 6:3841–3848
Silver PA, Hall MN (1988) Transport of proteins into the nucleus. In: Das RC, Robbins PW (eds) Protein transport and organelle biogenesis. Academic Press, Orlando, Florida
Silver PA, Keean LP, Ptashne M (1984) Amino terminus of the yeast GAL4 gene product is sufficient for nuclear localization, Proc Natl Acad Sci USA 81:5951–5955
Smith AE, Kalderon D, Roberts BL, Colledge WH, Edge M, Gillett P, Markham A, Paucha E, Richardson WD (1985) The nuclear signal. Proc R Soc Lond B 226:43–58
Smith CD, Wells WW (1983) Phosphorylation of rat liver nuclear envelopes. II. Characterization of in vitro lipid phosphorylation. J Biol Chem 258:9368–9373
Smith CD, Wells WW (1984) Solubilization and reconstitution of a nuclear envelope-associated ATPase. Synergistic activation by RNA and polyphosphoinositides. J Biol Chem 259:11890–11894

Snow CM, Senior A, Gerace L (1987) Monoclonal antibodies identify a group of nuclear pore complex glycoproteins. J Cell Biol 104:1143–1156
Stacey DW, Allfrey VG (1984) Microinjection studies of protein transit across the nuclear envelope of human cells. Exp Cell Res 154:283–292
Stevens BJ, Swift H (1966) RNA transport from nucleus to cytoplasm in *Chironomus* salivary glands. J Cell Biol 31:55–77
Stick R, Hausen P (1985) Changes in the nuclear lamina composition during early development of *Xenopus laevis*. Cell 41:191–200
Sugawa H, Imamoto N, Wataya-Kaneda M, Uchida T (1985) Foreign protein can be carried into the nucleus of mammalian cell by conjugation with nucleoplasmin. Exp Cell Res 159:419–429
Summers MD (1971) Electron microscope observations on granulosis virus entry, uncoating and replication processes during infection of the midgut cells of *Trichoplusia ni*. J Ultrastr Res 35:606–625
Suprynowicz FA, Gerace L (1986) A fractionated cell-free system for analysis of prophase nuclear disassembly. J Cell Biol 103:2073–2081
Theissen H, Etzerodt M, Reuter R, Schneider C, Lottspeich F, Argos P, Lührmann R, Philipson L (1986) Cloning of the human cDNA for the U1 RNA-associated 70K protein. EMBO J 5:3209–3217
Torrisi MR, Lotti LV, Pavan A, Migliaccio G, Bonatti S (1987) Free diffusion to and from the inner nuclear membrane of newly synthesized plasma membrane glycoproteins. J Cell Biol 104:733–737
Tsuneoka M, Imamoto NS, Uchida T (1986) Monoclonal antibody against non-histone chromosomal protein high mobility group 1 co-migrates with high mobility group 1 into the nucleus. J Biol Chem 261:1829–1834
Unwin NT, Milligan RA (1982) A large particle associated with the perimeter of the nuclear pore complex. J Cell Biol 93:63–75
Vale RD (1987) Intracellular transport using microtubule-based motors. Annu Rev Cell Biol 3:347–378
Velasquez JM, Lindquist S (1984) hsp70: nuclear concentration during environmental stress and cytoplasmic storage during recovery. Cell 36:655–662
Vorbrodt A, Maul GG (1980) Cytochemical studies on the relation of nucleoside triphosphatase activity to ribonucleoproteins in isolated rat liver nuclei. J Histochem Cytochem 28:27–35
Walter P, Gilmore R, Blobel G (1984) Protein translocation across the endoplasmic reticulum. Cell 38:5–8
Warner JR (1979) Distribution of newly formed ribosomal proteins in HeLa cell fractions. J Cell Biol 80:767–772
Warrick HM, Spudich JA (1987) Myosin structure and function in cell motility. Annu Rev Cell Biol 105:379–421
Watson MEE (1984) Compilation of published signal sequences. Nucleic Acids Res 12:5145–5164
Watson ML (1955) The nuclear envelope. Its structure and relation to cytoplasmic membranes. J Biophys Biochem Cytol 1:257–270
Welshons WV, Lieberman ME, Gorski J (1984) Nuclear localization of unoccupied oestrogen receptors. Nature 307:747–749
Welshons WV, Krummel BM, Gorski J (1985) Nuclear localization of unoccupied receptors for glucocorticoids, estrogens, and progesterone in GH3 cells. Endocrinology 117:2140–2147
Wieben ED, Madore SJ, Pederson T (1983) U1 small nuclear ribonucleoprotein studied by in vitro assembly. J Cell Biol 96:1751–1755
Wieben ED, Rohleder AM, Nenninger JM, Pederson T (1985) cDNA cloning of a human autoimmune nuclear ribonucleoprotein antigen. Proc Natl Acad Sci USA 82:7914–7918
Wolff B, Willingham MC, Hanover JA (1988) Direct visualization of nuclear protein import: specificity for transport across the nuclear pore. Exp Cell Res 178:318–334
Wu RS, Warner JR (1971) Cytoplasmic synthesis of nuclear proteins. J Cell Biol 51:643–652
Wychowski C, Benichou D, Girard M (1986) A domain of SV40 capsid polypeptide VP1 that specifies migration into the cell nucleus. EMBO J 5:2569–2576

Yamasaki L, Kanda P, Lanford RE (1989) Identification of four nuclear transport signal-binding proteins that interact with diverse transport signals. Mol Cell Biol 9:3028–3036

Yasuzumi G, Tsubo I (1986) The fine structure of nuclei as revealed by electron microscopy. III. Adenosine triphosphatase activity in the pores of nuclear envelope of mouse choroid plexus epithelial cells. Exp Cell Res 43:281–292

Yoneda Y, Imamoto-Sonobe N, Yamaizumi M, Uchida T (1987a) Reversible inhibition of protein import into the nucleus by wheat germ agglutinin injected into cultured cells. Exp Cell Res 173:586–595

Yoneda Y, Arioka T, Imamoto-Sonobe N, Sugawa H, Shimonishi Y, Uchida T (1987b) Synthetic peptides containing a region of SV40 large T-antigen involved in nuclear localization direct the transport of proteins into the nucleus. Exp Cell Res 170:439–452

Yoneda Y, Imamoto-Sonobe N, Matsuoka Y, Iwamoto R, Kiho Y, Uchida T (1988) Antibodies to asp-asp-glu-asp can inhibit transport of nuclear proteins into the nucleus. Science 242:275–278

Zeller R, Nyffenegger T, De Robertis EM (1983) Nucleocytoplasmic distribution of snRNPs and stockpiled snRNA-binding proteins during oogenesis and early development in *Xenopus laevis*. Cell 32:425–434

Zieve GW, Sauterer RA, Feeney RJ (1988) Newly synthesized small nuclear RNAs appear transiently in the cytoplasm. J Mol Biol 199:259–267

Zimmer FJ, Dreyer C, Hausen P (1988) The function of the nuclear envelope in nuclear protein accumulation. J Cell Biol 106:1435–1444

Cytoplasmic Assembly and Nuclear Transport of the snRNP Particles

G. W. ZIEVE and R. J. FEENEY[1]

A. Introduction

The snRNP particles, a family of six major (U1–U6) and a growing number of minor, less abundant (U7–U12) ribonucleoprotein particles, are stable components of the interphase nucleus (Table 1, Figs. 1A, 2). In the nucleus, the snRNP particles function in RNA processing including the removal of introns, 3′ end formation of pre-mRNA, and rRNA maturation. During the processing events several of the individual snRNPs assemble together into complexes with the substrate. Some of the snRNPs provide sequence specificity by base-pairing between the snRNAs and conserved sequence motifs in their substrates. With only limited exception, the snRNP particles contain a single snRNA and approximately eight proteins, including a shared core of six or seven proteins and several snRNP specific proteins. The common core in human cells includes the 29 kDa B′, 28 kDa B, 17 kDa D′, 16 kDa D, 13 kDa E, 12 kDa F, and 11 kDa G proteins in a stoichiometry of $BB'D'_2D_2EFG$ (Table 2, Fig. 4). Assembly of the common core proteins is directed by a sequence motif of PuA $(U)_nGPu$ ($n > 3$) present in single-stranded regions of the snRNAs. snRNP core assembly occurs in the cytoplasm where newly synthesized snRNAs appear transiently, immediately after transcription, before returning permanently to the interphase nucleus. Several recent reviews have summarized the structure and function of the snRNP particles (Brunel et al. 1985; Birnstiel 1988; Dreyfuss et al. 1988; Guthrie 1988; Zieve and Sauterer 1990). This report reviews current knowledge about the cytoplasmic assembly and nuclear transport of the snRNP particles in somatic mammalian cells and oocytes.

B. Maturation of the snRNAs

I. *snRNAs Appear Transiently in the Cytoplasm*

Early cell fractionation data identified the newly transcribed snRNAs in cytoplasmic fractions prepared from HeLa cells. As early as 2 min after the

[1] Department of Anatomical Sciences and program in Cellular and Developmental Biology, SUNY Stony Brook, Stony Brook, NY 11794-8081, USA

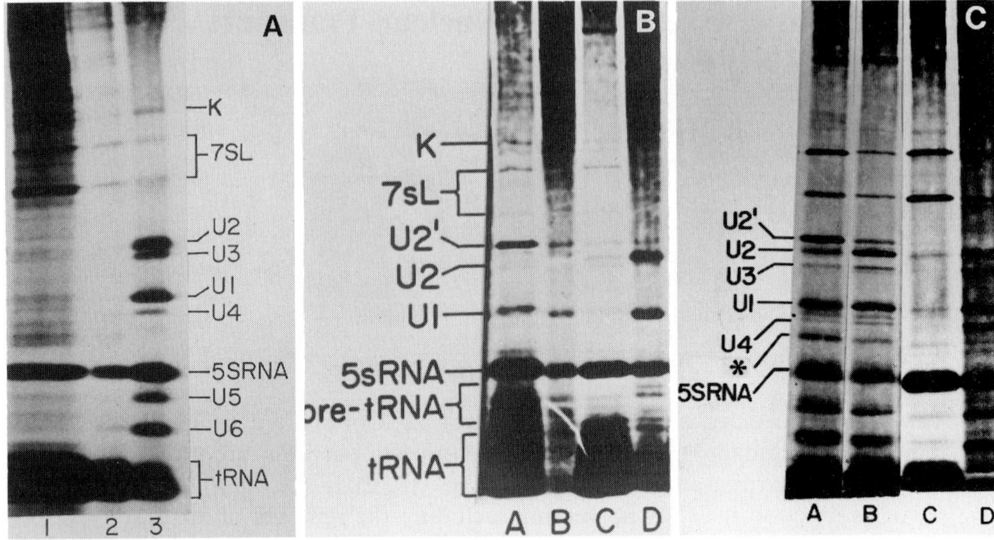

Fig. 1. snRNAs in the cytoplasm and nucleus of L929 cells. (*A*) L929 cells were labeled with 5 μC/ml 3H-uridine for 16 h and then fractionated into cytoplasm and nucleus using aqueous cell fractionation. *Lanes 1* and *2* are the solubilized cytoplasm and *lane 3* is the nuclear fraction. (*B*) L929 cells were fractionated into cytoplasm (*lanes A* and *C*) and nucleus (*lanes B* and *D*) after a pulse label (*lanes A* and *B*) and chase (*lanes C* and *D*). snRNAs were labeled for 20 min with 3H-uridine and chased for 45 min with 5 μg/ml actinomycin D and whole cell fractions were analyzed directly on gradient gels. Newly synthesized snRNAs exhibit quantitative maturation into nuclear species during a chase. (*C*) L929 cells were labeled with 3H-uridine and then pretreated for 10 min with 10 μg/ml cytochalasin B and enucleated on 12.5–25% Ficoll gradients. Cytoplasts and karyoplasts were harvested and the small RNA species were analyzed on 6–15% gradient gels. *Lane A* illustrates the small RNA species present in cytoplasts prepared from cells pulse labeled for 20 min with 80 μC/ml ^{3}H uridine. *Lane B* represents the small RNAs present in an identical preparation of cytoplasts cultured for 60 min after enucleation and before harvesting. *Lanes C* and *D* display the stable RNAs in cytoplasts and karyoplasts, respectively, from cells labeled for 16 h with 5μC/ml ^{3}H uridine

Table 1. snRNAs in mammalian cells

Size	Nucleotides	Abundance x 10^6	5′ End	Function
U1	165	1.0	m3GpppAmUmA	Pre-mRNA splicing
U2	189	0.9	m3GpppAmUmC	Pre-mRNA splicing
U3	216	0.2	m3GpppAmAmG	Pre-rRNA processing
U4	139	0.2	m3GpppAmGmC	Pre-mRNA splicing
U5	117	0.2	m3GpppAmUmA	Pre-mRNA splicing
U6	107	0.4	CH_3pppGUG	Pre-mRNA splicing
U7	56	< 0.05	m3GpppAUC	Histone 3′ end formation
U8	139	< 0.05	m3GpppAmUmC	Pre-rRNA processing
U9	130	< 0.05	m3GpppA	?
U10	60	< 0.05	m3GpppA	?
U11	131	< 0.05	m3GpppA	Pre-mRNA polyadenylation
U12	150	< 0.05	m3GpppN	?

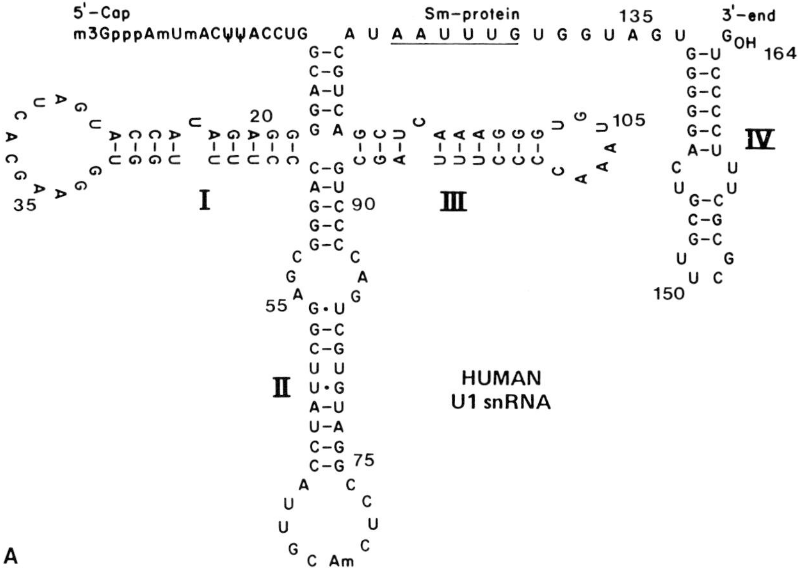

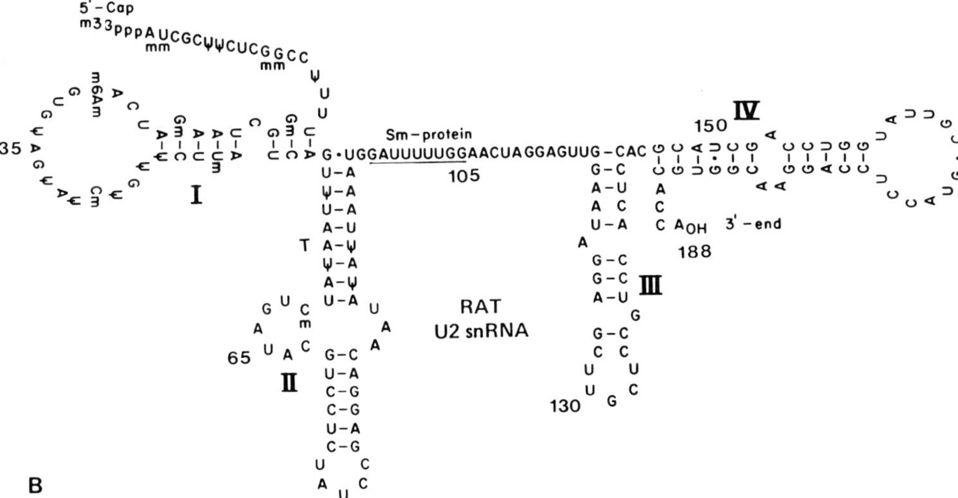

Fig. 2. Sequences and predicted secondary structures of U1 and U2 snRNAs. Sequences and predicted secondary structures are illustrated for human U1 (164 nucleotides) in *panel A*, rat U2 (188 nucleotides) in *panel B*. Stem loops are *numbered* and the Sm binding site is *underlined*. Methylated nucleotides are indicated with an *m* and pseudouridine as a ψ. Recent model suggests first stem loop of U2 is only nucleotides 7 to 28

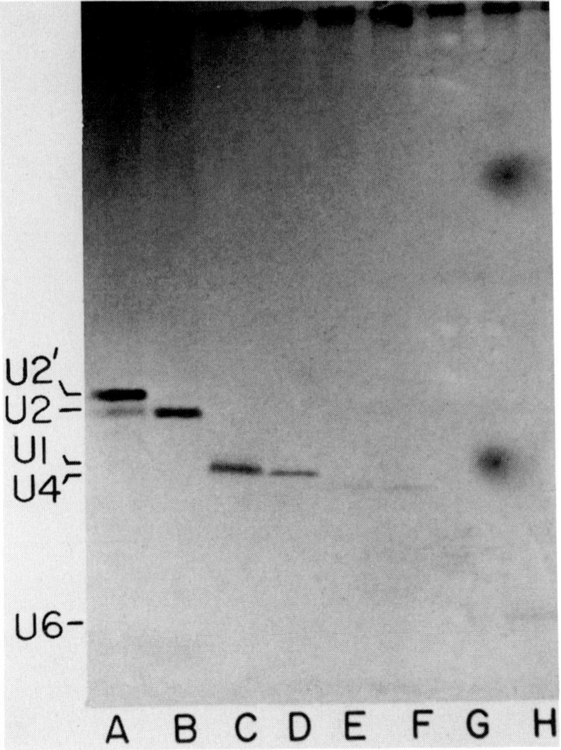

Fig. 3. Processing of snRNAs in the cytoplasm during a pulse and chase. L929 cells were pulse labeled for 12 min with 3H-uridine and then enucleated. Species *U1* (*lanes C* and *D*), *U2* (*lanes A* and *B*), *U4* (*lanes E* and *F*) and *U6* (*lanes G* and *H*) were hybrid selected from cytoplast fractions immediately after enucleation (*lanes A, C, E,* and *G*) and after cytoplasts were maintained in culture for 30 min (*lanes B, D, F,* and *H*)

initiation of labeling, the most abundant snRNAs, Ul and the U2 precursor U2′, are identifiable in the cytoplasmic fractions (Eliceiri 1974; Frederiksen and Hellung-Larsen 1975; Zieve and Penman 1976, Fig. 1B). The kinetics of accumulation suggest the snRNAs begin appearing in the cytoplasm almost immediately after the completion of transcription (Sauterer et al. 1988). With the exception of U6, which is transcribed by RNA polymerase III, the snRNAs are transcribed by RNA polymerase II and a 7-methylguanosine cap is added during transcription as in other polymerase II transcripts (for review, Parry et al. 1989). Later, during the cytoplasmic maturation, this cap is hypermethylated to the 2,2,7-trimethylguanosine cap which is unique to the snRNAs, as discussed below. It appears likely that the snRNAs are exported from the nucleus by mechanisms similar to those that export other polymerase II products (Agutter 1988). However, the pool of nuclear precursors is small and little is known about the proteins associated with the newly transcribed snRNAs in the nucleus before they assemble into snRNPs.

Table 2. Protein composition of the snRNPs

snRNP	Protein	Molecular weight (kDa) SDS-PAGE	cDNA	Reference
Shared "core"	B′	29	(same as B?)	
	B	28	29.1	Rokeach et al. 1990
	D′	17	—	
	D	16	13.3	Rokeach et al. 1988
	E	13	11	Stanford et al. 1987
	F	12		
	G	11		
Neural-specific variant of B	N	29	24.6	McAllister et al. 1989
U1 snRNP	"Core"	—		
	70 kDa	68–70	52	Query et al. 1989
	A	33	31	Sillekens et al. 1987
	C	22	17.4	Sillekens et al. 1988
U2 snRNP	"Core"	—		
	A′	32	28.4	Fresco and Keene 1989
	B″	29	25.5	Habets et al. 1987
U3 snRNP		74		Parker and Steitz 1987
		59		
		36		
		30		
		13		
		12.5		
U4 snRNP	"Core"	—		
		(23)		Lelay-Taha et al. 1986
		(12)		
		(10)		
		52		Bjørn et al. 1989
U5 snRNP	"Core"	—		
		25		Lelay-Taha et al. 1986
		70–100		Gerke and Steitz 1986
		260		Lossky et al. 1987

Because of the potential for nuclear leakage during cell fractionation, the appearance of the snRNAs in the cytoplasm required confirmation by techniques that prevented redistribution during cell lysis. Two fractionation procedures that minimize nuclear leakage, nonaqueous cell fractionation and cell enucleation, confirmed that all six of the major snRNAs appear in the cytoplasm of HeLa cells and mouse L929 fibroblasts immediately after transcription (Eliceiri and Gurney 1978; Gurney and Eliceiri 1980; Zieve et al. 1988; Figs. 1C, 3). Nonaqueous cell fractionation mechanically removes the cytoplasm from lyophilized cells, while cell enucleation extrudes the nucleus from cytochalasin treated cells and prepares a cytoplast fraction that represents a bona fide cytoplasm. Pulse and chase experiments, in which synthesis of snRNAs is halted by actinomycin D, indicate that all the newly synthesized cytoplasmic snRNAs mature and move into the nucleus (Zieve 1987; Fig. 1B). This strongly supports the hypothesis that all of the snRNAs appear transiently in the cytoplasm before returning to the nucleus.

The abundance of snRNA precursors in the cytoplasm of proliferating mouse L929 fibroblasts was analyzed using Northern blotting of cytoplast and karyoplast fractions prepared by cell enucleation (Sauterer et al. 1988). In proliferating cells the major snRNAs have relative abundances in the cytoplasm of ca. 2.5% of the nuclear abundance. Kinetic experiments employing both pulse and chase protocols and labeling to equilibrium indicated cytoplasmic half-lives of ca. 20 min. This rate of synthesis will double the total number of cellular snRNAs every 24 h, which is approximately the generation time of the L929 cells.

II. 3′ End Processing of snRNAs

The U1, U2, and U4 snRNAs appear in the cytoplasm as precursors that are slightly longer on the 3′ end then the mature snRNAs in the nucleus. In the cytoplasm, nucleotides are removed from these snRNAs to form the mature-sized species (Fig. 3). The U2 precursor, U2′, is approximately 11 nucleotides larger than mature U2 and is visible on gels as a discrete species in the cytoplasm. Pulse label and chase experiments indicate that processing of U2′ begins as early as 7 min after transcription (Eliceiri 1980; Zieve et al. 1988). The processing of U2′ occurs in cytoplasts, indicating that the majority of the trimming occurs in the cytoplasm, though the last few nucleotides are apparently trimmed in the nucleus (Zieve et al. 1988; Eliceiri 1980; Figs. 1C, 3).

The processing complex that trims the 3′ end of U2 has been isolated as a 7S complex on glycerol gradients (Kleinschmidt and Pederson 1987). The 7S complex will correctly process an in vitro transcribed U2′ molecule; however, the mature U2 degrades over time. The 7S activity appears to be a protein and the 3′ processing activity requires Mg^{+2} and ATP. Following the infection of BHK cells with the vesicular stomatitis virus, the processing of the U2′ precursor is rapidly inhibited and the precursors accumulate in the cell cytoplasm (Fresco et al. 1987).

U1 snRNA is also processed on the 3′ end in the cytoplasm, although the precursor is not a discrete species as observed with U2. The newly synthesized U1 precursors in the cytoplasm form a "ladder", extending at least eight nucleotides longer than mature U1 (Madore et al. 1984a; Zieve et al. 1988; Fig. 3). These precursors are processed to mature-sized U1 within 30 min, although some U1 snRNAs which are a few nucleotides longer than mature U1 are also found in the nucleus. This suggests that the final 3′ trimming may occur in the nucleus.

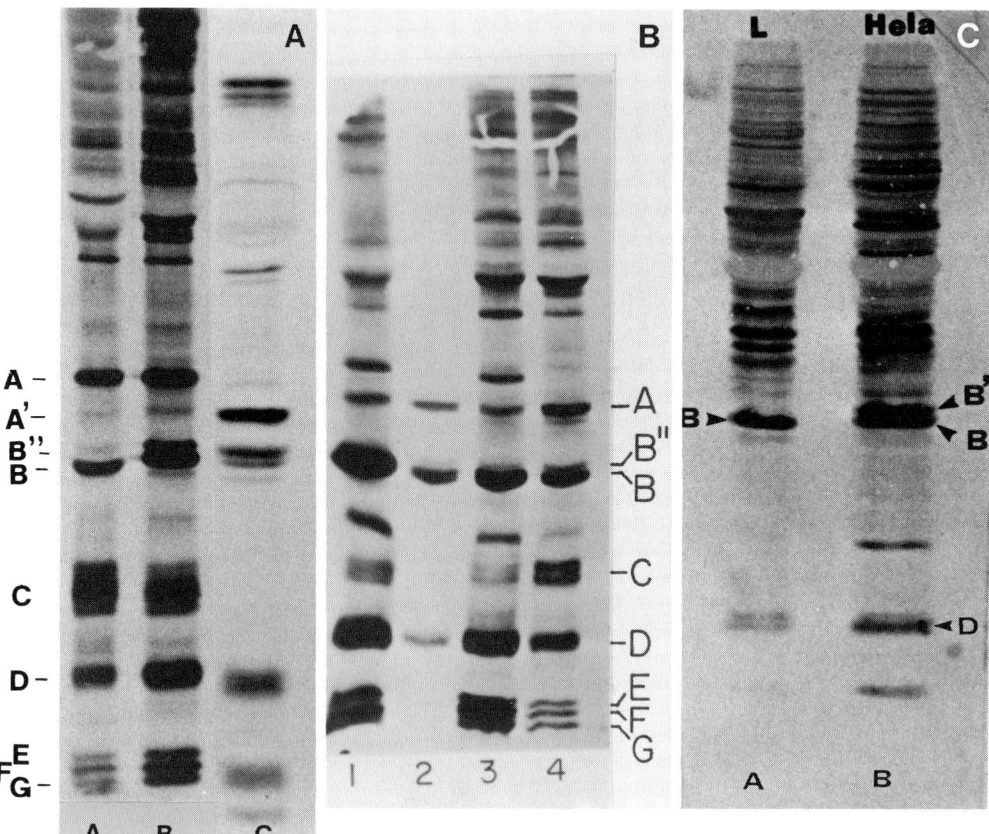

Fig. 4. snRNP proteins in the U1 and U2 snRNP particles. (*A*) L929 cells were labeled with 10 μC/ml ^{35}S- methionine (*lanes A* and *B*) or 10 μC/ml 3H-leucine for 16 h (*lane C*). Nuclear fractions prepared by aqueous cell fractionation were immunoprecipitated with a (U1) RNP monoclonal antiserum (*lane A*), the Y12 Sm antiserum (*lane B*) or a U2 patient antiserum (*lane C*). The *B*, *D*, *E*, *F*, and *G* common core proteins and the U1 specific *A* and *C* and the U2 specific *A'* and *B''* proteins are indicated. The U2 specific *A'* protein is leucine-rich and methionine-poor and is most obvious in cells labeled with leucine. The 70 kDa U1 specific protein is present in substoichiometric amounts and is difficult to identify on one-dimensional gels. (*B*) L929 cells were labeled with 50 μC/ml ^{35}S-methionine for 30 min (*lanes 1* and *2*) and chased with a 1000x excess of cold methionine for 90 min (*lanes 3* and *4*). Cytoplasmic (*lanes 1* and *3*) and nuclear (*lanes 2* and *4*) fractions were immunoprecipitated with Sm antiserum and resolved on 13% gels. The large pools of cytoplasmic snRNP proteins show only a small fraction maturing into nuclear particles during a 90-min chase. (*C*) Whole cell fractions of murine L929 cells (*L*) and human *HeLa* (H) cell line were analyzed on 13% polyacrylamide gels, transferred to nitrocellulose, and probed with a human Sm antiserum using an alkaline phosphatase coupled second antibody. The serum recognizes the *B* and *D* proteins in the murine cells and the *B*, *B'* and *D* proteins in human cells

The 3′ extensions on the U1 snRNA appear to be of heterogeneous sequence (Patton and Wieben 1987). The currently sequenced snRNA genes in human cells all have the same 3′ sequences, suggesting that some of the snRNAs are transcribed from genes that were previously considered nontranscribed pseudogenes (Manser and Gesteland 1982). At present, it is not known if these sequence variants correspond to specific variants in the coding region as well. Low abundance variants of the U1 snRNA that differ from the canonical sequence by a few nucleotides have been identified by RNA sequencing (Lund 1988). Some of the U1 3′ sequences contain the sequence $A(U)_nG$, where $n = 3$–6, which is the sequence motif responsible for the assembly of the core proteins with the mature snRNAs. Whether or not the 3′ sequences also bind snRNP proteins is not known (Patton and Wieben 1987).

A ladder of U4 precursors up to seven nucleotides longer than mature U4 has also been identified in the cytoplasm; processing to mature-sized U4 also occurs in this compartment (Madore et al. 1984b). Possible U3 precursors have been identified in pulse-labeled cytoplasmic extracts (Chandrasekharappa et al. 1983). Larger-sized cytoplasmic precursors of U5 and U6 have not been observed.

III. Nucleotide Modification Including the 5′ Cap

The snRNA species have a large number of modified nucleotides, including the hypermethylated 5′ cap, 2′-O-ribose methylated nucleotides, pseudouridine, and N-6 adenosine residues. Studies on tRNA and rRNA suggest pseudouridine and H-6 adenosine residues are formed in the nucleus (Melton et al. 1980; Nishikura and DeRobertis 1981). However, experimental data suggests that the hypermethylated caps and at least one 2-O-ribose methylation occur in the cytoplasm.

The major snRNAs, with the exception of U6, have a type II 5′ end with 2′-O-ribose methylations on the first two nucleotides 3′ to the cap structure. Cory and Adams (1975) first demonstrated that in mRNA, the first methylation took place in the nucleus, while the second was added later in the cytoplasm. snRNAs are the only nuclear RNAs with a type II 5′ end (Cory and Adams 1975). This suggested that the second methylation found on the nuclear snRNAs was generated during their transient appearance in the cytoplasm. However, this has not been documented experimentally to date.

The snRNAs, with the exception of U6, have the distinctive 2,2,7 trimethylguanosine cap. The snRNAs, again with the exception of U6, have a type I cap added during transcription like other polymerase II products (Eliceiri 1980; Skuzeski et al. 1984; Mattaj 1986). Experiments using *Xenopus* oocytes indicate that the snRNAs leave the nucleus with a standard 7-methylguanosine cap and that the extra methylations are added to the cap during their transient appearance in the cytoplasm (Mattaj 1986). The hypermethylation of the cap requires that the snRNA assemble into a bona fide snRNP particle. If the sequence motifs that direct snRNP assembly are altered and the snRNAs do not associate with the snRNP core proteins, the 5′ cap is not hypermethylated

(Mattaj 1986). The contribution of the snRNP core proteins to the hypermethylation is not clear; the U3 snRNP in the nucleolus, which lacks the common core of snRNP proteins found on nucleoplasmic snRNAs, also has a hypermethylated 5′ cap. Very little work has been done on the capping of snRNAs in mammalian cells.

The hypermethylated 5′ cap clearly distinguishes the snRNAs; it has been suggested that this prevents factors designed for recognizing the mRNA cap from binding to the snRNAs. If the monomethylated 5′ cap is a ligand for nuclear export of both the newly synthesized snRNAs and pre-mRNA, this would exclude the hypermethylated mature nuclear snRNPs. U6 snRNA, an RNA polymerase III transcript, does not have the trimethylguanosine cap, and phosphate is blocked with a methyl group (Kunkel et al. 1986; Reddy et al. 1987; Singh and Reddy 1989).

C. snRNP Particle Assembly

I. snRNP Proteins

With the exception of U6 and the nucleolar snRNAs U3 and U8, the mature snRNP particles share a common set of snRNP proteins in addition to several snRNP specific proteins (Bringmann et al. 1983; Petterson 1984; Kinlaw et al. 1983, Table 2, Fig. 4). Recent analyses suggest that in HeLa cells the common core has a stoichiometry of $BB'D'_2D_2EFG$ (Feeney et al. 1989). The assembly of the core proteins is directed by the short sequence motif $PuA(U)_nGPu$ ($n > 3$) (Liautard et al. 1982). The U1 and U2 snRNPs have a calculated molecular weight of ca. 400 kDa and are ca. 80% protein (Fig. 6). This is consistent with their density in cesium chloride or cesium sulfate at ca. 1.4 g/cm^3 (Lelay-Taha et al. 1986: Patton et al. 1987).

Analysis of the snRNP proteins has been aided by the availability of autoimmune antisera that recognize the snRNP proteins (Table 3, Figs. 4, 5). In the autoimmune disease systemic lupus erythematosus (SLE), 30% of patients

Table 3. Antibodies to the snRNPs

	Antigenic determinants	snRNPs precipitated
Anti-Sm	Mainly B and/or D. Rarely E or A	U1, U2, U4, U5, U6, U7, U8, U9, U10, U11
Anti-(U1) RNP	70 kDa protein	U1
Anti-(U1, U2)	A (U1) and B″ (U2) proteins	U1, U2
Anti-(U2)	A′ and B″ proteins	U2
Anti-(U3)	36 kDa protein	U3
Anti-La	50 kDa protein	U1, U6
Anti-m3G	2, 2, 7 Trimethyl guanosine	All except U6
Anti-m6A	N^6 Methyladenosine	U2, U4, U6

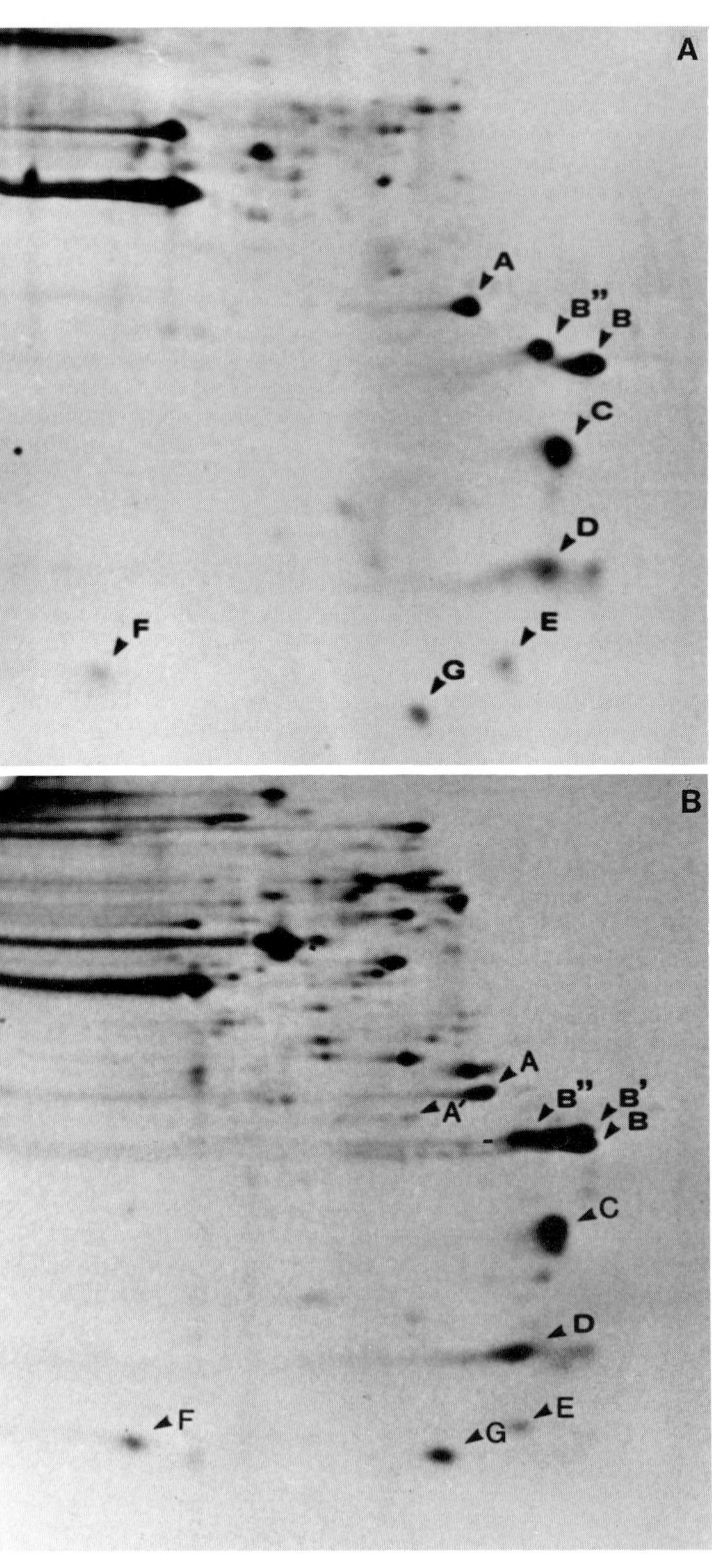
A
A
B"
B
C
D
F
E
G
B
A
A'
B"
B'
B
C
D
E
F
G

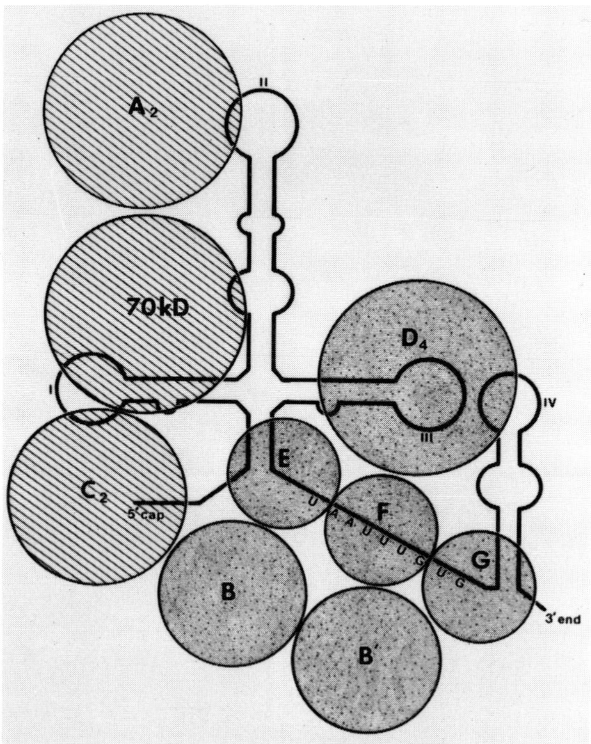

Fig. 6. Suggested structure and stoichiometry of the U1 snRNP particle. The snRNP core proteins (*B*, *D*, *E*, *F*, and *G*) and the U1 specific proteins (*A*, *C*, and 70kD) are positioned based on structural data discussed in the text. The cross-sections of each protein subunit are from spherical particles where the volume is proportional to the molecular weight

develop antisera against the B and D proteins (anti-Sm response) (Reichlin 1987). This is a polyclonal response and several monoclonal antibodies have been developed from autoimmune mice which recognize distinct epitopes on the B and D proteins (Lerner et al. 1981; Billings et al. 1985; Williams et al. 1986). SLE patients also develop activities against the U1 specific proteins 70 kDa, A, and C [anti-(U1) RNP response], which are also available as monoclonal antisera or as patient sera (Billings et al. 1982). Less frequent autoimmune responses are directed against the U2 and U3 specific proteins (Craft et al. 1988; Reimer et al. 1987, Table 3). It is not known why the snRNP proteins are often targets for the autoimmune response.

Fig. 5. Two-dimensional gel electrophoresis of Sm immunoprecipitates of nuclear fractions from HeLa and L929 cells. L929 (*A*) and HeLa (*B*) cells were labeled for 16 h with S35-methionine and nuclear fractions were immunoprecipitated with Sm antisera by standard procedures and analyzed by two-dimensional gel electrophoresis using nonequilibrium pH gradient gel electrophoresis in the first dimension. The snRNP core proteins (*B*, *B′*, *D*, *E*, *F*, and *G*) and the snRNP specific proteins (*A*, *C*, 70kD, and *A′*, *B″*) are identified

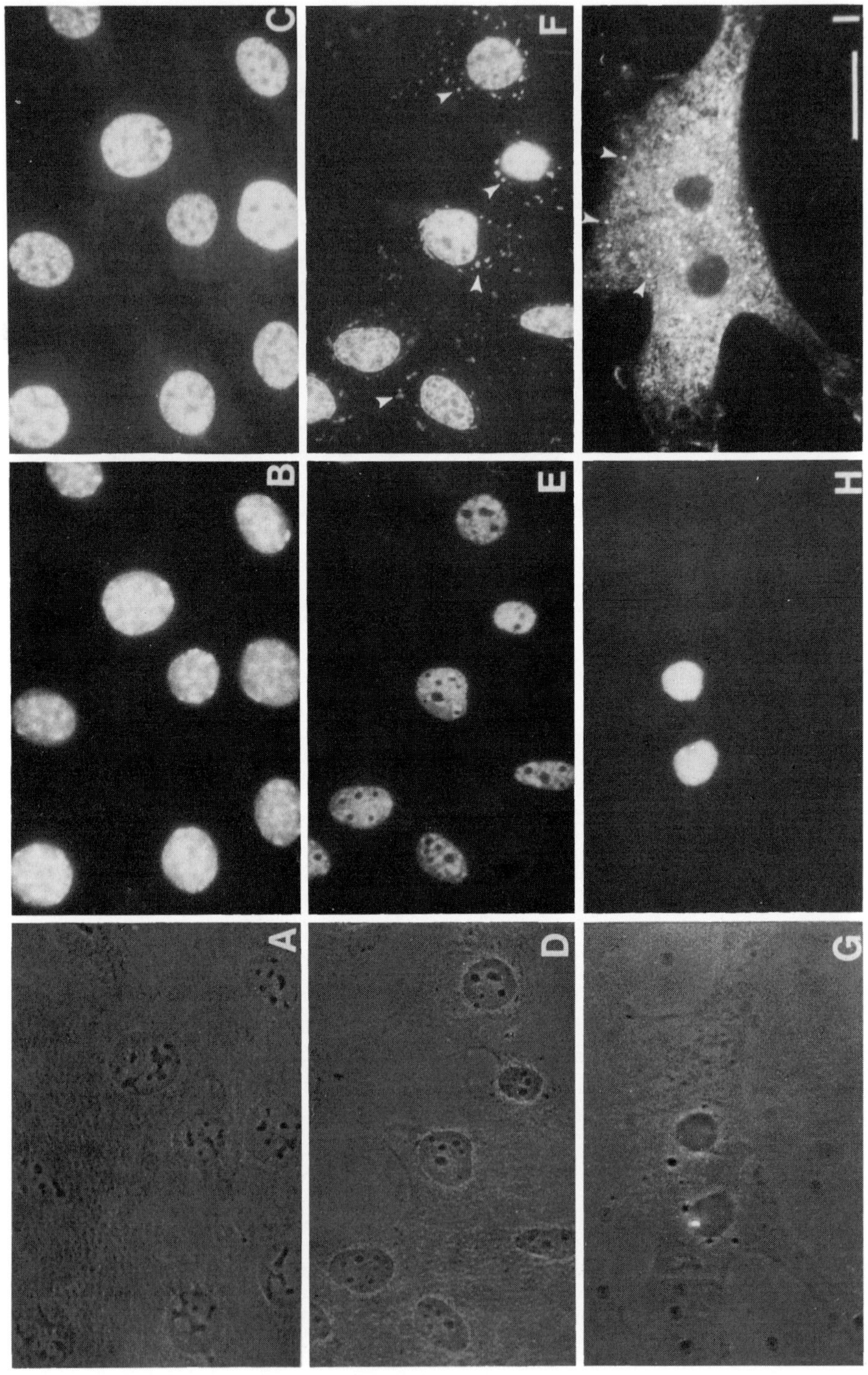
A
B
C
D
E
F
G
H
I

Newly synthesized snRNAs in the cytoplasm of somatic mammalian cells (with the exception of the nucleolar snRNAs and U6) are immunoprecipitated by the anti-Sm protein antibodies along with a full set of snRNP core proteins within 5 min of appearance in the cytoplasm (Chandrasekharappa et al. 1983; Zieve et al. 1988; Madore et al. 1984a). This suggests that snRNP assembly occurs very shortly after the snRNAs enter the cytoplasm, or alternatively, before they leave the nucleus. Cell fractionation and kinetic studies have defined the assembly pathway of the snRNP particles.

II. snRNP Core Protein Assembly

Quantitative analysis of the snRNP core proteins in both somatic mammalian cells and in amphibian oocytes identifies large pools of partially assembled RNA-free intermediates available for assembly with the newly transcribed snRNAs that appear transiently in the cytoplasm. The relative abundance of the snRNP core proteins in the cytoplasm of mammalian cells was calculated by Western blotting of karyoplast and cytoplast fractions prepared by cell enucleation. Blots with the anti-Sm sera indicate the abundance of the snRNP B protein in the cytoplasm to be 25% of the nuclear abundance (Sauterer et al. 1988). When compared to the 2.5% cytoplasmic abundance of the snRNAs, this suggests large pools of the B protein in the cytoplasm are not associated with snRNA. However, the cytoplasmic pools of snRNP protein are not readily identifiable in indirect immunofluorescent staining of fixed cells (Figs. 7, 10). Fluorescent staining with the anti-Sm antibody shows nuclear staining almost exclusively. This difficulty in identifying the cytoplasmic protein may be due to the problem of identifying a faint cytoplasmic staining in contrast to the concentrated nuclear staining; alternatively, the cytoplasmic antigens may be masked and not available for staning by the antibodies in fixed cells. However, in cells exposed to hypertonic medium where the volume of the cytoplasm is reduced by ca. 50%, foci of anti-Sm staining proteins are apparent in the cytoplasm (Zieve 1987; Fig. 7). This may be the result of the aggregation of the proteins induced by the removal of cellular water. In a possibly related phenomenon, the mature U1, U2, U4/U6, and U5 snRNPs in nuclear extracts assemble into a pseudospliceosome in hypertonic

Fig. 7. Hypertonic medium inhibits the intracellular transport of snRNPs during interphase and mitosis. Nil 8 hamster fibroblasts were exposed to hypertonic medium by the addition of 180 mM NaCl to the culture medium. Control and experimental cells were examined by phase microscopy (*A*, *D*, *G*), Hoechst staining (*B*, *E*, *H*), and indirect immunofluorescent staining with the Y12 anti-Sm monoclonal antiserum 1 h after the alteration in the tonicity of the culture medium. Control interphase cells (*A*, *B*, *C*) show typical nuclear localization of the Sm antigen. Interphase cells exposed to hypertonic medium (*D*, *E*, *F*) show the development of regions of Sm staining in the cytoplasm (*arrows*, panel *F*). Hypertonic medium prevents the action of the cleavage furrow and the reformation of the daughter nuclei in dividing cells (*G*, *H*, *I*). The chromatin remains condensed and the mature nuclear snRNPs dispersed throughout the cytoplasm as the cell spreads back out on its substratum. *Bar* = 10 μm

medium without association with substrate pre-mRNA (Konarska and Sharp 1988). This suggests that the snRNP core proteins have an intrinsic tendency to oligomerize in hypertonic medium.

The half-life of the cytoplasmic snRNP proteins was investigated by kinetic studies using both labeling to equilibrium, and pulse label and chase protocol, followed by immunoprecipitation of cytoplasm fractions. This data suggested that the snRNP proteins have a half-life in the cytoplasm of ca. 2.5 h (Sauterer et al. 1988). This indicates that a large, more stable pool of snRNP proteins is available for assembly with the smaller pool of more rapidly turning-over snRNAs. This is consistent with studies on the inhibition of protein synthesis which indicate that snRNP particle assembly occurs normally for over 30 min after the inhibition of protein synthesis with cycloheximide or emetine. Apparently, the large pools of snRNP protein are capable of supporting snRNP assembly when protein synthesis is arrested (Chandrasekharappa et al. 1983; Zieve 1987). This is in contrast to ribosome synthesis where assembly arrests soon after protein synthesis is halted (Willems et al. 1969).

To investigate the assembly pathway of the snRNPs, cells were pulse labeled, and the entrance of radioactivity into fully assembled snRNP particles in the cytoplasm and mature snRNP particles in the nucleus was assayed by immunoprecipitation with snRNP-specific antisera (Fig. 4B). Among the snRNP core proteins, the B protein in assembled snRNP particles becomes radioactive before the D, E, F, and G proteins (Fisher et al. 1985; Feeney et al. 1989). This suggests that the B protein is the last protein to add to the particles. As discussed below, the snRNP-specific proteins also become radioactive quickly; however, it is likely that they exchange with the mature snRNP particles (Fig. 8). In contrast, the common core of snRNP proteins are permanently associated with the snRNAs. More detailed fractionation studies combined with kinetic analysis have characterized the cytoplasmic pools of snRNP protein as a set of partially assembled RNA-free intermediates.

snRNP protein intermediates in the cytoplasm can be separated by sucrose gradient centrifugation of cytoplasmic fractions, followed by the identification of the proteins by either immunoprecipitation or two-dimensional gel electrophoresis (Fig. 9). Fisher et al. (1984, 1985) were the first to report that newly synthesized human snRNP D, E, F, and G proteins, labeled in a short pulse, are found in a 6S particle that is immunoprecipitable by Sm antisera both in vivo and in vitro. They suggested that this represents a 6S core that is a fundamental unit of the shared set of snRNP proteins. Recently available sequence data (Rokeach et al. 1988; Stanford et al. 1989; Ohosone et al. 1989) allows the correction of radioactive labeling to determine relative abundance, and suggests that the 6S core is a particle of D_2EFG (Feeney et al. 1988). In pulse and chase experiments the D_2EFG shifts to 10S and larger structures that also contain snRNA and the B and D′ protein. This suggests that snRNP core assembly requires the initial formation of the 6S core, which assembles with snRNA and then the D′ and B proteins. Subsequent studies of Zieve and coworkers (Sauterer et al. 1989; Feeney et al. 1989) extended this two-step model.

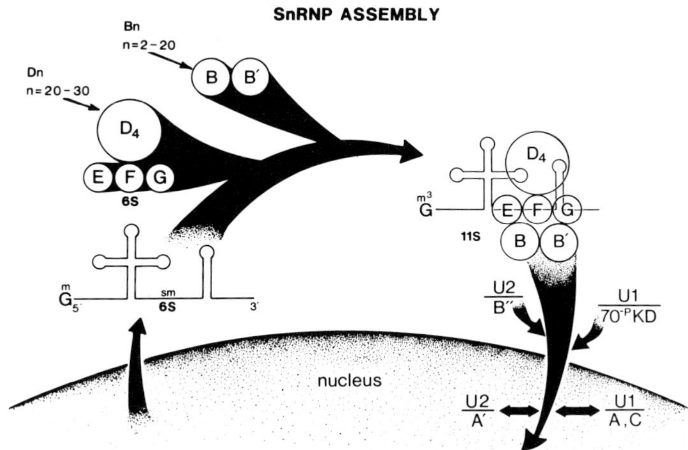

Fig. 8. Cartoon model of the cytoplasmic assembly and nuclear transport of the snRNP particles. Newly synthesized snRNAs appear transiently in the cytoplasm where they undergo 3′ end processing and cap hypermethylation and assemble with the snRNP core proteins stored in large, partially assembled pools in the cytoplasm. The *D*, *E*, *F*, and *G* core proteins preassemble into a 6S RNA free particle and homooligomers of *B* and *D* protein (B_n and D_n) are also present. The D_4EFG particle is actually D'_2D_2EFG. The dynamic behavior of the U1 and U2 snRNP specific proteins are also illustrated. There are large pools of the *A* and *C* U1 specific proteins and the *A′* U2 specific protein in the nucleus. However, there are no pools of the U2 specific B″ protein or the U1 specific 70 kDa phosphoprotein

Sedimentation analysis of pulse-labeled cytoplasmic extracts from rodent cells identified newly synthesized snRNP proteins sedimenting from 4S to 20S. Prior treatment with actinomycin D to deplete the cytoplasm of newly synthesized snRNAs did not alter the distribution of these proteins, indicating that the vast majority are snRNA free (Sauterer et al. 1989; Sauterer and Zieve 1989; Fig. 9). The authors suggest that these structures represent (a) a particle of D_2EFG at 6S; (b) particles containing the D′ protein at 20S; (c) a heterodisperse distribution of the B protein from 4S to 20S, all of which are immunoprecipitable by the Y12 anti-Sm monoclonal antibody and patient autoimmune Sm antisera. The D′ protein at 20S has a more acidic pI than D protein at 6S (Feeney et al. 1989). The heterodisperse sedimentation of the B protein suggests this protein has an intrinsic activity to oligomerize. The exact precursor of the B protein that assembles into mature snRNP particles is not known. However, several experiments suggest that the cosedimenting B and D protein at 6S and B and D′ at 20S are in independent or loosely associated structures (Sauterer and Zieve 1989).

When the same extract is immunoprecipitated with the 713 anti-Sm sera, a subset of the proteins are detected. B but not D′ is immunoprecipitated at 20S, and D, E, F, G but not B are precipitated at 6S. This activity of the 713 anti-Sm antisera is unusual because it recognizes primarily the D protein in Western

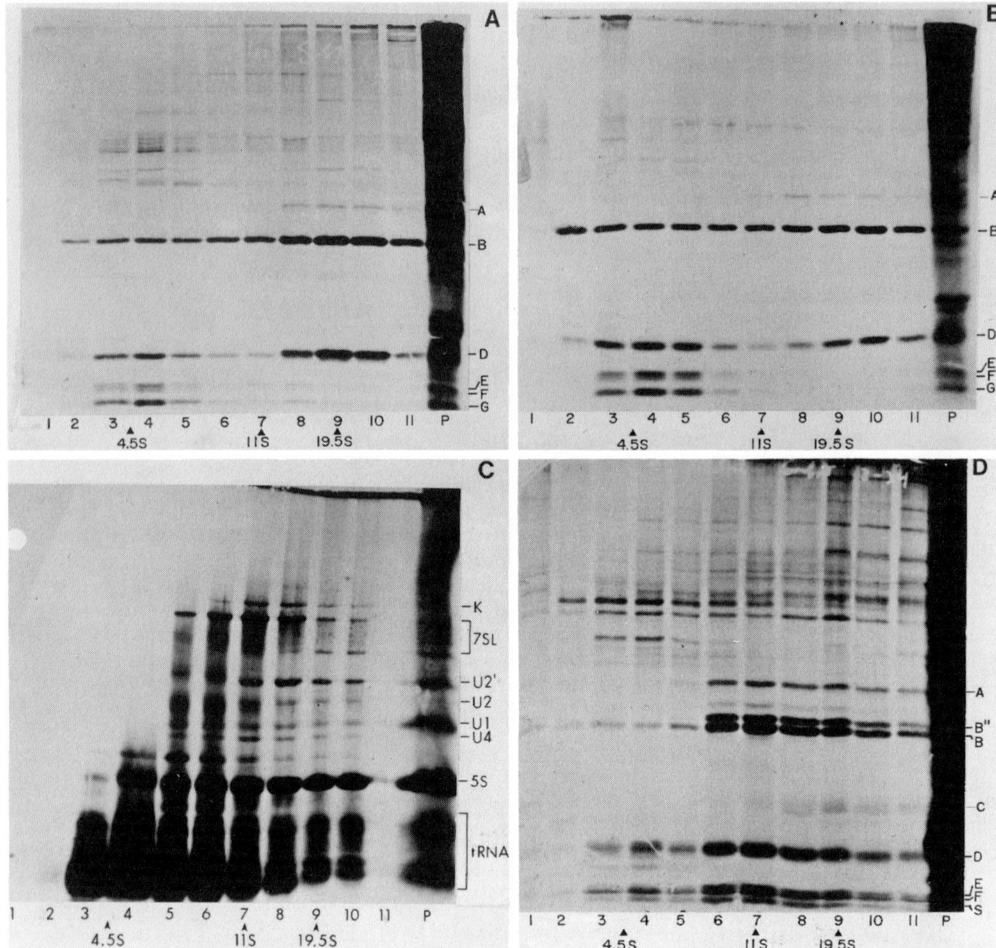

Fig. 9. Sedimentation analysis of mature nuclear snRNP particles and newly synthesized snRNP proteins in the cytoplasm. L929 cells were either labeled 1 h in methionine-free SMEM with 50 μCi/ml ^{35}S (*Panel A*) or pretreated 1 h with 10 μg/ml actinomycin D, then labeled for 1 h with 50 μCi/ml ^{35}S in methionine-free SMEM with 10 μg/ml actinomycin D (*Panel B*). CSK-Triton cytoplasmic extracts were fractionated on 5–15% sucrose gradients and immunoprecipitated with the anti-SM monoclonal antibody Y12. L929 cells were labeled in normal SMEM for 25 min with 100 μCi/ml ^{3}H uridine (*Panel C*), then the CSK-Triton cytoplasmic extract was fractionated on a sucrose gradient and the RNA was analyzed directly. Mature nuclear snRNPs were labeled with 10μC/ml 35S-methionine for 14 h and a nuclear fraction was analyzed on a 5–15% sucrose gradient and immunoprecipiated with the Y12 Sm antiserum (*Panel D*). Gradients were collected into 11 equal fractions and a pellet and the proteins were identified by precipitation with Sm antiserum. Markers run with a parallel gradient were identified by optical density and were BSA 4.5S, catalase 11S, and beta-galactosidase 19.5S. Note the snRNP particles sediment from 10–16S and the RNA-free proteins in the cytoplasm sediment distinctly different

blots (Billings et al. 1985). In addition, denaturation of the extracts with low concentrations of SDS disrupts the structures containing the D protein; however, the B protein remains in large particles. Both lines of evidence support the hypothesis that B and D are in independent structures at 6S (Sauterer et al. 1990). If these structures are homooligomers, the B protein would be in structures of B_n where n = 2–20; the particle of D′ at 20S is D'_n, n = 25–35.

This data suggests the mature snRNP particles assemble by a pathway where newly synthesized snRNAs in the cytoplasm bind initially to a 6S particle of D_2EFG then two copies of D′ and then two copies of the B protein, most likely through protein:protein interactions with the $D_2D'_2$FG core (Fig. 9). Structural studies are consistent with this model. The B protein can be stripped from this complex at high ionic strength in low magnesium (Liautard et al. 1982), leaving the $D_2D'_2$EFG core associated with the snRNA. However, in high magnesium the snRNP particles are particularly stable and retain their integrity without prior fixation after isopycnic banding in 1.2M cesium sulfate (Patton et al. 1987).

UV cross-linkage suggests that the F protein is most intimately associated with the snRNA (Luhrmann 1988). In addition, protein cross-linkage suggests the B and D core proteins can be cross-linked to the E and G core proteins but not each other, and that the Ul-specific proteins can cross-link to each other but not to the core proteins (Harris et al. 1988a, b). Taken together, this suggests the snRNP core proteins and the snRNP specific proteins are in different domains, and that the contacts of the B protein with the $D_2D'_2$FG core are through the E and G protein, not the D_2D′ tetramer (Fig. 5).

III. Relationship of B, B′, and N snRNP Core Proteins

In the HeLa cell line the B and B′ snRNP proteins are found in the cytoplasm and nucleus in a ratio of 1:1 and have a similar sedimentation distribution (Fisher et al. 1984, Figs. 4C, 5). Both the U1 snRNP, precipitated by U1 specific antibodies, and the full family of snRNPs, precipitated by the anti-Sm antisera, include both the B and B′ proteins in a similar ratio. A phylogenetic analysis suggests that in nonprimate cell lines, including rodent, avian, and amphibian cell lines, the B′ protein is absent (Feeney and Zieve, submitted; Figs. 4C, 5).

The B and B′ proteins in human cells have similar amino acid compositions and peptide maps, cross-react with the same antibodies, and have the identical N terminal sequence (Reuter et al. 1987; Rokeach et al. 1989). Also, Northern blotting with a B protein cDNA fails to identify more than one mRNA (Rokeach et al. 1990). This suggests that in human cells the B′ protein is a post translational modification of the B protein, or a very closely related gene product. The exact difference between the two proteins has not been identified.

Recently a cDNA was cloned for an snRNP protein, called the N protein, that is closely related to the B protein and is restricted primarily to neural tissue (McAllister et al. 1989). The N protein sequence is quite similar to that of the B protein (Schmauss et al. 1989). The N protein is recognized by the anti-Sm-class of autoantibodies and may represent a tissue-specific variant of the B protein. The N protein migrates with a molecular weight that is slightly larger than the B protein on polyacrylamide gels in the region of B′ and the U2-specific B″ protein (Table 2).

An additional protein termed D′ has been identified in the snRNP core (Bringmann and Luhrmann 1986). This protein is of slightly higher molecular weight than the D protein. D and D′ comigrate in many gel systems however the addition of urea shifts D′ to a higher molecular weight (Andersen, Feeney and Zieve, in preparation).

IV. U1 and U2 Specific Proteins

In contrast to the snRNP core proteins, which exist in large pools in the cytoplasm, the snRNP specific proteins are restricted primarily to the nucleus (Fig. 8) (Feeney and Zieve 1990). Data accumulated on the most abundant snRNP specific proteins, the U1-specific A, C, and 70 kDa proteins, and the U2-specific A′ and B″ proteins, has failed to identify cytoplasmic pools of these species, and the assembly kinetics differ for the individual proteins (Feeney et al. 1989). Several specific proteins associated with the less abundant snRNP particles have been identified, but little is known about their assembly kinetics (Table 2). The cDNAs for all the U1 and U2 specific proteins are now cloned and sequenced (Query and Keene 1987; Yamamoto et al. 1988; Sillekens et al. 1987; Habets et al. 1987; Spritz et al. 1987; Sillekens et al. 1988). The U1-specific A protein has sequence homology to the U2-specific B″ protein and this explains why some antibodies cross-react between these two proteins. Also, the 70 kDa, A, and B″ proteins contain the RNA recognition motif (RRM) (Swanson et al. 1987; Dreyfuss et al. 1988; Mattaj 1989) identified on a large family of RNA binding proteins. This sequence, which includes an octamer of conserved amino acids in the middle of a 80 amino acid region is also found on poly-A binding proteins and some of the hnRNP core proteins. This domain is essential for the recognition of the U1 snRNA by the 70 kDa protein and is actually present in two copies in the B″ protein (Query et al. 1989). This observation and the kinetic results described below suggest that several of the snRNP specific proteins may bind directly to the snRNAs.

Quantitative cell fractionation using the cell enucleation protocol demonstrates that all the U1 and U2 specific proteins are localized in the nucleus. However, during aqueous cell fractionation, substantial quantities of the A and C U1-specific and the A′ U2-specific proteins leak from isolated nuclei and appear in the cytoplasm (Fig. 4B) (Feeney and Zieve 1990). Stoichiometric and kinetic analyses suggest that the 70 kDa U1-specific protein is associated with some, but not all U1 snRNPs, and that B″ is stably associated with all U2 snRNPs. No unassembled forms of either the 70 kDa or B″ protein are detected. In contrast, the U1-specific A and C proteins and the U2-specific A′ protein exist in both assembled and unassembled forms (Feeney et al. 1989). It is the unassembled but not the assembled forms that leak from the nucleus during aqueous cell fractionation. The unassembled C protein that leaks sediments in sucrose gradients at 2–6S and the unassembled A protein sediments from 18–22S (Sauterer et al. 1990).

In pulse label and chase experiments, the A and C proteins rapidly associate with the stable snRNP particles in the nucleus (Feeney et al. 1989). This suggests that the pools of these proteins are in a dynamic equilibrium with the mature snRNP particles. The significance of this exchange is not known, one possibility being that the exchange occurs during the functional cycle of the snRNP particles in the spliceosome.

During a chase, the mol. wt. of the C protein increases by approximately 2 kDa. The increase in molecular weight occurs on both assembled and unassembled forms of the protein (Fisher 1985; Feeney et al. 1989). This suggests this protein undergoes a posttranslational modification after synthesis. 70 kDa is the only snRNP protein that is phosphorylated; no alterations in the phosphorylation have been observed during the cell cycle. The lack of a pool of the U2-specific B″ protein may explain why the assembly of the U2 snRNP particle is more sensitive to the inhibition of protein synthesis than the U1 snRNP particle (Chandrasekharappa et al. 1983; Zieve 1987). The B″ protein appears as stable as the U2 snRNA, and unlike the U1-specific proteins, does not exchange in the nucleus (Feeney et al. 1989).

The La antigen is a predominantly nuclear phosphoprotein that binds transiently to the 5′ end of polymerase III transcripts (Rinke and Steitz 1982; Chambers et al. 1988). Small amounts of the La protein are also found in the cytoplasm, where they bind several polymerase III transcripts, including the U6 snRNA and a small fraction of the U1 snRNA (Madore et al. 1984b; Rinke and Steitz 1985). It has been suggested the La antigen functions in RNA maturation by either facilitating polymerase termination, 5′ end processing, or alternatively, intracellular transport (Rinke and Steitz 1982). The U1 snRNA is the only polymerase II transcript associated with the La antigen. The U1 snRNA has an oligouridylate stretch on the 5′ end which is a binding motif for the La protein; however, less that 1% is associated with La antigen (Madore et al. 1984b; Stefano 1985).

The mature U3, U8, and U13 snRNAs are localized in the nucleolus. These snRNAs do not contain the Sm sequence motif that binds the snRNP core proteins and are associated with a distinct set of proteins. A recently isolated autoimmune antisera recognizes a 34 kDa component of the U3 snRNP protein, termed fibrillarin, which is a major component of the fibrillar region of the nucleolus (Ochs et al. 1985; Parker and Steitz 1987; Reimer et al. 1987). Immunoprecipitated U3 snRNPs include two phosphorylated proteins of 74 and 59 kDa and four nonphosphorylated proteins of 36, 30, 13, and 12.5 kDa (Parker and Steitz 1987). U3 snRNA appears transiently in the cytoplasm and has a diagnostic 2,2,7 trimethylguanosine cap; however, little is known about the assembly of this particle in the cytoplasm.

V. Independent Synthesis and Assembly of snRNP Proteins in Xenopus Oocytes

The first indications of large pools of partially assembled snRNA-free snRNP protein came from studies on *Xenopus* oocytes. *Xenopus* oocytes contain a large pool of RNA-free snRNP proteins in the oocyte cytoplasm (Zeller et al. 1983; Forbes et al. 1983; Fritz et al. 1984). snRNA synthesis in the oocyte stops in early oogenesis before the vitellogenic stage, when oocytes have the snRNA equivalent to 8000 somatic cells (Forbes et al. 1983). snRNP protein synthesis continues throughout oogenesis, resulting in the accumulation of large pools of snRNP proteins in the mature oocyte (Zeller et al. 1983; Fritz et al. 1984). Following fertilization, RNA synthesis begins again at the midblastula transition (4000 cell stage). The snRNAs are among the most abundant RNAs transcribed at this time (Forbes et al. 1983). The U1 snRNAs synthesized in embryos upon resumption of transcription are two variants found in somatic cells, but are distinctly different from the four isoforms synthesized early in oogenesis (Forbes et al. 1984). Presumably, snRNAs assembled into snRNP particles and stored in the oocyte during early oogenesis are sufficient for the early embryo, and additional snRNPs are needed after the midblastula transition. The snRNAs transcribed at the midblastula transition assemble with the snRNPs stored in large pools in the cytoplasm. The subtle differences in sequence of the oocyte versus embryonic snRNAs may contribute to stage-specific regulation of RNA processing.

Immunological staining of oocyte sections with Sm antisera, as well as immunoprecipitation and Western blots of extracts from manually isolated *Xenopus* oocyte nuclei and enucleated oocytes (Zeller et al. 1983; Fritz et al. 1984) indicate the snRNP proteins to be predominantly cytoplasmic in late-stage oocytes and early embryos. Immunoprecipitations reveal the cytoplasmic pool consists of the core proteins D, E, F, and G, as well as B (Zeller et al. 1983).

Estimates of the size of the pool of cytoplasmic snRNP proteins in *Xenopus* oocytes using Western blots (Fritz et al. 1984) indicate it is equal to the snRNP protein content of up to 200000 somatic cells, and thus is in at least a 10–20-fold excess over the snRNA present in the oocyte nucleus. The size of this pool does not change significantly during fertilization and early embryogenesis, but starts to decline in the late blastula stage of development (Fritz et al. 1984). This decline is coincident with an increase in anti-Sm staining in the nucleus of embryonic cells as newly synthesized snRNAs assemble with the stored proteins and move into the nucleus. The excess cytoplasmic pool of snRNP proteins is essentially depleted by the midgastrula stage, with the majority of the snRNP proteins visible by immunological staining in the nucleus (Zeller et al. 1983). The assembly strategy of the amphibian oocyte appears to be an exaggerated form of the normal assembly pathway in somatic cells. The cytoplasmic to nuclear ratio of snRNP proteins in the oocyte is ca. 40 times greater than that found in somatic mammalian cells. This large stockpile of proteins is available for the rapid assembly of the snRNP particles that occurs in early development.

VI. In Vitro Assembly of snRNP Particles

Several experimental systems are available that assemble snRNP particles in vitro. In combination with mutated snRNAs, these systems have helped define many of the sequence requirements for snRNP core and snRNP specific protein binding. Intact *Xenopus* oocytes, or extracts from oocytes, and extracts from mammalian cells will support snRNP assembly with added snRNAs. Experiments with these systems have helped identify the Sm-binding sequence motif as a necessary and sufficient structure for binding the common core of snRNP proteins. In vitro studies have also identified the 5′ stem loops of U1 snRNA as the sites of U1-specific protein binding and the 3′ stem loops of the U2 snRNA as the site of U2-specific protein binding.

Xenopus oocytes have been a particularly powerful system for studying snRNP assembly. snRNAs injected into the oocyte cytoplasm of snRNAs transcribed from an introduced gene will assemble with snRNP protein and accumulate in the nucleus (DeRobertis et al. 1982). Mattaj (1986) investigated the requirement for the proper assembly and capping of the snRNAs by introducing mutated snRNA genes into *Xenopus* oocytes. Mutants of U1 and U2 genes were injected with labelled nucleotides into the nucleus of *Xenopus* oocytes; the resultant snRNPs were analyzed by immunoprecipitation. Deletion of U1 or U2 coding sequences, but not nontranscribed regions of the gene, affected snRNP assembly and cap trimethylation of the mutant U2 (Mattaj 1986; Skuzeski et al. 1984; Hamm et al. 1987). Deletions near the 3′ end of U2 abolished binding of the U2-specific proteins A′ and B″, but not the binding of the Sm antigen (the core complex) nor cap trimethylation (Bringmann et al. 1983a). Deletion of the Sm binding site prevented both association of the Sm-reactive proteins and cap trimethylation. The mutant U2 was neither immunoprecipitated by trimethylguanosine cap antisera nor did direct analysis of extracted U2 show anything but the 7-methylguanosine cap typical of RNA polymerase II transcripts (Mattaj 1986). Like U2, cap trimethylation in U1 is dependent on binding of the Sm proteins (Hamm et al. 1987), since deletion of the Sm binding site caused loss of immunoprecipitability with trimethylguanosine antibodies. In contrast to the results with U2, deletions of the three 5′ stem-loop regions of the U1 snRNP prevented assembly of the U1-specific proteins, but had no effect on trimethylation of the 5′ cap, indicating the important role of the Sm core proteins in this process.

Insertion of an Sm binding site consensus sequence, AAUUUUUGG, into two different locations in the mutant U2 gene lacking the wild type Sm binding site, resulted in both immunoprecipitability of the RNA with Sm antisera and trimethylguanosine antibodies, indicating that trimethylation of the cap had occurred. The efficiency of the cap trimethylation was independent of the insertion point of the Sm binding sequence into the mutant U2 gene, although immunoprecipitation with Sm antisera was partially dependent on location of the insertion (Hamm et al. 1987). Furthermore, insertion of the Sm binding site into a commercial cloning vector (Mattaj 1986) and subsequent injection of the in vitro transcribed RNA, capped with a 7-methylguanosine, into either whole or enucleated *Xenopus* oocyte cytoplasm, showed formation of a trimethylguanosine cap and association of the Sm reactive core proteins after 16 h of incubation in the oocyte, but not 1 min after injection. This shows that cap trimethylation is dependent only on the presence of the Sm binding site and binding of the Sm core proteins. It also demonstrates that cap trimethylation is a cytoplasmic process because it occurs at equal levels in both control and enucleated oocytes.

The exact role of the Sm core proteins in cap trimethylation is unknown. Since U3 has a trimethylguanosine cap, but is not immunoprecipitable by Sm antibodies, the core snRNP proteins are not absolutely essential for cap trimethylation. Whether one or more of the snRNP proteins is the actual trimethylase, or if the proteins merely serve as a recognition site for the trimethylase, is unknown.

In vitro transcribed snRNAs incubated with HeLa cell cytoplasmic extracts will assemble into snRNPs with efficiencies of ca. 10% (Fisher et al. 1983; Wieben et al. 1983; Patton et al. 1987) compared to the extracts from the oocytes which assemble snRNPs with efficiencies of over 75% (Hamm et al. 1987). The snRNPs produced have the same buoyant density, nuclease sensitivity, immunogenicity, and protein composition as native particles. The particle assembly is not dependent on the presence of a hypermodified 5′ cap or internal modified nucleotides. The presence of excess heterologous RNA to absorb nonspecific RNA binding proteins and low ionic strength are important conditions for the assembly reaction. In vitro translated proteins will also assemble with added snRNA although yields are quite low (Fisher et al. 1984; Wieben et al. 1983). Studies on the reconstituted U1 snRNP particles suggest the 70 kDa and A proteins bind to the first stem loop in the U1 snRNA (Hamm et al. 1987; Patton and Pederson 1988; Query et al. 1989).

Taken together, this data suggests the cytoplasm has a high concentration of snRNP core proteins that immediately assemble with available snRNAs in a two-step, irreversible process, generating a stable snRNP particle. The snRNP specific proteins subsequently add to this particle, either immediately after translation in the cytoplasm or after return of the particle to the nucleus.

VII. U6 snRNP

The U6 snRNA is unusual; unlike the other snRNAs, it is transcribed by RNA polymerase III (Parry et al. 1989). In the nucleus, the majority of U6 is base-paired with the U4 snRNA into a single snRNP particle (Bringmann et al. 1984; Hashimoto and Steitz 1984; Rinke et al. 1985). They remain associated during splicing although the strength of their association changes during the splicing cycle (Blencowe et al. 1989).

U6 appears transiently in the cytoplasm in a manner similar to the other snRNAs. U6 lacks the Sm binding sequence motif and does not associate with the snRNP core proteins, and nothing is currently known about the proteins specifically associated with the mature U6 snRNA (Reddy et al. 1987). However, in the nucleus, U6 is precipitable by Sm antisera because of its association with U4. In the cytoplasm the U6 snRNA is transiently associated with the 50 kDa La antigen, as are other polymerase III transcripts; however, the functional significance of this protein is unknown (Rinke and Steitz 1985). The majority of U6 in the cytoplasm is not associated with U4; if transcription of U4 snRNA by RNA polymerase II is inhibited, transcription of U6 snRNA by polymerase III continues and the U6 snRNA accumulates in the cytoplasm (Zieve et al. 1977, 1988). This suggests that the nuclear accumulation of U6 snRNA is a result of its base-pairing with U4 snRNA, which returns to the nucleus in a manner analogous to the other Sm-associated snRNP particles.

D. Nuclear Accumulation of snRNP Particles

I. Interphase

1. snRNP Core Particles

The nuclear localization of the assembled snRNP particles shares many features with the localization of nuclear proteins. For proteins larger than ca. 70 kDa which are unable to diffuse passively through the nuclear pores, a short amino acid stretch, the nuclear localization signal (NLS), is required for the nuclear accumulation of the proteins. Data suggests the NLS is a ligand for a receptor that is either soluble or a component of the nuclear pore complex. When bound to the receptor, the ligand is targeted for transport through the nuclear pore. Many proteins also have intrinsic affinity for components of the nucleus, so that they remain in the nucleus even if the nuclear envelope is removed (For review: Dingwall and Laskey 1986). Nuclear transport is a two-step process in which the NLS first binds to the nuclear pore complex and is then actively translocated into the nucleus (Newmeyer and Forbes 1988; Richardson et al. 1988). The fully assembled snRNP particles in the cytoplasm, but not unassembled precursors, are present in a detergent-insoluble fraction which may represent association with the nuclear transport apparatus (Zieve 1987). A unique aspect of snRNP transport is that the unassembled core proteins remain in the cytoplasm while assembled particles move into the nucleus (DeRobertis 1983). This suggests that the NLS for snRNPs is formed (or at least exposed) when snRNA binds to the proteins.

Binding of the snRNP core proteins is an absolute requirement for translocation of the snRNAs into the nucleus. Mutant U2 genes, lacking the Sm binding site, produce transcripts that are not immunoprecipitable by anti-Sm antibodies, and are not transported into the nucleus (Mattaj and DeRobertis 1985). Other mutant U2 transcripts, including those that prevent binding of one or more U2 specific proteins (probably A′) but could still bind the core proteins, are transported into the nucleus normally. Thus, it seems that the NLS is formed or exposed by the interaction of the snRNA and the common core proteins that are recognized by anti-Sm antibodies, and that the unique proteins are not involved to a significant extent. Nucleolar U3, which does not share the common core of proteins, but has its own unique set of proteins, must have a NLS, and more specifically, a nucleolar transport signal. Whether the interaction of an snRNA and the core protein complex produces a conformational change in the proteins that exposes a NLS, or whether the NLS includes both RNA and protein, is not known (De Robertis 1983).

The secondary structure of the snRNA also affects the nuclear transport of snRNP particles (Konings and Mattaj 1987). U2 mutants with deletions and substitutions in the stem and loop nearest the 3′ end initially had 3′ extensions on the transcripts, which were slowly processed down to the proper 3′ end over a period of several hours. Both the 3′ extended and processed transcripts could be immunoprecipitated with anti-Sm antisera, but only the processed transcripts could migrate to the nucleus when purified from *Xenopus* oocytes and reinjected. The 3′ extended transcripts of these mutants were found only in the cytoplasm. Secondary structural analysis of the 3′ extended mutants predicted an interaction between the extension and the stem and loop closest to the 5′ end, causing a radical conformational change (Konings and Mattaj 1987). Although this change blocked the nuclear transport, it did not inhibit core protein binding, indicating that core protein binding is not the only factor involved in nuclear transport of snRNPs.

Zieve (1987) investigated the affects of a wide range of metabolic inhibitors and alterations in cell culture conditions on the nuclear transport of the snRNP particles in HeLa cells (Fig. 1B). Pretreatment of cells with a wide variety of inhibitors of intermediary metabolism of the cytoskeleton all failed to affect snRNP maturation or transport into the nucleus. Only hypertonic medium, prolonged inhibition (60 min or more) of protein synthesis, or cold shock blocked maturation and transport (Fig. 7; Zieve 1987). Treatment of cells with medium adjusted to ca. twice the normal osmolarity with either salts or sugars (the addition of 180 mM NaCl or 360 mM sorbitol to normal medium) blocked mutration and transport of snRNPs into the nucleus. This effect is completely reversible when the cells are re-incubated in normal medium. Hyperosmotic medium withdraws water from the cytoplasm and the entire cell shrinks in volume. One hypothesis to explain these results is that the collapse of the cytoplasmic matrix under these conditions blocks the normal diffusion of the particles in the cytoplasm. The effects of prolonged protein synthesis inhibition and cold are likely to be due to the depletion of essential proteins, and the general slow-down of cell metabolism, respectively.

The assembled snRNP particles sediment at 10S and larger, and have an estimated molecular weight of 450 kDa. In high resolution electron micrographs, the snRNP particles appear as roughly spherical particles 10 nm in diameter (Spector et al. 1983; Kastner and Luhrmann 1989). This is far larger than those proteins able to passively cross the nuclear pore (Paine and Horowitz 1980). This clearly eliminates the possibility that nuclear accumulation is solely due to passive diffusion with the snRNPs binding to specific sites in the nucleus. In addition, the mature nuclear snRNP particles readily diffuse out of isolated nuclei, which suggests that unlike pre-mRNA, they are not firmly attached to intranuclear structures (Agutter 1988). This is consistent with the function of the snRNP particles, in which they cyclically engage different pre-mRNA transcripts to carry out RNA splicing. This cycle implies that in analogy to cytoplasmic ribosomes, there are pools of active snRNP particles bound to pre-mRNA and unbound particles available for use.

2. snRNP Specific Proteins

The presence of large, unassembled pools of the U-1 specific A and C proteins and the U2-specific A′ protein in the nucleus suggests these proteins enter the nucleus independently of snRNP assembly (Feeney et al. 1989). The U1-specific 70 kDa protein and the U2-specific B″ protein are not present in unassembled pools; it is not known if they associate with snRNP particles in the cytoplasm immediately after translation, or enter the nucleus independently and assemble with mature nuclear snRNPs. These observations suggest that some of the snRNP specific proteins have nuclear localization signals (NLS). Studies on a variety of viral and cellular proteins have identified nuclear recognition signals as quite heterogeneous, although they are usually a combination of basic and hydrophobic residues, and their context within the proteins is also important (Roberts et al. 1987; Dingwall et al. 1988). The sequences of all the U1 and U2 snRNP specific proteins are now available (Table 2). Table 4 lists sequence motifs in the U1 specific A and 70 kDa proteins and the U2 specific B″ and A′ proteins that are candidates for NLS. Genetic analysis of the snRNP proteins will be required to determine if these are indeed true NLS.

II. Mitosis

In most higher eucaryotes the nuclear envelope breaks down at the onset of mitosis at the end of prophase. The nuclear and cytoplasmic compartments are

Table 4. Putative nuclear localization signals in U1 and U2 specific proteins

A	U1 specific arg glu lys arg lys pro lys 107 113
70 kDa	U1 specific arg lys arg arg ser ser arg ser arg 288 296
B″	U2 specific lys lys lys glu lys lys lys ala lys thr val 103 113
A′	U2 specific lys lys lys gly gly pro ser pro 191 198

free to mix during mitosis and then faithfully redistribute when the daughter nuclei reform. This cyclical recompartmentalization is one reason that nuclear localization signals are permanent features of nuclear proteins. Like many other nuclear components, the mature snRNPs redistribute throughout the cell cytoplasm when the nuclear envelope breaks down, with only a small fraction remaining associated with the surface of the chromosomes (Fig. 10). The punctate distribution of the particles observed in the interphase nucleus is lost and the particles appear uniformly distributed throughout the cytoplasm (Deng et al. 1981; Zieve and Slitzky 1986; Reuter et al. 1985; Spector and Smith 1986). The snRNP particles retain their normal antigenicity and protein composition during this time, as determined by immunoprecipitation and indirect immunofluorescent staining with SLE autoimmune antisera. The 70 kDa protein associated with the U1 snRNP, which binds to the nuclear matrix in interphase cells, remains associated with the dispersed U1 snRNPs during mitosis (Verheijen et al. 1986). Sedimentation analysis indicates the snRNPs remain in heterodisperse structures, ranging from individual 12S particles up to structures of over 100S. Selective extraction of metaphase cells with buffers that stabilize the cytoskeleton suggest that ca. 40% of the snRNP particles are soluble in the cytoplasm, with the remainder associated with large insoluble structures (Zieve and Slitzky 1986).

The snRNP particles begin returning to the daughter nuclei immediately after the chromatin begins decondensing in telophase. The particles return quantitatively to the daughter nuclei during early G1. The mechanisms responsible for the return of the particles to the daughter nuclei are not known. However, the rapid return of the snRNPs to the region of decondensing chromatin suggests that the snRNPs have an affinity for the nuclear environment and that it is not necessary for all the mature particles to enter the daughter nuclei by active transport through nuclear pores, like the newly assembled snRNPs during interphase. In an effort to analyze the return of mature particles to daughter nuclei following the completion of mitosis, Zieve and Slitzky (1986) investigated a variety of metabolic inhibitors for their ability to interfere with this movement.

None of the well-characterized reagents that disrupt the cytoskeleton or inhibit cellular metabolism blocked this movement. Only the exposure of cells to hypertonic medium inhibited the return of the snRNP particles to daughter nuclei. When cells in anaphase or telophase were exposed to hypertonic medium, further movement of the chromosomes and formation of the cleavage furrow were inhibited. However, the cells flattened out as if returning to interphase. The chromatin remained condensed and the stable snRNP particles remained dispersed throughout the cytoplasm (Fig. 10.I). This data is consistent with other suggestions that the return of the particles to daughter nuclei is a result of diffusion in the cytoplasm, coupled with binding to specific sites in the chromatin and at the nuclear pores (Paine and Horowitz 1980). As discussed earlier, hypertonic medium also blocks the movement of newly synthesized snRNP particles into the interphase nucleus (Zieve 1987). This is consistent with the hypothesis that the targeting of newly synthesized snRNP particles to the nucleus during interphase and the return of mature stable particles to daughter nuclei at the completion of mitosis occur by similar mechanisms.

An unusual exception to the obligatory return of mature snRNP particles to daughter nuclei occurs in sea urchin embryos where maternal snRNPs from the oocyte nucleus do not return to the daughter nuclei after fertilization. Mature sea urchin oocytes are arrested after the second metaphase of meiosis and mature snRNPs are found distributed throughout the cytoplasm (Ruzdijic and Pederson 1987; Nash et al. 1987; Lobo et al. 1988). Using in situ hybridization of U1 antisense RNA to thin sections of sea urchin oocytes, fertilized eggs, and embryos, Nash et al. (1987) found that U1 snRNA was predominantly nuclear during

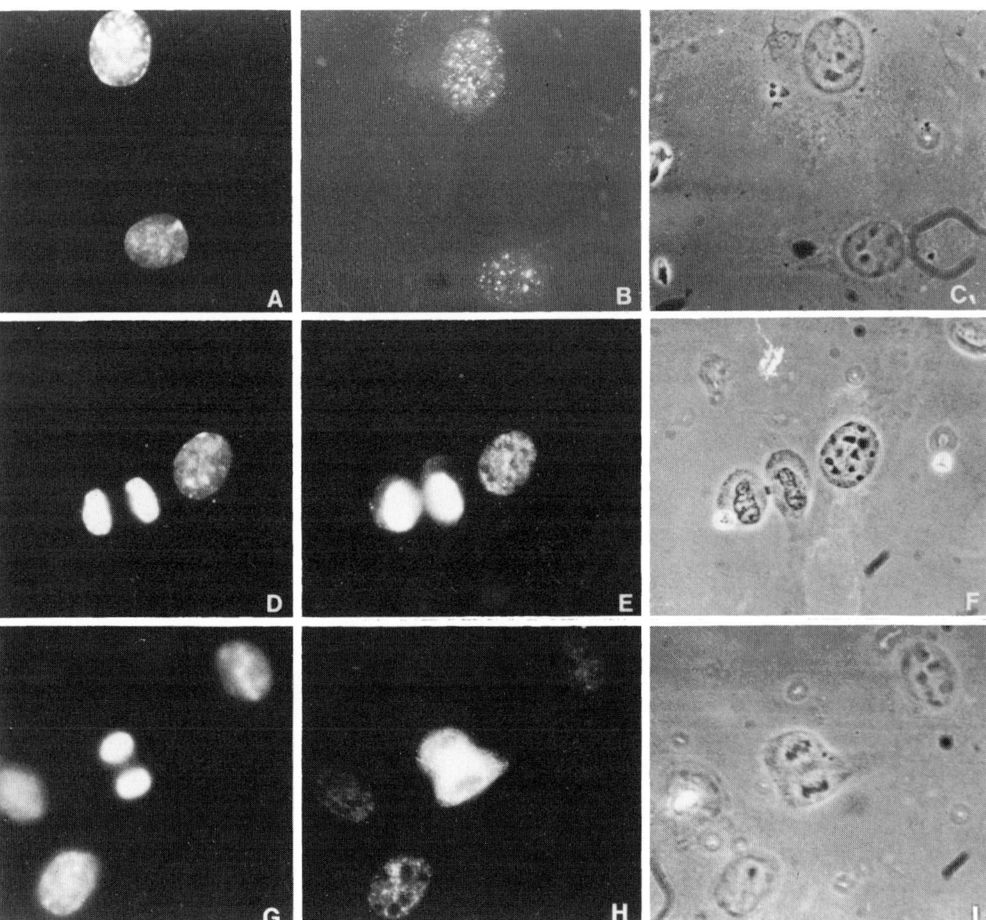

Fig. 10. Indirect immunofluorescent staining of snRNP particles during interphase and mitosis in Nil 8 hamster fibroblasts. Hoechst (*A, D, G*), indirect immunofluorescent staining (*B, E, H*), and phase micrograph (*C, F, I*) of interphase Nil 8 hamster fibroblasts stained with (U1) RNP antiserum (*A, B,* and *C*), of interphase and late mitosis cells (*D, E, F*), and of an anaphase cell (*G, H, I*) stained with the Y12 anti-Sm monoclonal antibody × 900

oogenesis, but migrated almost entirely to the cytoplasm during the final stages of maturation when the germinal vesicle breaks down, remaining there during early cleavage divisions of fertilized eggs. Some nuclear localization of U1 was noted by the fourth cleavage, when synthesis of new embryonic snRNAs commences, and U1 snRNA was predominantly nuclear by the blastula stage of development. The distribution of the (U1) RNP antigen was the same as that of the U1 snRNA, and snRNPs could be immunoprecipitated from sea urchin egg extracts with both (U1) RNP and Sm antisera, indicating that at least some of the U1 snRNA and U1-specific proteins are assembled into snRNP particles. Labeling early embryos with 32P orthophosphate showed that the newly synthesized U1 was exclusively nuclear, while maternal U1 snRNA was exclusively cytoplasmic (Nash et al. 1987). This suggests that the bulk of the maternal, fully assembled snRNPs remain in the cytoplasm after the second meiotic division and do not enter the nuclei of embryonic cells. Rather, the embryonic cells accumulate snRNPs assembled with newly transcribed snRNAs, suggesting that some mechanism exists to modify the maternal snRNPs after germinal vesicle breakdown so that they do not return to embryonic nuclei.

Using psoralen cross-linking of enucleated sea urchin eggs, Ruzdijic and Pederson (1987) found that cytoplasmic U1 snRNA was base paired to poly-A containing mRNA in the oocyte cytoplasm that contained interspersed repeated elements. This RNA resembles the pre-mRNA that is the substrate for RNA splicing in the nucleus; however, it is unlikely that this RNA ever enters polyribosomes (Thomas et al. 1982). This data suggests that the snRNPs in the oocyte cytoplasm are associated with unspliced mRNA precursors; it is not known if this RNA is processed during development. This observation raises a number of questions about how the unspliced pre-mRNA and the mature snRNP particles remain in the cytoplasm.

E. Summary and Perspectives

The snRNP particles are stable components of the interphase nucleus, where they participate in repeated rounds of RNA processing. The family of particles include a common core with a suggested stoichiometry of $B_2D'_2D_2$ EFG in addition to several snRNP specific proteins. The core proteins are present in large pools of partially assembled RNA-free intermediates in the cytoplasm. The snRNAs assemble with the common core proteins in a two-step reaction of first the D'_2D_2 EFG intermediate, and then B_2, when they appear transiently in the cytoplasm before returning permanently to the interphase nucleus. Kinetic studies indicate that the snRNAs and the common core proteins are metabolically stable; however, the U1 and U2 snRNP specific proteins are found only in the nucleus and have a diverse set of kinetic behaviors. Several of the snRNP specific proteins exchange between assembled particles and unassembled pools in the nucleus, and the 70 kDa U1 specific protein is associated with some but not all of the U1 snRNPs. This suggests the intriguing possibility that the snRNP specific proteins exchange on the snRNP particles during their functional cycle in the nucleus. This poses complex regulatory problems for coordinating the synthesis of the snRNAs, common core proteins and the snRNP specific proteins.

The coordinate synthesis of snRNAs and snRNP proteins is less coupled than that of ribosomal RNAs and proteins. Ribosomal RNA transcription and ribosome assembly arrest almost immediately after the inhibition of protein synthesis, unlike snRNP assembly, which continues for over 1 h. The presence of large pools of partially assembled RNA-free protein intermediates in the cytoplasm suggests the most sensitive regulation of snRNP assembly is at the level of snRNA transcription. The system is designed to rapidly assemble snRNA which enters the cytoplasm into snRNP particles, then return it to the nucleus.

During their functional cycle in RNA splicing, five different snRNPs, including four sets of core particles, transiently assemble into a spliceosome. The forces that stabilize this structure are not known, but are likely to involve a combination of RNA-RNA, RNA-protein, and protein-protein contacts. The presence of four identical core protein complexes in the spliceosome opens the possibility of extensive homotypic interactions in spliceosome assembly. It is intriguing that the RNA-free core proteins in the cytoplasm assemble into large complexes, several of which are possibly homo-oligomers. The interactions in the cytoplasm may be analogous to the homotypic interactions that occur in the spliceosome. The tissue and species specific diversity in the B snRNP core protein and the presence of the 70 kDa U1-specific protein in some but not all U1 snRNPs, offer the possibility of assembling spliceosomes with altered structures. It remains to be determined if this contributes to patterns of alternative pre-mRNA splicing.

snRNPs have been identified in almost all eukaryotes. The assembly of the snRNP particles in the cytoplasm suggests that the snRNPs developed after the emergence of the eucaryotic cell. In support of this hypothesis is the observation that self-splicing pre-mRNAs in organelles can remove introns by a mechanism that is identical to that catalyzed by snRNPs in the nucleus (Cech 1986). This suggests that in eucaryotes the snRNPs supply functions in trans that were previously supplied by the substrate itself. This would then free the substrate to evolve in less constrained directions.

A large family of snRNAs have been identified in yeast; this organism is proving to be an attractive system for studying snRNP particles (Riedel et al. 1986). However, the snRNP particles are substantially less abundant than in mammalian cells. This corresponds to the smaller number of transcribed introns and subsequent pre-mRNA splicing in yeast. Also, studies of nucleocytoplasmic interactions of the snRNP particles are difficult in yeast because the cell wall creates problems for effective cell fractionation. However, the advantages of genetic analysis in yeast make it an attractive system for studying the function of individual snRNP proteins in pre-mRNA splicing.

C. elegans trans-splicing presents an unusual variation on snRNP assembly. The first exon of a set of trans-spliced mRNAs is synthesized and assembled initially as an snRNP with a 5′ trimethylguanosine cap and a set of snRNP core proteins (Thomas et al. 1988; Van Doren and Hirsch 1988; Bruzik et al. 1988). This suggests that this small RNA appears transiently in the cytoplasm where it is processed and assembled with snRNP proteins like a typical snRNP particle. However, when this particle returns to the nucleus and participates in the splicing reaction, and the first 22 nucleotides of its RNA component is attached to the substrate as the first exon.

The snRNP proteins are major autoantigens in systemic lupus erythematosus (SLE). This autoimmune disease is associated with circulating antibodies to a limited set of cellular proteins which include the snRNP proteins (Hardin 1987). Immune responses in SLE are analogous to those that are seen when animals are experimentally immunized with intact snRNP particles (Reuter and Luhrmann 1986). Immunologists are attempting to understand what is unusual about the snRNP proteins that predisposes them to be targeted as antigens in autoimmune disease. The major autoantigens, the B and D core proteins of the Sm response, and the U1-specific 70 kDa protein of the (U1) RNP response have different assembly pathways, and there are no obvious similarities in the kinetic behavior of the proteins. Further studies will be required to understand why these proteins are specifically targeted by the immune response.

The snRNPs are a major focus of research in modern cell biology. They are an essential link in the control of gene expression because of their function in RNA processing. In addition, the snRNP particles are a valuable model system for studying ribonucleoprotein assembly and nucleocytolasmic interactions. Also, because of their involvement in autoimmune disease, it is important to understand why the snRNP proteins are targeted by the immune system in SLE, so that methods can be developed for treatment and prevention.

References

Agutter PS (1988) Nucleo-cytoplasmic transport of mRNA: Its relationship to RNA metabolism, subcellular structures and other nucleocytoplasmic exchanges. Prog Mol and Subcell Biol 10:15–96

Billings PB, Allen RW, Jensen FC, Hoch SO (1982) Anti-RNP monoclonal antibodies derived from a mouse strain with lupus-like autoimmunity. J Immunology 128:1176–1180

Billings PB, Barton JR, Hoch SO (1985) A murine monoclonal antibody recognizes the 13 000 molecular weight polypeptide of the Sm small nuclear ribonucleoprotein complex. J Immunol 135:428–432

Birnstiel ML (ed) (1988) Structure and function of major and minor small nuclear ribonucleoprotein particles. Springer Berlin Heidelberg, New York

Bjørn SP, Soltyk A, Beggs JD, Friesen JD (1989) PRP4 from S. cerevisiae: Its gene product is associated with the U4/U6 small nuclear ribonuclearprotein particle. Mol and Cell Biol 9, 3698–3709

Blencowe BJ, Sproat BS, Ryder U, Barabino S, Lamond AI (1989) Antisense probing of the human U4/U6 snRNP with biotinylated 2′-DMc RNA oligonucleotides. Cell 59:531–539

Bringmann P, Luhrmann R (1986) Purification of the individual snRNPs U1, U2, U5, and U4/U6 from HeLa cells and characterization of their protein constituents. EMBO J 5:3509–3516

Bringmann P, Rinke J, Appel B, Reuter R, Luhrmann R (1983b) Purification of snRNPs U1, U2, U4, U5 and U6 with 2, 2,7- trimethylguanosine-specific antibody and definition of their constituent proteins reacting with anti-Sm and anti-(U1)RNP antisera. EMBO J 2:1129–1135

Bringmann P, Appel B, Rinke J, Reuter R, Theissen H, Luhrmann R (1984) Evidence for the existence of snRNAs U4 and U6 in a single ribonucleoprotein complex and for their association by intermolecular base pairing. EMBO J 3:1357–1363

Brunel C, Sri-Widada J, Jeanteur P (1985) SnRNPs and scRNPs in eucaryotic cells. Prog Mol Cell Biol 9:1–52

Bruzik JP, Van Doren K, Hirsh D, Steitz JA (1988) Trans splicing involves a novel form of small nuclear ribonuclearprotein particles. Nature 335:559–562

Cech TR (1986) The generality of self-splicing RNA: relationship to nuclear mRNA splicing. Cell 44: 207–210

Chambers JC, Kenan D, Martin BJ, Keene JD (1988) Genomic structure and amino acid sequences domains of the human La autoantigen. J Biol Chem 263:18043–18051

Chandrasekharappa SC, Smith JH, Eliceiri GL (1983) Biosynthesis of small nuclear RNAs in human cells. J Cells Phys 117:169–174

Cory S, Adams JM (1975) Modified 5′-termini in small nuclear RNAs of mouse myeoloma cells. Mol Biol Regp 2:287–294

Craft J, Mimori T, Olsen TL, Hardin JA (1988) The U2 small nuclear ribonucleoprotein particle as an autoantigen. Analysis with sera from patients with overlap syndromes. J Clin Invest (United States) 81 (6):1716–1724

De Robertis EM (1983) Nucleocytoplasmic segregation of proteins and RNAs. Cell 32:1021–1025

De Robertis EM, Lienhard S, Parisot RF (1982) Intracellular transport of microinjected 5S and small nuclear RNA. Nature 295:572–577

Deng JS, Takasaki Y, Tan EM (1981) Nonhistone nuclear antigens reactive with autoantibodies. Immunofluorescent studies of distribution in synchronized cells. J Cells Biol 91:654–660

Dingwall C, Laskey RA (1986) Protein import into the cell nucleus. Ann Rev Cell Biol 2:367–390

Dingwall C, Robbins J, Dilworth SM, Roberts B, Richardson WD (1988) The nucleoplasmin nuclear localization sequence is larger and more complex than that of SV-40 large T antigen. J Cell Biol 107:841–849

Dreyfuss G, Philipson L, Mattaj IW (1988) Ribonucleoprotein particles in cellular processes. J Cell Biol 106:1419–1425

Eliceiri GL (1974) Short-lived, small RNAs in the cytoplasm of HeLa cells. Cell 3:11–14

Eliceiri GL (1980) Formation of low molecular weight RNA species in HeLa cells. J Cell Phys 102:199–207

Eliceiri GL, Gurney Jr T (1978) Subcellular location of precursors to small nuclear RNA species C and D and of newly synthesized 5S RNA in HeLa cells. Biochem Biophys Res Commun 81:915–919

Feeney RJ, Zieve GW (1990) Nuclear exchange of the U1 and U2 snRNP specific proteins. J Cell Biol 110 (in press)

Feeney RJ, Sauterer RA, Feeney JL, Zieve GW (1989) Cytoplasmic assembly and nuclear accumlation of mature snRNP particles. J Biol Chem 264:5776–5783

Fisher DE, Conner GE, Reeves WH, Blobel G, Kunkel HG (1983) Synthesis and assembly of human small nuclear ribonucleoproteins generated by cell-free translation. Proc Natl Acad Sci USA 80:6356–6360

Fisher DE, Conner GE, Reeves NH, Wisniewolski R, Blobel G (1985) Small nuclear ribonucleoprotein particle assembly in vivo: demonstration of a 6S RNA-free core precursor and posttranslational modification. Cell 42:751–758

Fisher DE, Reeves HW, Conner GE, Blobel G, Kunkel HG (1984) Pulse labeling of small nuclear ribonucleoproteins in vivo reveals distinct patterns of antigen recognition by human. Proc Natl Acad Sci USA 81:3185–3189

Forbes DJ, Kornberg TB, Kirschner MW (1983) Small nuclear RNA transcription and ribonucleoprotein assembly in early Xenopus development. J Cell Biol 97:62–72

Frederiksen S, Hellung-Larsen P (1975) Precursors to small molecular weight RNA components. FEBS Letters 58:374–378

Fresco LD, Kurilla MD, Keene JD (1987) Rapid inhibition of processing and assembly of small nuclear ribonucleoproteins after infection with vesicular stomatitis virus. Mol and Cell Biol 7:1148–1155

Fritz A, Parisot RF, Newmeyer D, De Robertis EM (1984) Small nuclear U-RNPs in *Xenopus laevis* development: uncoupled accumulation of the protein and RNA components. J Mol Biol 178:273–285

Gerke V, Steitz JA (1986) A protein associated with small nuclear ribonucleoprotein particles recognizes the 3′ splice site of premessenger RNA Cell 47:973–984

Gurney Jr T, Eliceiri GL (1980) Intracellular distribution of low molecular weight RNA species in HeLa cells. J Cell Biol 87:398–403

Guthrie C, Patterson B (1988) Spliceosomal snRNAs. Annu Rev Genet 22:387–419

Habets WJ, Sillekens PT, Hoet MH, Schalken JA, Roebroek AJ, Leunissen JA, van de Ven WJ, van Venrooij WJ (1987) Full-length sequence of the U2 small RNA-associated B″ antigen. Proc Natl Acad Sci USA 84:2421–2425

Hamm J, Kazmaier M, Mattaj IW (1987) In vitro assembly of U1 snRNPs. EMBO J 6:3479–3485

Hardin JA (1986) The lupus autoantigens and the pathogenesis of systemic lupus erythematosus. Arth Rheum 29:457–460

Harris SG, Hoch SO, Smith HC (1988) Chemical cross-linking of Sm and RNP antigenic proteins. Biochemistry 27:4595–4600

Harris SG, Matin TE, Smith HC (1988) Reversible chemical cross-linking and ribonuclease digestion analysis of the organization of proteins in ribonucleoprotein particles. Mol and Cell Biochem 84:17–28

Hashimoto C, Steitz JA (1984) U4 and U6 RNAs coexist in a single small nuclear ribonucleoprotein particle. Nucleic Acids Res 12:3283–3293

Kastner B, Luhrmann R (1989) Electron microscopy of U1 small nucler ribonucleoprotein particles: shape of the particle and position of the 5′ RNA terminus. EMBO Journal 8:277–286

Kinlaw CS, Robberson BL, Berget SM (1983) Fractionation and characterization of human small nuclear ribonucleoproteins containing U1 and U2 RNAs. J Biol Chem 258:7181–7189

Kleinschmidt AM, Pederson T (1987) Accurate and efficient 3′ processing of U2 small nuclear RNA precursor in a fractionated cytoplasmic extract. Mol and Cell Biol 7:3131–3137

Konarska MM, Sharp PA (1988) Association of U2, U4, U5, and U6 small nuclear ribonucleoproteins in a spliceosome-type complex in absence of precursor RNA. Proc Natl Acad Sci USA 85:5459–5462

Konings DAM, Mattaj IW (1987) Mutant U2 snRNAs of *Xenopus* which can form an altered higher order RNA structure are unable to enter the nucleus. Exp Cell Research 172:329–339

Kunkel GR, Pederson T (1988) Upstream elements required for efficient transcription of a human U6 RNA gene resemble those of U1 and U2 genes even though a different polymerase is used. Genes Dev 2:196–204

Lamond AI, Konarska MM, Grabowski PJ, Sharp PA (1988) Spliceosome assembly involves the binding and release of U4 small nuclear ribonucleoprotein. Proc Natl Acad Sci USA 85:411–415

Lelay-Taha MN, Reveillaud I, Sri-Widada J, Brunel C, Jeanteur P (1986) RNA-protein organization of U1, U5, and U4–U6 small nuclear ribonucleoproteins in HeLa cells. J Mol Biol 189:519–532

Lerner EA, Lerner MR, Janeway CAJr, Steitz JA (1981) Monoclonal antibodies to nucleic acid-containing cellular constituents: probes for molecular biology and autoimmune disease. Proc Natl Acad Sci USA 78:2737–2741

Liautard JP, Sri-Widada J, Brunel C, Jeanteur P (1982) Structural organization of ribonucleoproteins containing small nuclear RNAs from HeLa cells. Proteins interact closely with a similar structural domain of U1, U2, U4, and U5 small nuclear RNAs. J Mol Biol 162:623–643

Lobo SM, Marzluff WF, Seufert AC, Dean WL, Schultz GA, Simerly C, Schatten G (1988)

Localization and expression of U1 RNA in early mouse embryo development. Dev Biol 127:349–361

Lossky M, Anderson GJ, Jackson SP, Begg J (1987) Identification of a yeast snRNP protein and detection of snRNP-snRNP interactions. Cell 51:1019–1026

Luhrmann R (1988) snRNP proteins. In: Structure and function of major and minor small nuclear ribonucleoproteins 71–99:Springer-Verlag, New York

Lund E (1988) Heterogeneity of human U1 snRNAs. Nucleic Acids Res (England) 16:5813–5826

Madore SJ, Wieben ED, Kunkel GR, Pederson T (1984b) Precursors of U4 small nuclear RNA. J Cell Biol 99:1140–1144

Madore SJ, Wieben ED, Pederson T (1984a) Intracellular site of U1 small nuclear RNA: processing and ribonucleotide assembly. J Cell Biol 98:188–192

Madore SJ, Wieben ED, Pederson T (1984c) Eukaryotic small ribonucleoproteins: anti-La human autoantibodies react with U1 RNA-protein complexes. J Biol Chem 259:1929–1933

Manser T, Gasteland RF (1982) Human U1 loci: genes for human U1 RNA have dramatically similar genomic environments. Cell 29:257–264

Mattaj IW (1986) Cap trimethylation of U snRNA is cytoplasmic and dependent on U snRNP protein binding. Cell 46:905–911

Mattaj IW (1989) A binding consensus: RNA-protein interactions in splicing, snRNPs and sex. Cell 57:1–3

Mattaj IW, De Robertis EM (1985) Nuclear segregation of U2 snRNA requires binding of specific snRNP proteins. Cell 40:111–118

McAllister G, Roby-Shemkovitz A, Amara SG, Lerner MR (1989) cDNA sequence of the rat U snRNP-associated protein N: description of a potential Sm epitope. EMBO Jour 8:1177–1181

Melton DA, DeRobertis EM, Cortese R (1980) Order and intracellular location of the events involved in the maturation of a spliced tRNA. Nature 284:143–148

Mowry, KL, Steitz JA (1988) snRNP mediators of 3′ end processing: functional fossils? Trends in Biochem Sci 13:447–451

Nash MA, Kozak SE, Angerer LM, Angerer RC, Schatten H, Schatten G, Marzluff WF (1987) Sea urchin maternal and embryonic U1 RNAs are spatially segregated in early embryos. J Cell Biol 104:1133–1142.

Newmeyer DL, Forbes DJ (1988) Nuclear import can beparated into distinct steps in vitro: nuclear pore binding and translocation. Cell 52:641–653

Nishikura K, De Robertis EM (1981) RNA processing in microinjected *Xenopus* oocytes. J Mol Biol 145:405–420

Ochs RL, Lischwe MA, Spohn WH, Busch H (1985) Fibrillarin : a new protein of the nucleolus identified by autoimmune sera. Biol Cell 54:124–134

Ohosone Y, Mimori T, Griffith A, Akizuki M, Homma M, Craft J, Hardin JA (1989) Molecular cloning of an Sm autoantigen: derivation of a cDNA for a B polypeptide of the U series of small nuclear ribonucleoprotein particles. Proc Natl Acad Sci USA 86:4249–4253

Paine PL, Horowitz SB (1980) The movement of material between nucleus and cytoplasm. Cell Biol 4:299–338

Parker KA, Steitz JA (1987) Structural analyses of the human U3 ribonucleoprotein particle reveal a conserved sequence available for base-pairing with pre-rRNA. Mol and Cell Biol. 7:2899–2913

Parry HD, Scherly D, Mattaj IW (1989) "Snurpogenesis": the transcription and assembly of U snRNP components. Trends in Biochem Sci 14:12–16

Patton JR, Pederson T (1988) The Mr 70,000 protein of the U1 small nuclear ribonucleoprotein particle binds to the 5′ stem-loop of U1 RNA and interacts with the Sm domain proteins. Proc Natl Acad Sci USA 85:747–751

Patton JG, Wieben ED (1987) U1 precursors: variant 3′ flanking sequences are transcribed in human cells. J Cell Biol 104:175–182

Patton JR, Patterson RJ, Pederson T (1987) Reconstitution of the U1 small nuclear ribonucleoprotein particle. Mol and Cell Biol 7:4030–4037

Petterson I, Hinterberger M, Mimori T, Gottlieb E, Steitz JA (1984) The structure of mammalian small nuclear ribonucleoproteins: identification of multiple protein components reactive with anti-(U1) RNP and anti-Sm autoantibodies. J Biol Chem 259:5907–5914

Query CC, Keena JD (1987) A human autoimmune protein associated with U1 RNA contains a region of homology that is cross-reactive with retroviral p30gag antigen. Cell 51:211–220

Query CC, Bentley RC, Keene JD (1989) A common RNA recognition motif identifed within a defined U1 RNA binding domain of the 70K U1 snRNP protein. Cell 57:89–101

Reddy R, Henning D, Das G, Harless M, Wright D (1987) The capped U6 small nuclear RNA is transcribed by RNA Polymerase III. J Biol Chem 262:75–81

Reichlin M (1987) Measurement of antibodies Sm and nRNP by ELISA: clinical and serological correlations. In: Kasukawa R and Sharp GC (eds.) Mixed connective tissue disease and anti-nuclear antibodies. Elsevier Science Publication:85–96

Reimer G, Pollard KM, Penning CA, Ochs RL, Lischwe MA, Busch H, Tan EM (1987) Monoclonal autoantibody from a F1 mouse and some human scleroderma sera target a Mr 34,000 nucleolar protein of the U3 snRNP particle. Arth Rheum 30:793–800

Reuter R, Luhrmann R (1986) Immunization of mice with purified U1 small nuclear ribonucleoproteins (RNP) induces a pattern of antibody specificities characteristic of the anti-SM and anti-RNP autoimmune response of patients with lupus erythematosis, as measured by monoclonal antibodies. Proc Natl Acad Sci USA 83:8689–8693

Reuter R, Rothe S, Luhrmann R (1987) Molecular relationships between U snRNP proteins as investigated by rabbit antisera and peptide mapping. Nucleic Acids Res 15:4021–4034

Reuter R, Appel B, Rinke J, Luhrmann R (1985) Localization and structure of snRNPs during mitosis. Exp Cell Research 159:63–79

Richardson WD, Mills AD, Dilworth SM, Laskey RA, Dingwall C (1988) Nuclear protein migration involves two steps: rapid binding at the nuclear envelope followed by slower translocation through nuclear pores. Cell 52:655–664

Riedel N, Wise JA, Swerdlow H, Mak A, Guthrie C (1986) Small nuclear RNAs from Saccharomyces cerevisiae: unexpected diversity in abundance, size, and molecular complexity. Proc Natl Acad Sci USA 83:8097–8101

Rinke J, Steitz JA (1982) Precursor molecules of both human 5S ribosomal RNA and transfer RNAs are bound by a cellular protein reactive with the anti-La lupus antibodies. Cell 29:149–159

Rinke J, Steitz JA (1985) Association of the lupus antigen La with a subset of U6 snRNA molecules. Nucleic Acids Res 13:2617–2629

Rinke J, Appel B, Digweed M, Luhrmann R (1985) Localization of a base-paired interaction between small nuclear RNAs U4 and U6 in intact U4/U6 ribonucleoprotein particles by psoralen crosslinking. J Mol Biol 185:721–731

Roberts BL, Richardson WD, Smith AE (1987) The effect of protein context on nuclear location signal function. Cell 50:465–475

Rokeach LA, Haselby JA, Hoch SO (1988) Molecular cloning of a cDNA encoding the human Sm-D autoantigen. Proc Natl Acad Sci USA 85:4832–4836

Rokeach LA, Jannatipour M, Hoch SO (1990) Heterologous expression and epitope mapping of a human small nuclear protein associated Sm-B′/B autoantigen. J Immunol 145(3) (in press)

Ruzdijic S, Pederson T (1987) Evidence for an association between U1 RNA and interspersed repeat single-copy RNAs in the cytoplasm of sea urchin eggs. Develop 101:107–116

Sauterer RA, Goyal A, Zieve GW (1990) Cytoplasmic assembly of snRNP particles from 6S and 20S RNA- free intermediates. J Biol Chem 265:1048–1058

Sauterer RA, Feeney RJ, Zieve GW (1988) Cytoplasmic assembly of snRNP particles from stored proteins and newly transcribed snRNAs in L929 mouse fibroblasts. Exp Cell Res 176:344–359

Schmauss C, McAllister G, Ohosome Y, Hardin JA, Lerner MR (1989) A comparison of snRNP-associated Sm-autoantigens: human N, rat N and human B/B′. Nucleic Acids Res 17:6777

Sillekens PT, Habets WJ, Beijer RP, van Venrooij WJ (1987) cDNA cloning of the human U1 snRNA-associated A protein: extensive homology between U1 and U2 snRNP-specific proteins. EMBO J 6:3841–3848

Sillekens PT, Beijer RP, Habets WJ, Venrooij WJ (1988) Human U1 snRNP-specific C

protein: complete cDNA and protein sequence and identification of a multigene family in mammals. Nucleic Acids Res 16:8307–8321
Singh R, Reddy R (1989) γ-monomethyl phosphate: A cap structure in spliceosomal U6 small nuclear RNA. Proc Natl Acad Sci USA 86:8280–8283
Skuzeski JM, Lund E, Murphy JT, Steinberg TH, Burgess RR, Dahlberg JE (1984) Multiple elements upstream of the coding region are required for accumulation of human U1 RNA in vivo. J Biol Chem 259:8345–8352
Spector DL, Smith HC (1986) Redistribution of U-snRNPs during mitosis. Exp Cell Research 163:87–94
Spector DL, Schrier WH, Busch H (1983) Immunoelectron microscopic localization of snRNPs. Biol Cell 49:1–9
Spritz RA, Strunk K, Surowy CS, Hoch SO, Barbon DE, Francke U (1987) The human U1-70K snRNP protein: cDNA cloning, chromosomal location, expression, alternative splicing and RNA-binding. Nucl Acids Res 15:10373–10391
Stanford DR, Kehl M, Perry CA, Holicky EL, Harvey SE, Rolhetter NM, Rehder JrK, Luhrmann R, Wieben ED (1988) The complete primary structure of the human snRNP E protein. Nucleic Acids Res 16:10593–10605
Stefano JE (1984) Purified lupus antigen La recognizes an oligouridylate stretch common to the 3′ termini fo RNA polymerase III transcripts. Cell 36:145–154
Swanson MS, Nakagawa TY, LeVan K, Dreyfuss G (1987) Primary structure of human nuclear ribonucleoprotein particle C proteins: conservation of sequence and domain structures in heterogeneous nuclear RNA, mRNA and pre-rRNA-binding proteins. Mol Cell Biol 7:1731–1739
Symington J, Gurney T Jr, Eliceiri GL (1984) Subcellular location of polypeptides that react with anti-Sm and anti-RNP antibodies. Biochem Biophys Res Comm 120:81–87
Thomas JD, Conrad RC, Blumentahl T (1988) The C. elegans trans-spliced leader RNA is bound to Sm and has a trimethylguanosine cap. Cell 54:533–539
Thomas TL, Britten RJ, Davidson DH (1982) An interespersed region of the sea urchin genome represented in both maternal poly (A) RNA and embryo nuclear RNA. Dev Biol 94:230–239
Van Doren K, Hirsh D (1988) Trans spliced leader RNA exists as small nuclear ribonucleoprotein particles in *Caenorhabditis elegans.* Nature 335:556–559
Verheijen R, Kuijpers H, Vooijs P, van Venrooij W, Ramaekers F (1986) Distribution of the 70K U1 RNA-associated protein during interphase and mitosis. J Cell Sci 86:173–190
Wieben ED, Madore S, Pederson T (1983) U1 small nuclear ribonuclear protein studies by in vitro assembly. J Cell Biol 96:1751–1755
Willems M, Penman M, Penman S (1969) The regulation of RNA synthesis and processing in the nucleolus during the inhibition of protein synthesis. J Cell Biol 41:177–187
Williams DG, Stocks MR, Smith PR, Maini RN (1986) Murine lupus monoclonal antibodies define five epitopes on two different Sm polypeptides. Immunol 58:495–500
Yamamoto K, Miura H, Moroi Y, Yoshinoya S, Goto M, Nishioka K, Miyamoto R (1988) Isolation and characterization of a complementary DNA expressing human U1 small nuclear ribonucleoprotein C polypeptide. J Immunol 140:311–317
Zeller R, Nyffenegger T, De Robertis EM (1983) Nucleocytoplasmic distribution of snRNPs and stockpiled snRNA-binding proteins during oogenesis and early development in *Xenopus laevis.* Cell 32:425–434
Zieve GW (1987) Cytoplasmic maturation of the snRNAs. J Cell Physio 131:247–254
Zieve GW, Penman S (1976) Small RNA species of the HeLa cell: metabolism and subcellular localization. Cell 8:19–31
Zieve GW, Sauterer RA (1990) Cell biology of the snRNP particles. CRC Crit Rev Biochm and Mol Biol 25 (1) (in press)
Zieve GW, Slitzky B (1986) Removal of cellular water prevents the reformation of the interphase nucleus. J Cell Physio 128:85–95
Zieve GW, Benecke B, Penman S (1977) Synthesis of two classes of small RNA species in vivo and in vitro. Biochemistry 16:4520–4525
Zieve GW, Sauterer RA, Feeney RJ (1988) Newly synthesized snRNAs appear transiently in the cytoplasm. J Mol Biol 199:259–267

The Centrosome: Recent Advances on Structure and Functions

M. BORNENS, E. BAILLY, F. GOSTI and G. KERYER[1]

The centrosome acts as the microtubule-organizing center in interphasic animal cells. It duplicates only once at each cell cycle and the two products function as mitotic poles during cell division. Recent advances in the isolation of centrosomes have opened the way to experimental studies on this minute and potentially important organelle. Here we will review the literature from only the last five years, including quite recent data, as previous reviews have covered earlier reports (Peterson and Berns 1980; Brown et al. 1982; Wheatley 1982; McIntosh 1983; Bornens and Karsenti 1984; Brinkley 1985; Vorobjev and Nadehzdina 1987).

A. Definitions

Some definitions are necessary, as authors are not always thinking of centrosomes in the same sense. This in itself indicates how young the field is, despite the fact that the centrosome was discovered and named in the beginning of cell biology (one could not imagine a similar situation in the case of mitochondria or of the nucleus). The criterion of definition for the centrosome has been primarily morphological until now. Depending on the cell system under study, the size of microtubule asters varies greatly; the centers of these asters vary accordingly in size. Marine eggs, for example, possess huge centers, whereas most somatic animal cells display a tiny corpuscular center. The old definition from Boveri (1901) of the centrosome as a polar corpuscule containing two centrioles has been often replaced by the operational and restricted definition of a microtubule-organizing center (MTOC, coined by Pickett-Heaps 1969). In many cells, the MTOC is the pericentriolar material, (PCM). In other cells, it is the arrangement of microtubules which indicates where to look for MTOCs. Today, these centers, aggregates, or osmiophilic regions can be more accurately localized by immunocytochemical mean, thanks to spontaneously reacting sera. In this definition of centrosomes, the centrioles are dispensable structures or "passengers"

[1]Centre de Genetique Moleculaire du CNRS, 2 Avenue de la Terrasse, 91190 GIF sur yvette, France

(see Bornens and Karsenti 1984) or even "advertisements of centrosomes", possibly "helping us to locate centrosomes and perhaps to count the number of subunits in a centrosome" (Mazia 1987). We propose a more objective definition of centrosomes, made possible by recent experimental developments in their study. In this review, centrosome designates an organelle which, once isolated from cells, is able to perform in controlled conditions the two basic functions normally associated with centrosomes, i.e., (1) the nucleation of microtubules and (2) the establishment of an efficient mitotic spindle. This may bring us back to the old distinction between centrosome and centrosphere.

B. Isolation of Centrosomes from Somatic Cells

Two different approaches have been used to isolate centrosomes. In the first one, centrosomes were isolated as centrosome-nucleus complexes (Bornens 1977) which were further dissociated in several ways (Nadezhdina et al. 1978; Maro and Bornens 1980). However, the yield was low and centrosomes were contaminated with perinuclear cytoskeleton. In the second approach, centrosomes were dissociated from the nucleus by cell lysis at very low ionic strength. Introduced by Blackburn et al. (1978) on CHO cells, this was further developed by Mitchison and Kirschner (1984). N115 cells were lysed with nonionic detergents, after rapid equilibrium in media of decreasing ionic strength. Subsequent purification on a sucrose gradient was monitored by a quantitative immunofluorescent assay (Evans et al. 1985). Adapting this approach, Bornens et al. (1987) obtained high yields of isolated centrosomes from the human lymphoblastic cultured KE37 cell line. This cell line was chosen because cells grow in suspension and possess a low cytoplasmic to nuclear ratio. An example of such a preparation is presented in Fig. 1. Centrosomes were recovered in their native paired configuration. This was visible at the optical level, using specific antibodies. Double immunofluorescence for centrioles and PCM was necessary to identify centrosomes without ambiguity, as their size is very small. The major potential contaminants of centrosome preparations were small pieces of chromatin. They were eliminated by treating lysate supernatants with DNase II before gradient purification of the centrosomes. Electron microscopy demonstrated the purity of the preparations.

The method is rapid and quantitative, with a centrosome yield of ca. 60% of the starting material, assuming one centrosome per cell. The centrosome yield is directly dependent on the cell lysis step. Recovery of functional centrosomes depends on the care taken to inhibit proteases during cell lysis, as the microtubule nucleating activity has been shown to be sensitive to proteolysis (Kuriyama 1984). The method should be adaptable to other cell types, provided that cell lysis is optimized. This was recently achieved using cells from intact tissue instead of cultured cells (Komesli et al. 1989). Calf thymus was chosen, as it is a source of cells with the lowest known cytoplasmic to nuclear ratio. This resulted in being a very favourable starting material, providing many highly purified centrosomes, and using a simplified and cheap procedure. In particular, drug pretreatment to

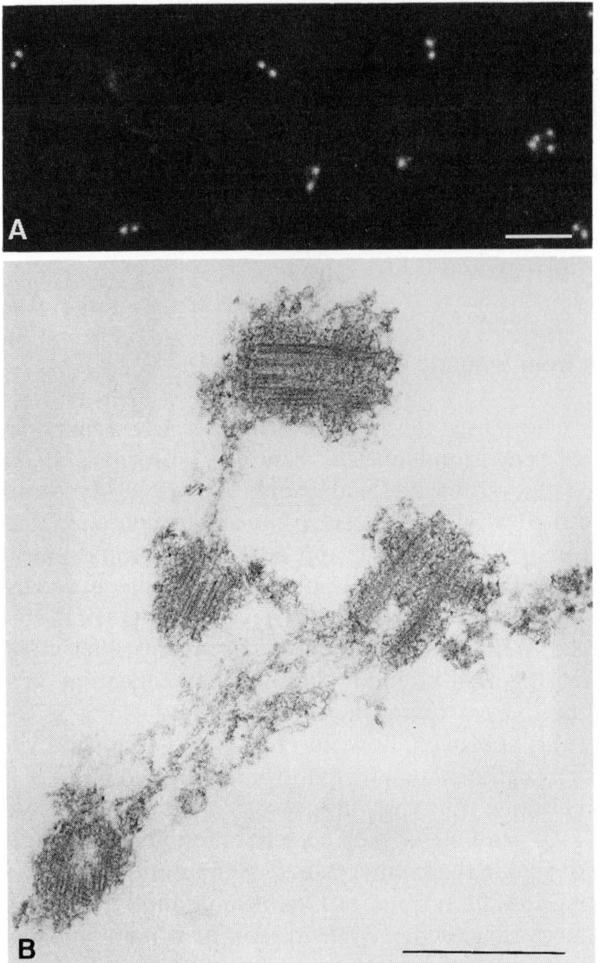

Fig. 1. Centrosomes isolated from human lymphoblasts. They are recovered in their native paired configuration. (*A*) Observation by immunofluorescence using an antitubulin antibody. Individual centrioles can be identified; *bar* = 5 μm. (*B*) A link of variable length is observed between centrioles in a pair. Sections are parallel to the coverslip on which isolated centrosomes have been sedimented; *bar* = 0.5 μm

disassemble actin was not necessary, as the cytoskeleton is not consequential in thymocytes.

Centrosomes have also been prepared either from mitotic CHO cells or from metaphase sea urchin eggs (Kuriyama 1984; Kuriyama and Borisy 1983). The CHO cells were blocked in a "pseudo-metaphase" state with anti-microtubule drugs and further lysed at low ionic strength as for interphase cells. In the sea urchin eggs, huge mitotic centrospheres could be prepared by extracting the metaphase spindles with 0.5 M KCI without effect on the nucleating capacity of the mitotic centers.

C. The Structure of Isolated Centrosomes

Ultrastructural studies of centrosomes in situ have always been confronted with the problem of orientating ultrathin sections with respect to the complex 3-D organization of this organelle. To obviate this difficulty, Bornens et al. (1987) oriented isolated centrosomes by sedimentation on a coverslip before processing them for electron microscopy. In this way, centrosomes were positioned with centrioles parallel or perpendicular to the coverslip (see Fig. 1B). New structural features were observed in this way. In particular, a structural basis for the paired configuration of centrosomes was established. A link exists which appears as part of a complex filament network surrounding each individual centriole, often displaying a periodic organization in its narrow part. The chemical nature of this link is not known. There have been several reports on centrosome splitting, i.e., substantial separation of the two centrioles, sometimes by great distances (Schliwa et al. 1982; Sherline and Mascardo 1982). Evidence has been provided for a role of actin in the positioning and the motility of the centrosome (Schliwa and Euteneuer and Schliwa 1985; see below). Actin is consistently associated with centrosome preparations (see below). Association of actin with sperm centrioles has also been demonstrated in hydractinia (Kleve and Clark 1980). However, attempts to decorate the link between centrioles with myosin S1 fragment have failed.

The lumen of each centriole is filled for about three-fifths of its length by a cylindric hub, with a diameter of ca. 40 nm, showing a tapered internal extremity. The other end of the centrioles presents an apparently empty lumen. The pericentriolar material possesses a proximo-distal organization, which might be incomplete on one of the two centrioles. At the proximal end of each centriole, the pericentriolar material appears as a sheath ca. 40 nm thick and covers one-half of the total length. At the other end apparently of one centriole only, the pericentriolar material displays radial arms distributed according to a ninefold axial symmetry. These arms possess in themselves a complex structure, with a multilayered transverse plate and possibly other substructures.

As a whole, the pericentriolar material appears highly complex. Accordingly, a description obtained from random sectioning of whole cells is highly variable. Moreover, we must emphasize that differences exist between isolated centrosomes and those described in situ. Isolated centrosomes have lost most of their loosely associated material, or cloud, often identified as part of the pericentriolar material in situ (cf. Figs. 1 and 2 in Gosti-Testu et al. 1986). This material might correspond to some unkown functional compartment within the "centrosphere", for example, to an excess of nucleating material, nonessential for the complete expression of centrosomal functions (see below). This view can be illustrated in Sluder and Rieder (1985). Using semi-thick sections for observation in a high-voltage eletron microscope, they documented a particularly good description of the complete ultrastructure of the huge "centrosomes" of sea urchin blastomeres. The centrioles, which were shown in this study to be the markers of the duplicative capacity of spindle poles, appear as tiny corpuscules embedded in a large cloud of granular material. From their results one may infer that these centrosomes, once isolated free of most of the surrounding cloud, would keep the essential functions of centrosomes. Admittedly, this view is at variance with that described by Mazia (1987). Others examples of the ultrastructure of the pericentriolar cloud, here described as an unessential centrospheric compartment can be found in Brown et al. (1982) and Rieder and Borisy (1982). Alternatively, this compartment could serve some cytoskeletal function (see Salisbury et al. 1986) and could be in a highly contracted form after centrosome isolation.

The centrioles themselves have an average length of 0.4 μm. The most external microtubule of each triplet was incomplete at the distal end, as already reported for basal bodies (Wilsman and Farnum 1983). A recent report has convincingly demonstrated the presence of tektins in the centrioles (Steffen and Linck 1988), suggesting that the structural similarities of the latter with axonemes are corroborated by biochemical homologies.

An unexpected result has arisen from the study of centrosomes from thymocytes, since they possess a peculiar structure: the two centrioles are tightly associated with each other by their proximal ends, in a linear configuration (Komesli et al. 1989). This could help in understanding the morphogenesis of the intercentriolar link that was observed in centrosomes from KE37. In any case, these observations demonstrate variable differentiation in the centrosomal structure of one cell type to another, suggesting the intriguing possibility that the centrosome, despite the ubiquitous structure of individual centrioles, could conceal properties associated with a differentiated state. Moreover, the centrosomes from thymocytes nucleate few microtubules from the distal ends of the centrioles, as would basal bodies. The functional significance of these observations is under study.

D. Centrosomal Proteins

The total protein content per isolated centrosome is $2–3 \times 10^{-2}$ pg. The one-dimensional protein profile is complex but distinct from either detergent-soluble or -insoluble cellular proteins. Two-dimensional analysis further demonstrated the specificity of the protein pattern (Bornens et al. 1987). High molecular weight proteins (180–300 kDa) and a group of proteins between 50 and 65 kDa, are the major features of the centrosomal pattern. The complexity of the protein profile is not too surprising, as the isolated centrosomes are structurally quite complex. Related structures such as axonemes contain more than 100 polypeptides, despite their periodic organization (Piperno et al. 1977). However, it is likely that the proteins observed in the profile do not all belong to the centrosome proper, although morphological controls and total protein content both suggest a high enrichment of isolated centrosomes in the preparations. It is necessary to demonstrate independently that the proteins belong to the centrosome, because it is not surrounded by a membrane in situ, but is immersed within the cytoplasm. Little is known of the interactions which maintain the centrosome in its location, except that it is linked to the nucleus (Bornens 1977; Fais et al. 1984). The possible role of intermediate filaments in linking centrosomes with their environment has been raised in some reports (Aubin et al. 1980; Blose and Bushneel 1982) and dismissed by others (Nelson and Traub 1982; Maro et al. 1984). A recent report shows direct connections of intermediate filaments with centrioles, the nucleus and the plasma membrane (Katsuma et al. 1987). During cell lysis, the centrosome is dissociated from its environment in an unkown manner. Contaminating proteins could be present for different reasons. For example, fodrin has been consistently found in centrosome preparations but cannot be demonstrated at the centrosome in situ by the use of specific antibodies (Klotz and Bornens, unpubl. obser.). This protein could be artifactually adsorbed on centrosomes during the isolation procedure because of its insolubility at low ionic strength. The same holds for actin and myosin, which are both present in centrosome preparations. There is no argument as yet to decide if these proteins are contaminants or not, although actin has been shown to be involved in the splitting of centrioles (Schliwa et al. 1982).

Centrosomes probably consist of ubiquitous proteins associated in a specific way (i.e., tubulins) and of specific components found only therein. On immunocytochemical grounds, several proteins have been reported to be associated with centrosomes. Some such as MAP I (Sherline and Mascardo 1982; Bonifacino et al. 1985), tektins (Steffen and Linck 1988) or kinesin (Neighbors et al. 1988) are not unexpected, as they are known to interact with microtubules. The others are less obvious candidates for a centrosomal localization, i.e., the cAMP-dependent protein kinase II (Nigg et al. 1985; de Camilli et al. 1986), which is also specifically associated with the Golgi apparatus and the purine nucleotide phosphorylase (Oliver et al. 1981), which is otherwise homogeneously distributed in the cytoplasm.

When rabbit sera are used, caution must be taken before conclusions are drawn as to a centrosomal localization, since pre-immune activity against centrosomes or basal bodies is quite frequent in this species. One has either to use affinity-purified antibodies when the antigen is available, or to prove independently that the antigen is associated with centrosomes. This holds even when no obvious anti-centrosome activity is observed in the pre-immune serum; experimental immunization can induce a transient increase of cryptic activities.

Unprovoked sera can be very active and some have been used to identify centrosomal proteins. The human auto-immune serum 5051 has been widely used and has been shown to react by immunofluorescence with centrosomes or equivalent structures in all cells tested so far, from plant to mammals (Calarco-Gillam et al. 1983; Clayton et al. 1985). These data suggest that proteins of centrosomes, be they centriole-associated or not, are highly conserved through evolution. The rabbit serum 0013 has an activity essentially restricted to human and monkey cells (Maunoury 1978). It has led to the identification of new centrosomal proteins in human cells (Gosti-Testu et al. 1986), such as a family of high molecular weight proteins. From more recent estimations, the largest component is significantly larger than 250 kDa and the others could be degradation products. Several indirect lines of evidence argue for a role of this antigen in the microtubule nucleation. It is localized within the pericentriolar material. The variation of the centrosome labeling during the cell cycle coincides with the cycling change of the nucleating activity of centrosomes demonstrated in the past (Snyder and McIntosh 1975; Kuriyama and Borisy 1981). When the immunoreacting material is dissociated from the centrioles, either physiologically, as in myotubes (Tassin et al. 1985a; see below), or artificially, as in Taxol-treated cells (Gosti-Testu et al. 1986), it redistributes as expected for a capping or nucleating protein. No direct demonstration of such a function has been obtained for this antigen as the antibodies do not inhibit tubulin nucleation on isolated centrosomes, nor has the antigen been purified. This antigen shares a common epitope with a protein of the Nucleolar Organizing Center (Courvalin et al. 1986) and more surprisingly with the human B isoform of lactate dehydrogenase (Gosti et al. 1987; Gosti and Bornens in prep.).

In order to establish these cross-reactivities, it was necessary to use immunoglobulins purified by affinity on immunoreacting bands after Western blotting, as nonimmune sera are often polyspecific. This is an obligatory condition before any conclusion can be drawn from Western blotting experiments with centrosome-reacting sera. In the case of the rabbit serum 0013, for example, immunoglobulins purified to one cytoplasmic reacting band were shown not to stain centrosomes nor to react with centrosomal proteins on Western blots (Gosti et al. 1987). A counter example is provided by the report from Bastmeyer and Russell (1987). Using a human serum, they claimed to have identified an MTOC-associated polypeptide of 112 000 Mr, despite the fact that this protein was quite abundant among cellular proteins. They should have demonstrated that immunoglobulins affinity-purified to this polypeptide do react with centrosomes, and should have eliminated the possibility of a specific centrosomal antigen different from the 112 000 Mr antigen. In the absence of such evidence, there is no reason to believe that the 112 000 Mr polypeptide is related to the centrosome.

Antibodies deliberately raised against centrosomes are still rare. A 190 kDa protein has been reported in the centrosomes of sea urchin eggs (Kuriyama and Borisy 1985). These centrosomes are also specifically decorated by a monoclonal antibody against *Drosophila* vimentin which reacts with a 68 kDa protein (Schatten et al. 1987).

Monoclonal antibodies have been raised in the author's laboratory by using purified centrosomes from KE 37 cells as immunogens. Several classes of anti-centrosome antibodies could be distinguished on the basis of their cellular staining: (1) centrosome or centrioles; (2) centrosome and Golgi apparatus; (3) centrosome and nucleus. Most of them exhibited cell-cycle dependent staining of the centrosome, sometimes in an all-or-none manner. They should be useful tools for the future study of centrosomes or related structures. Several of these antibodies have been shown to react with cortical or nuclear MTOC of ciliates and with specific structures of their cortex (Keryer et al. 1989).

Antibodies raised against mitotic Hela cells (Davis et al. 1983) decorate MTOCs in cells of several organisms often in a cell cycle-dependent manner (Vandre et al. 1986). In ciliates, all MTOC are permanently decorated throughout the life cycle (Keryer et al. 1987).

Antibodies raised against nuclear proteins have in some cases led to anti-centrosome specificities. An example is the monoclonal antibody Bx63 raised against nuclear proteins of early embryos of *Drosophila* (Frasch et al. 1986), which strongly decorates centrosomes in this species together with the nuclei in a more diffuse manner. This antibody identifies two proteins with apparent molecular weights of 185 and 66 kDa which have been used to prepare antisera (Whitfield et al. 1988). This strategy allowed the authors to demonstrate that the 185 kDa protein was associated with centrosomes and to identify cloned DNAs, encoding this protein among those which were selected by screening expression libraries of *Drosophila* DNA with Bx63. The gene occurs as a single copy and has been mapped on chromosome 3. The function of the protein is unknown. A similar approach in yeast has been taken by Hurt (1988), who obtained a serum reacting with an antigen localized in the nucleus periphery and concentrated at the spindle pole body. The gene has been cloned and sequenced. The predicted aminoacid sequence corresponds to a protein of 823 amino acids, with particular domains (a highly repetitive nine amino acid sequence in the middle, the amino- and carboxy-terminal domains revealing similarities to cytokeratins and calcium-binding proteins). Gene disruption experiments have demonstrated that the protein is essential for cell division. Interestingly, centrosomes are decorated in animal cells with this serum, suggesting an evolutionary conservation between the spindle pole body of yeast and the centrosome of higher animal cells.

E. The Centrosome and the Nucleation of Microtubules

Nothing is known on the microtubule nucleation reaction at the centrosome, except that it can be very efficiently produced on isolated centrosomes from different sources (Mitchison and Kirschner 1984; Bornens et al. 1987; an example is shown on Fig. 2). The true MTOC corresponds to the pericentriolar material, but the precise sites of microtubule nucleation within the centrosome are still unknown and we do not know if nucleation and anchoring of the microtubules are one or two distinct events.

Many examples of MTOCs not associated with centriolar structures are known (see Sect. A). The transition from one type of MTOC to the other can be observed during cell development of differentiation (see below, Sect. I). Cell cycle-dependent modifications of the pericentriolar material take place in parallel with the duplication cycle of the centrosome. Finally, the association of pericentriolar material with centrioles is sensitive to tubulin drugs, indicating that microtubule inhibitors also affect the organizing centers. Further examples have been documented (Gosti-Testu et al. 1986; Hauser 1986; Sellitto and Kuriyama 1988).

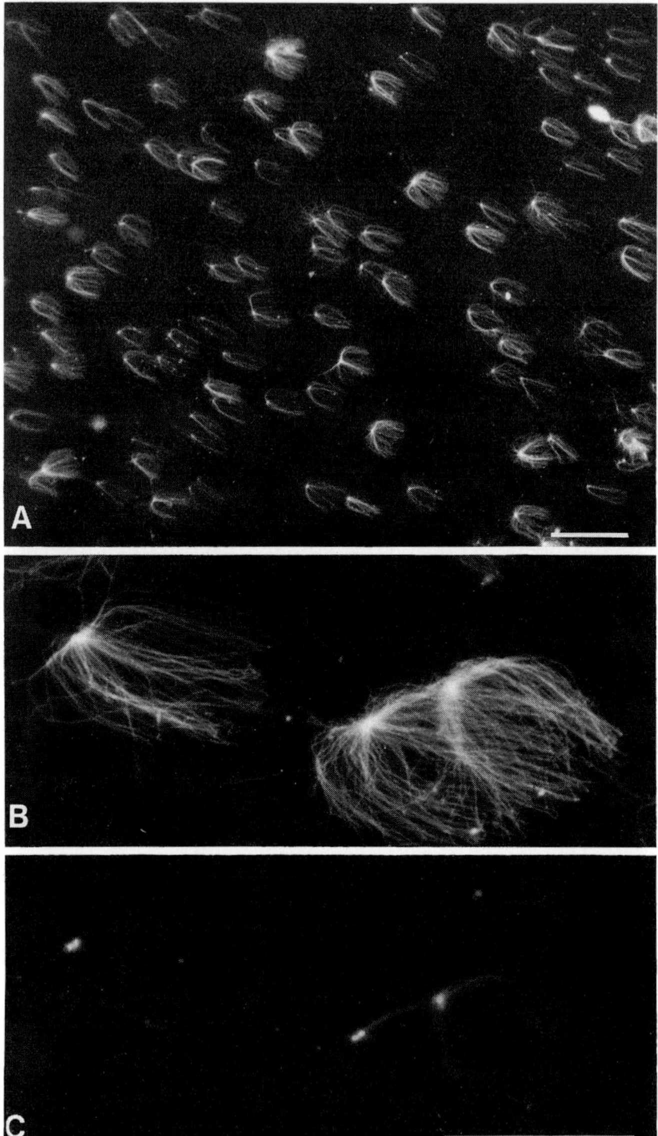

Fig. 2. Isolated centrosomes nucleate microtubules from purified tubulin.(*A*) Low magnification view of a nucleation experiment in which centrosomes were incubated at 37°C during 8 min with 12 μM tubulin (from beef brain) purified on phosphocellulose. The asters were visualized by an antitubulin antibody; *bar* = 10 μm. (*B–C*) Higher magnification which demonstrates by double immunofluorescence the presence of an individual centrosome in the center of each individual aster. (*B*) Antitubulin antibody. (*C*) Anticentrosome antibody (rabbit serum 0013). Note that the paired configuration of the centrosomes is visible; *bar* = 10 μm

F. The Centrosome Cycle in the Cell Cycle

The molecular mechanisms which govern centrosome duplication are unknown, although the morphological description of centriole duplication has been known for years. However a temperature-sensitive lethal mutation, *esp 1*, has been recently discovered in yeasts which deregulates spindle pole duplication (Baum et al. 1988). The gene product participates in the mechanism which limits spindle body duplication to a single occurrence in each cell division cycle.

Our understanding of the duplication of the pericentriolar material and its redistribution on the daughter centrioles has not progressed in recent years. By contrast, several lines of evidence have clearly established that the tight coupling between nuclear events and the doubling of centrosomes at each cycle are not due to the sequential control of one compartment on the other. This was done in early embryos, in which most of the substances required for the progress through the cell cycle have been stockpiled ahead of time. In these systems, the cleavage cycle has been shown to be driven by a cytoplasmic clock independent of the zygote nucleus. Sluder et al. (1986), by removing the nucleus from the eggs of the sea urchin *Lytechinus variegatus* at prophase of the first mitosis, demonstrated that the centrosome reproduced in a precise doubling manner, with a periodicity slightly slower than the control cycle. The cell cycle-dependent changes in astral morphology were identical to those of control eggs. They further demonstrated that all centrosomes produced in enucleated eggs contain two centrioles apiece. Using starfish eggs, Picard et al. (1988) further investigated whether the centrosome could duplicate in the absence of any material from the oocyte germinal vesicle, as the egg cytoplasm in fact contains nuclear components from the oocyte (the female pronucleus which forms after completion of meiosis is much smaller than the germinal vesicle of the oocyte). By the hormonal induction of meiotic maturation in enucleated oocytes, they observed the growth of the two meiotic asters normally present at the animal pole and their division at the normal time of the first meiotic cleavage. The sperm centrosome underwent regular duplications and showed the periodical changes in the organization of asters correlated with cell surface reorganization. Uncleaved eggs with 2^9 centrosomes ultimately cytolysed. This number corresponds to the blastomer number at the mid-blastula transition. When enucleation was achieved after fertilization by removing both pronuclei, as in the sea urchin experiment mentioned above 2^9 empty blastomeres were formed, as already demonstrated in this species by Nagano et al. (1981), using chemical enucleation with aphidicolin. Therefore, even in the complete absence of nuclear material from the oocyte, the centrosome cycle takes place as long as the mid-blastula transition has not been reached. A similar dissociation between centrosomal and nuclear division has been observed in the recessive, maternal-effect mutation *gnu* of *Drosophila* (Freeman et al. 1986). Embryos from homozygous females are defective in nuclear division, but not in DNA replication. They develop a small number of giant nuclei. Centrosomes divide and migrate at the surface of the syncitial blastoderm where they nucleate the formation of asters. Phenotypic copies of the *gnu* mutation have been recently produced by the same group, using aphidicolin treatment (Raff and Glover 1988). Enucleated polar cells were even observed in this case.

Centrosomes have been shown to be powerful and exclusive parthenogenetic agents in amphibians (Maller et al. 1976). Amphibian eggs are therefore favorable systems to study the initiation of centrosome duplication, and to hopefully identify the active component capable of starting the successive rounds of doubling. One can also attempt to study the coupling between the centrosome cycle and the cell cycle, as the first successful cleavage is obtained by complementation with an exogenous centrosome, which can be selected according to various criteria. A striking feature of this system is that there is apparently no species requirement for centrosomes: they have been shown to be active when isolated from sea urchin (Maller et al. 1976), mouse (Karsenti et al. 1984), and man (Bornens et al. 1987).

The unfertilized egg in *Xenopus* is laid arrested at the second meiotic metaphase, due to the presence of a cytostatic factor (Meyerhof and Masui 1979). During fertilization, the block is released, probably through a calcium wave believed to inactivate the cytostatic factor. The same calcium wave can be induced by pricking the egg with a microinjection needle. In this case, the cell cycle is reinitiated, as revealed by the periodic occurrence of surface contraction waves, of DNA duplication, and of mitotic kinase activities (Karsenti et al. 1987), but no cleavage occurs. Cleavages can be restored if centrosomes are injected in the egg at the pricking step. This result is interpreted as indicating that *Xenopus* eggs lack a functional centrosome, as it is often the case in many eggs, and that under normal conditions, the sperm contributes the centrosome used in development. This corresponds to the view of Boveri on the centrosome as "the division organ" (see Wilson 1925), a view which was abandoned for many years on the ground of misinterpreted experiments (Bataillon 1911). It clearly indicates that frog eggs are unable to assemble a centrosome from its elements in the absence of a preexisting centrosome, in contrast to mouse eggs, where it happens physiologically (Szollosi et al. 1972) or to sea urchin eggs, where it can be induced under various treatments (Kuriyama and Borisy 1983, among many others).

In order to induce a true parthenogenesis, the injected centrosome must be able to assemble microtubules from the egg tubulin, to duplicate, and to interact properly with the egg nucleus. Centrosomes or related structures which lack one of these properties would be unable to induce parthenogenesis. For example, basal bodies isolated from ciliates or flagellates were shown to be capable of assembling egg tubulin in a radial aster of microtubules like a regular centrosome. They were unable, however, to induce parthenogenesis, suggesting that they were unable to duplicate properly or to interact in an effective way with the nucleus (Heideman and Kirschner 1975).

Is the whole centrosomal structure, including the centrioles and the surrounding material, required to start the centrosome duplication cycle – which would suggest a structural continuity – or is the structural integrity of the centrosome dispensable – which would suggest a generative process? A relevant experimental strategy aims at chemical or enzymatic dissection of centrosomes to identify the active subfraction. This was recently attempted by Klotz et al. (1988, 1990). Starting with isolated centrosomes (from hunman KE37 cells), sequential extraction with salts, urea, or detergents, as well as treatment with nucleases or proteases, were monitored by protein analysis, by Western blotting using specific markers of centrioles (anti-tubulin) and pericentriolar material (serum 0013; Gosti-Testu et al. 1986), and by transmission electron microscopy. Structural modifications were correlated with the loss of nucleating activity in vitro and the loss of parthenogenetic activity. The data indicated that the parthenogenetic activity did not require nucleic acids and was preserved under conditions which abolished the nucleation activity in vitro. It was associated with an insoluble proteinaceous structure which was not significantly simpler than the native centrosome, as judged by the protein content and the structural organization. A correlation between the loss of the parthenogenetic activity and the disorganization of the centriolar triplets was observed. Overall, the results of these studies are compatible, with the injected centrosome acting as a structural template in the initiation of centrosome duplication.

Many questions are unanswered in the process of centrosome-induced parthenogenesis. A precise description of the duplication of the injected centrosome is necessary, as it is an essential step in the formation of a functional mitotic spindle. Do centrosomes need to be in a particular position in their duplicative cycle to induce cleavage, i.e., can they initiate their duplication in response to the egg cytoplasm, or can they only elongate a preformed centrioles? Isolation of centrosomes from synchronized cells has recently allowed Tournier et al. (1989) to answer this question: centrosomes from G_1, G_2, G_0 human cells possess a similar parthenogenetic activity, demonstrating that centrosome duplication can be triggered in *Xenopus* eggs.

One will have also to understand in biochemical terms how the injected centrosome responds to the egg cytoplasmic clock. Some insights have been recently obtained in our laboratory by the demonstration that the centrosome could be one of the substrates directly controlled by the mitotic kinase (Bailly et al. 1989). A crucial element of the internal clock is the maturation-promoting factor (MPF), which acts as a general control in the induction of mitosis, not only in the eggs, but in most cells from yeast to man (see Maller 1985). Although MPF activity has been studied for years, its purification is very recent (Lohka et al. 1988) and a wealth of data has been gathered in several laboratories, which all indicate that one component of MPF is a 34 kDa protein kinase homologue of the product of the cell-cycle gene cdc2 of fission yeasts, or cdc28 of budding yeasts (Dunphy et al. 1988; Gauthier et al. 1988; Labbé et al. 1988). The human homologue of cdc2 has been identified (Lee and Nurse 1987; Draetta et al. 1987) and its expression studied together with the activity of the protein during the cell cycle, in relation with its own state of phosphorylation and its association with putative regulatory proteins (Lee et al. 1988; Draetta and Beach 1988). The protein kinase activity is maximum during mitotic metaphase. Little is known, however, about the endogenous substrates. MPF activity has often been imagined as triggering a cascade of kinases; one can reasonably expect, however, some of the substrates of protein p34 to be associated with the chromosomes and/or the mitotic spindle. Histone H1 is one of the candidates among the nuclear proteins (Gauthier et al. 1988; Arion et al. 1988).

As for the spindle components, the use of monoclonal antibodies to mitotic HeLa cells (Davis et al. 1983) has lead to the observation that phosphoproteins were associated with the mitotic poles at the onset of mitosis (Vandre et al. 1986). On the other hand, structural modifications of the centrosomes at the G2-M transition and during mitosis can be observed in HeLa cells, which parallel the cycle of p34 described by Draetta and Beach (1988): an increase of centrosome-specific staining with anti-centrosome antibodies is observed during G2, whereas a dramatic decrease takes place at the onset of anaphase (Gosti-Testu et al. 1986), when a rapid inactivation and subunit rearrangement of p34 occurs. These centrosomal modifications, which are likely to correspond to a rise and fall of microtubule nucleating activity (for a review, see Bornens and Karsenti 1984), might be controlled by phosphorylation.

An immunocytochemical study of $p34^{cdc2}$ in HeLa cells (Bailly et al. 1989) has demonstrated an accumulation of p34 at the centrosome in some cells, which could be identified as G2 cells by increased staining with anti-PCM monoclonal antibodies. In late G2, p34 was still associated with centrosomes, while the nuclear staining appeared in a few large zones. Part of the staining could be suppressed by Triton extraction before fixation, but the centrosomal protein was apparently insoluble in these conditions. In mitotic cells, a redistribution of p34 at the onset of anaphase takes place as a very rapid sequestration process of the protein into a tubular system, localized at the intermediary part of dividing cells.

Most of the protein p34 could be recovered in the detergent extract of cells. A clear and sometimes abundant presence of p34 was observed in the preparations of isolated centrosomes, and was shown to correspond to the association of the protein with each individual centrosome.

From this study, it appears that the association of p34 with the centrosome corresponds precisely with the increase in centrosomal staining observed with anti-PCM antibodies (Gosti-Testu et al. 1986). It coincides also with ultra-structural modifications of the PCM (Robbins and Gonatas 1964; Rieder and Borisy 1982) and with the rise of the nucleating activity of centrosomes (Snyder and McIntosh 1975; Kuriyama and Borisy 1981). This suggests that the modifications of the centrosome might be achieved through the phosphorylation of centrosomal proteins by p34. Control of centrosomal activity by p34 in G2-M is further suggested by the precise coincidence between the apparent dissociation of p34 from the mitotic poles and the dramatic decrease of their staining with anti-PCM antibodies. It is also at this moment that a dramatically reduced centrosomal microtubule nucleation capacity was demonstrated in other cell systems (Snyder et al. 1982).

The association of p34 with the centrosome might also serve its duplicative cycle. Two steps in the centrosomal cycle are potentially important in the control of the cell cycle: (1) the initiation of centriole duplication in G1 or early S phase (Kuriyama and Borisy 1981) and (2) the separation of daughter centrosomes in late G2 or early prophase. The latter event apparently occurred in HeLa cells after the association of $p34^{cdc2}$ with the centrosome.

Involvement of the centrosome, centrioles, or spindle pole bodies in the control of the cell cycle has been proposed in the past (Byers and Goetsch 1975; Brooks et al. 1980). Some experimental support for this proposal was reported for the G0 to G1 transition, since a temporal coincidence between structural modifications of the centrosome and cell commitment to divide was observed (Tucker et al. 1979; Sherline and Mascardo 1982). However, no causal link was ever established. The association of kinase p34 with the centrosome at the G2-M transition observed by Bailly et al. (1989) suggests that centrosomal components might be among the substrates of this key activity for the mitotic control. More work is necessary to know the precise role of the centrosome in mitotic induction, and whether it exerts a feedback control on the cell cycle oscillator.

One may recall here that both regulatory and catalytic subunits of cAMP-dependent protein kinase have also been localized at the centrosome and the Golgi apparatus (Nigg et al. 1985; De Camilli et al. 1986), and that calmodulin accumulates at the poles of the mitotic spindle (Andersen et al. 1978; Welsh et al. 1979). Finally, the product of *CDC31* gene required for spindle pole body duplication in budding yeasts has significant homology with Ca^{2+}-binding proteins and calmodulin (Baum et al. 1986) and with basal body-associated proteins (Huang et al. 1988a, b; see below). All these data suggest that the centrosome could be critical for cell cycle regulation. In this sense, the release of mature starfish oocytes from interphase arrest by injection of centrosomes isolated from KE37 cells (Picard et al. 1987) could be related to associated kinase activities.

G. Centrosome Continuity

Obviously, different strategies have evolved by different species to restart the centrosome cycle during early development, and we will perhaps know more of the precise role of centrioles within the centrosome, before we understand how these patterns have been selected during evolution. Paternal inheritance has been selected in marine eggs and in amphibians, together with a structural continuity of the centrosome, since the first microtubule aster in the egg is formed around the sperm kinetosome. Marine eggs are, however, capable of maternal inheritance when activated parthenogenetically in proper ways (Kuriyama and Borisy 1983; Kallenbach 1985), whereas amphibian eggs are not. Maternal inheritance is apparently observed in the mouse (Szollosi et al. 1972; Calarco-Gillam et al. 1983; Maro et al. 1985; Schatten and Schatten 1986) together with a structural discontinuity, as numerous discrete MTOC are scattered within the oocyte and participate in the formation of the spindle poles. This is not the case in sheep eggs, where the sperm aster seems to control the fusion of pronuclei (Crozet 1988; Le Guen and Crozet 1989).

There is indeed something intriguing about the centrosome organization at the early steps of development. A quite original theory for the short term evolutionary maintenance of sexual reproduction has been recently proposed by Grafen (1988), which postulates that the centrosome is inherited in a selectively ambiguous way, i.e., a sexual offspring receives a contribution from each parent and selects the better centrosome to pass on to its own offspring. We perhaps do not know enough about centrosomes and their functions to envisage how they could compete with each other for presence in the germ line, but this paper contains an intrepid and interesting discussion on the issue of the replicator nature of the centrosome.

Structural discontinuity of the centrosome, i.e., transient disappearance of centrioles, is not infrequent, not only during early development, but also during many vegetative cycles. In no case is the mechanism of centriole reassembly understood. Often described as a de novo process, the reformation of centrioles might occur through a generative mechanism involving some sort of cryptic precursor. In the case of the myxamoeba *Physarum polycephalum*, a study on the continuity between centriolar-associated MTOC and acentriolar MTOC has been attempted (Akhavan-Niaki and Wright, pers. commun.) In this system, the amoeba possesses a centrosome with a pair of centrioles and divides through an open mitosis, whereas the plasmodium produced by the conjugation between two amoeba from different mating types is plurinucleated, acentriolar, and displays synchronous endonuclear divisions. Amoeba with several centrosomes can be selected; these display an increased number of abnormal mitosis. Symmetrical crosses between amoebae possessing one, two, or three centrosomes produced plasmodia with an increasing proportion of mitotic abnormalities. These observations suggest either that both the amoebal and plasmodial centrosomes are different organelles controlled by a single genetic regulatory mechanism, or that both types of centrosomes correspond to two different morphological states of a unique organelle. The analysis of the mitotic abnormalities in plasmodia obtained from asymmetrical crosses between amoeba possessing different numbers of centrosomes favors the second possibility.

Until recently, very few instances of mutations bearing on the duplication or morphogenesis of centrosomes were known. One case has been described in *Paramecium* (Ruiz et al. 1987), which apparently concerns a diffusible factor necessary for the initiation of basal body duplication. Its nature is unknown. Recent mutations described in *Drosophila* could also be associated with a defect in centrosome functions, opening the way to genetic analysis of this organelle in a particularly favorable system. They are the mutation *mgr* ("merry-go-round") which is associated with the appearance of mitotic and meiotic figures, where chromosomes are arranged in a circle (Gonzalez and Ripoll 1988). Direct evidence on the primary target of the mutation is still lacking, but the phenotype observed fits well with the idea of a defect in the centrosome behavior during mitosis. Another mutation (*polo*) is characterized by a high frequency of abnormal mitotic spindles with broad poles, both during early embryogenesis and in diploid cells (Sunkel and Glover 1988). Use of a specific anticentrosome antibody demonstrated that the distribution of centrosomes in *polo/polo* embryos was profoundly disturbed.

H. Centrosome and the Spindle Formation

This section covers several questions, one being the respective contributions of the centrosomes and the nucleus in the assembly of the spindle microtubules around the chromosomes. This has been discussed in previous reviews (Bornens and Karsenti 1984; Karsenti and Maro 1986). Recent data have established that the dynamics of spindle microtubules are one order of magnitude higher than those of interphasic microtubules (Schulze and Kirschner 1986; Soltys and Borisy 1985). It has been argued that the increase in the nucleating capacity of centrosomes, which is known to take place at the G2-M transition (Snyder and McIntosh 1975; Kuriyama and Borisy 1981), is sufficient in itself to explain both the spindle morphogenesis and the increase in microtubule dynamics (Kirschner and Mitchison 1986).

The other question is the specific role of the centrosomes at the spindle poles. Use of a spontaneous human "anticentrosome" serum has demonstrated that immunologically related materials are present at the poles of most of the meiotic spindles in the mouse oocyte (Calarco-Gillam et al. 1983; Maro et al. 1985; Schatten and Schatten 1986), in tipulid spermatocytes (Bastmeyer et al. 1986), as well as in plant cells (Wick 1985; Clayton et al. 1985; see however Harrer et al. 1989). The reacting material in mouse oocyte is considered as a genuine and complete centrosome by dedicated students of centrosomes (Mazia 1987). However, one of the basic properties classically associated with centrosomes, the capacity to duplicate at some point during the cell cycle, has not been established. Evidence is rather against the duplication of the microtubule-nucleating material during the early cycles of the developing mouse embryo: the maternal MTOC is apparently progressively diluted out by successive divisions, before centrosomes similar to those of somatic cells are formed (Calarco-Gillam et al. 1983). The question of the duplicative capacity of spindle poles has been studied in sea urchin eggs by Sluder and Rieder (1985) who fully analyzed the classical experiment of Mazia (1961). In this experiment, sea urchin eggs treated with mercaptoethanol contained spindle poles, apparently normal, but which had only half of the reproductive capacity. Such a study and others had lead to the concept of "polar organizer", as the essential determinant around which the centrosome is elaborated (Mazia et al. 1960; Mazia 1961; Sluder and Begg 1985). Sluder and Rieder (1985), using correlative light and high-voltage electron microscopy, demonstrated that the functional behavior of the polar organizers were coincident with, if not identical to, centrioles: i.e., the reproductive capacity of a spindle pole was exactly correlated to the number of centrioles it contained. The authors were hesitant to conclude that centrioles themselves were the polar organizers, accounting for the acentriolar spindle poles of higher plants, some animals, and rare mutant cell lines (Debec et al. 1982). As a matter of fact, many lower eukaryotes have spindle poles which contain pole bodies of various shapes, from rods to plates instead of a centriole. Higher plants have none of these geometrical bodies, as far as we know. The study of Sluder and Rieder (1985) sheds some light upon polar organizers of sea urchin eggs and proposes a structural counterpart to the old operational definition. Their work also demonstrated that the splitting apart of mother and daughter centrioles does not depend upon centriole duplication, and that a daughter centriole in a centrosome can also acquire pericentriolar material without first becoming a parent, as previous studies in somatic cells had suggested (Rieder and Borisy 1982).

I. Centrosome and the Spatial Organization of Microtubules in Terminally Differentiated Cells

Many immunofluorescent studies dealing with the spatial organization of microtubules have been done on cultured cell lines where cells were spread on coverslips. Few studies have been achieved on unsectioned tissue cells fixed in situ. This has been done in sheets of cells that remain in situ on the surface, of certain fish scales after removal from the organism (Byers et al. 1980; Dane and Tucker 1986). Microtubular networks appear remarkably similar from one cell to the other in these cellular sheets. Stereotypic patterns of microtubule alignment have been observed in areas proximal or distal to the centrosome. These intracellular alignments or reorientations of microtubules display a relationship with the supracellular pattern of alignment of extracellular collagen or bone, which suggest that they are causally related. Whatever the direction of causality, the changes in microtubule orientation take place at great distances from centrosomes, suggesting that the microtubular organization is largely independent from the latter.

Other examples of departure from the classical centrosome-centered microtubular network have been reported in differentiated cells, which involve the presence of acentriolar MTOC and the disappearance of centrioles. One example has been documented during myogenesis in vitro in the human system and points to the nuclear periphery as an alternative site for microtubule nucleation (Tassin et al. 1985a). An illustration of such a situation is shown in Fig. 3. Another example developed in an ultrastructural study of *Drosophila* wings points to the plasma membrane as another possible site for microtubule nucleation (Tucker et al. 1986; Mogensen and Tucker 1987). In this case, the majority of cells from developing wings lose their centrosomes before they stop assembling large bundles of microtubules between apical hemidesmosomes and basal desmosomes. Each trans-alar bundle includes up to 1500 microtubules and most of them are composed of 15 protofilaments. The latter in vivo observation supports the conclusion drawn from a study in vitro, which showed that the protofilament number is influenced by the centrosome (Evans et al. 1985). The functional

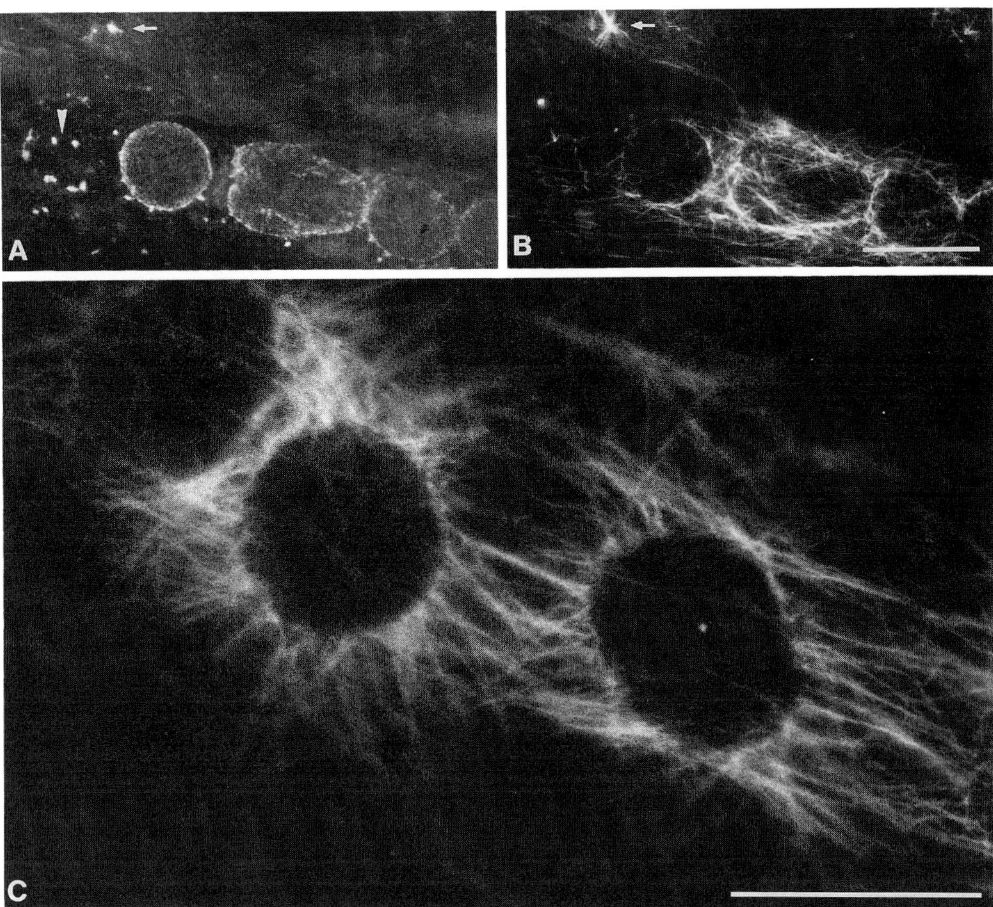

Fig. 3. In young myotubes, centrosomes dissociate from the nuclei and the MTOC redistributes on the nuclear periphery where microtubules assemble. (*A–B*) Double immunofluorescence on human myotubes during early regrowth of microtubules after Nocodazole treatment. (*A*) Anticentrosome antibody (rabbit serum 0013) decorates the centrosome in a myoblast (*arrow*) and the periphery of the nuclei in myotubes together with a cluster of dissociated centrosomes (*arrow-head*). (*B*) Antitubulin antibody demonstrates microtubule assembly at the nuclear periphery in myotubes and at the centrosome in myoblasts (*arrow*). (*C*) High magnification of the microtubule assembly at the surface of myotube nuclei; *bars* = 10 μm

significance of such switches in microtubular patterns during differentiation are indeed unknown. They are concomitant with changes in cell locomotion, cell polarity or with the establishment of cell-cell contacts (see below). The possibility of a similar switch from a microtubular network assembled on the centrosome to a network assembled on other sites was documented with cultured cells during the establishment of confluency: using centrosome-free cytoplasts, Karsenti et al. (1984) have demonstrated that confluent L929 cells can assemble microtubules whereas nonconfluent cells cannot. Epithelial cells capable of building a

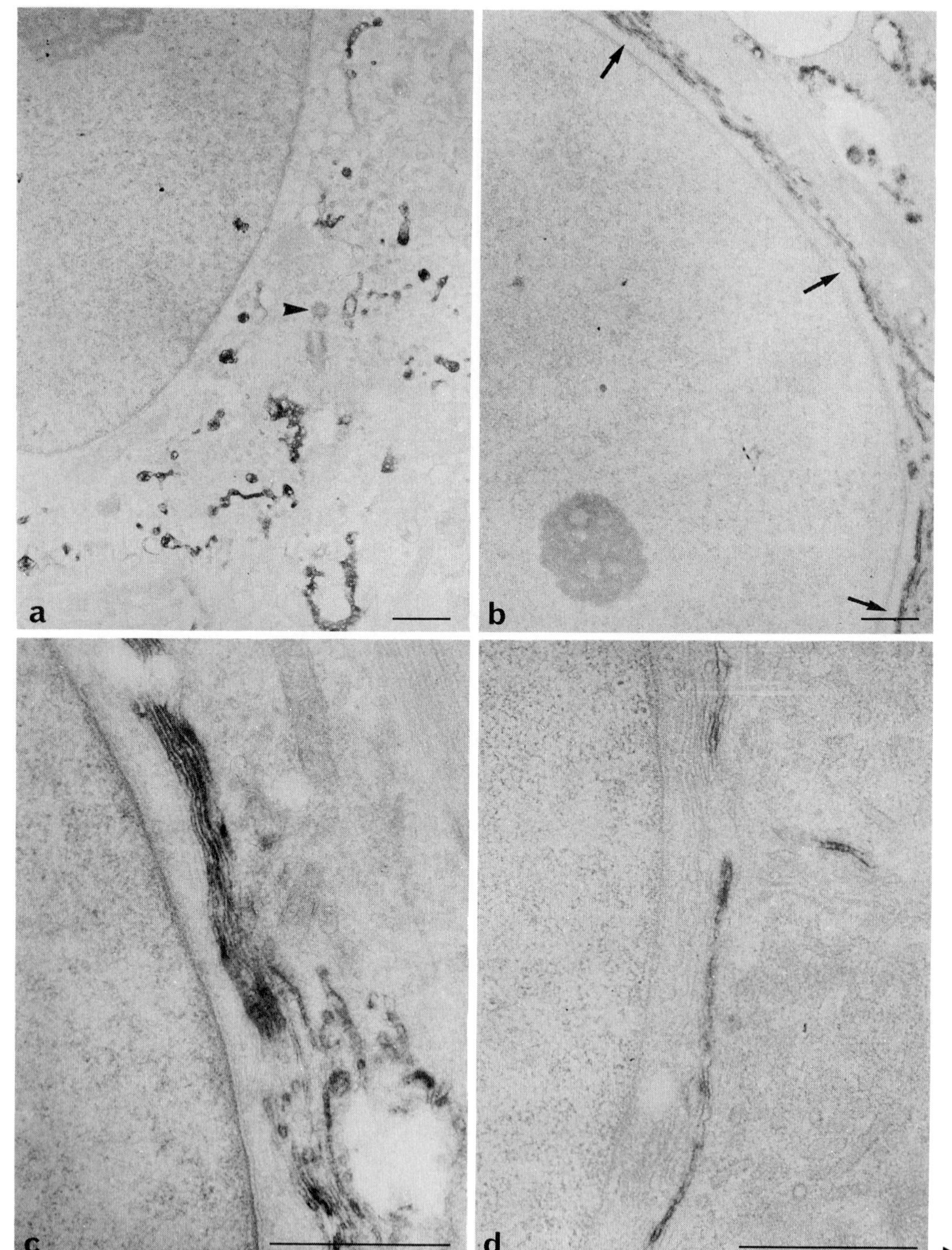
a
b
c
d

polarized epithelium in culture, such as MDCK cells, progressively display a microtubular network significantly different from the usual organization, with specific domains more stable than the others (Bre et al. 1987).

J. Centrosome and Cell Polarity/Movement

The idea of the centrosome as a determinant of cell polarity has been present since the beginning of cell biology. It has been recently argued in the frame of the dynamic instability of microtubules, that the role of the centrosome could be a passive one: selective stabilization of microtubules upon a polarized external signal could be sufficient in the establishment of cell polarity (Kirschner and Mitchison 1986).

A contribution of the centrosome in determining cell polarity is, however, suggested by the study of differentiating systems in which significant changes in cell polarity take place; a correlative dramatic change in the structure and the organization of the centrosome is observed. In the case of myogenesis, the fate of centrosomes has been studied in relation to another important compartment for cell polarity, namely, the Golgi apparatus (Tassin et al. 1985a, b). Myotubes produced by the fusion of competent myoblasts do not show any obvious antero-posterior polarity, nor do they migrate. A dramatic reorganization of the microtubular network takes place at the stage of fusion: centrioles are eliminated and microtubules are nucleated on the nuclear periphery where the pericentriolar material relocalizes (Fig. 3). Microtubules are distributed evenly in the cell according to a parallel organization along the cell axis. The Golgi apparatus displays a perinuclear distribution which is strikingly different from the polarized juxtanuclear organization observed in myoblasts (Fig. 4). Therefore, the association between the Golgi apparatus and the MTOC, which is a basic feature of cell polarity, is maintained in myotubes. This example provides some insight on the possible roles of the two parts of the centrosome, the centrioles and the MTOC itself. The MTOC is apparently capable of interacting with both the nuclear periphery and the centrioles. When present, the centriolar apparatus appears to mobilize the MTOC material which in turn organizes the Golgi apparatus in its immediate vicinity. As a result, cell polarity is defined. The cell axis can be reoriented by the relocation of the centrosome, and consequently of the Golgi apparatus, in response to certain stimuli (reviewed in Bornens and Karsenti 1984). By contrast, in the myotube the localization of both the MTOC and the

Fig. 4. The association between the Golgi apparatus and the MTOC is maintained in myotubes: the Golgi apparatus displays a perinuclear distribution strikingly different from the polarized juxtanuclear observed in myoblasts. (*a*) Mononucleate cell: the Golgi apparatus (here decorated with an anti-galactosyl transferase antibody) is organized in a complex way around the centrosome (*arrowhead*). (*b*–*d*) Myotube. (*b*) Perinuclear Golgi apparatus (here labeled by wheat germ agglutinin) appears at a constant distance from the nuclear periphery (*arrows*). (*c*–*d*) High magnification of the perinuclear Golgi apparatus labeled by wheat germ agglutinin (*c*) and by anti-galactosyl transferase antibody (*d*). The trans side is distal with respect to the nucleus. *Bars* = 1 μm

Golgi apparatus is permanent and does not display any preferential orientation. Such an organization may represent a prerequisite for allowing the establishment of muscle polarity by external clues. A functional polarity is apparently established later through innervation (Jasmin et al. 1989).

There is another model of cellular differentiation in culture which, like myogenesis, involves the fusion of precursors into a syncitial product, i.e., the monocyte-derived osteoclast-like cells (Testa et al. 1981). It provides a complementary example leading to similar conclusions because monocyte-derived giant cells, unlike myotubes, are capable of active oriented migration (Marchisio et al. 1984). Not only do they possess the centrosomes from their precursor but these are distributed in a regular manner in the giant cytoplasm, suggesting that they play an active role in the definition of cell polarity (Moudjou et al. 1989).

From such examples, it appears that the centrosome, provided it contains a centriolar apparatus, has two basic properties: (1) it is concentrated in a small volume, i.e. on the surface of the centrioles or in their immediate proximity; (2) it relocates according to cell reorientation in some circumstances. For example, preferential orientation of centrosomes toward the heart was observed in endothelial cells of major blood vessels and shown to be reestablished after reversal of a vessel segment (Rogers et al. 1985). How the latter property is brought about is not known. This question has been approached by Euteneuer and Schliwa (1985) in human neutrophils, where they had observed a dramatic centrosome splitting, i.e., separation of the centrosome into two solitary centrioles, each surrounded by an aster of microtubules which was related with cell activation and motility (Schliwa et al. 1982). They could induce centrosome splitting in a permanent fashion by the tumor promotor TPA. They demonstrated that the centriole-aster complexes were in rapid microtubule-dependent motion through the cytoplasm, and that centrosome splitting was microtubule-dependent and inhibited by the disruption of the actin network. Actin is therefore apparently capable of acting on the position of the centrosome through interaction with the microtubules radiating from it. The cortex plays a decisive role in the response of cells capable of chemotactic behavior. The centrosome/microtubule complex maintains the motile machinery as an integral part of the cell. This integrative role probably requires more than a passive relocation behind the leading lamella, since it must be achieved through elaborate interactions with other cellular compartments, particularly with the nucleus (Bessis et al. 1976; Malawista and Chevance de Boisfleury 1982; Schliwa et al. 1982).

Using actively motile newt leukocytes that display a highly visible centrosomal area, Koonce et al. (1984) studied the effect of laser irradiation of centrosome on cell behavior. The motility stopped transiently, resumed in a directionless manner, the average rate being significantly decreased. The authors provided evidence for a specific damage of centrioles, as microtubules reappear associated with the centrosomal material several minutes after irradiation. They concluded that the centrosome plays an important role in controlling the rate and direction of cell motility. A different conclusion was drawn from the study of fish epidermal cells, or cytoplasmic fragments, which show persistent directional motility in the absence of microtubules (Euteneuer and Schliwa 1984). The canoe-shaped leading edge of these very actively moving cells is, however, made of a quasi-paracrystalline organization of actin microfilaments. This could correspond to a built-in organization for unidirectional movement adapted to the wound-heating function of these cells.

The possibility also exists: that the actin system could interact directly with the centrosome. Evidence has been recently reported that basal body/centriole migration during differentiation of ciliated cells in Beroë is driven by the directed assembly of actin filaments attached to a centriole-associated rootlet (Tamm and Tamm 1988). Striated rootlets (or rhizoplasts) are often associated with basal bodies, but also with centrosomes. This is the case in epithelial PtK2 and many other cells, which are calcium-sensitive contractile organelles (Salisbury and Floyd 1978). Immunological evidence suggests that homologous proteins are present in the striated rootlets associated with basal bodies or centrosomes of many cells, from unicellular algae to mammalian cells (Klotz et al. 1986; Salisbury et al. 1986). A functional role has been proposed for these calcium-sensitive proteins in altering the orientation of centrioles or basal bodies in response to calcium fluxes (Salisbury et al. 1986). Interaction of the rootlets with the actin system could have important functional implications. Alternatively, morphological evidence has been reported for an association of striated rootlets with intermediate filaments in ciliated epithelia (Gounon et al. 1987).

The centrosome-nucleus association is apparently an important feature in the function of the centrosome/microtubule complex in cell polarization and motility. Progress on this topic has been achieved essentially in lower eukaryotes. A nucleus-basal body connector has been identified in *Chlamydomonas reinhardtii* and in many other unicellular algae (Wright et al. 1985). It is made essentially of the same calcium-sensitive proteins identified in flagellar rootlets. This connector can apparently modify the distance between centrioles/basal bodies and the nucleus upon the addition of calcium in vitro. The rapid movement of the nucleus toward the flagellar basal apparatus which occurs in vivo at the time of flagellar excision is achieved by the contraction of the connector (Salisbury et al. 1987). This contraction is not sensitive to colchicine or cytochalasin. It may serve flagellar regeneration in one way or another. One could also propose that in normal conditions, the contractile connector has a dynamic role, with a periodic contraction phased on the flagellar beating in order to prevent fish tailing. This could perhaps explain the permanent contraction observed upon flagellar excision.

The centrosome-nucleus association might be important for an accurate segregation of nuclear and cytoplasmic components. In their report, Wright et al. (1985) speculated after examining mutants from *Chlamydomonas* with a variable number of flagella that the basal body-nucleus union was important for accurate segregation of parental and daughter basal bodies at cell division, or for accurate basal body localization within the cell. The recent isolation and molecular characterization of the basal body-associated Ca^{2+}-binding protein from *Chlamydomonas* (Huang et al. 1988a, b) support such a view as they reveal a great homology with the yeast CDC31 gene product which is required for spindle pole duplication (Baum et al. 1986). A study on the reversible induction of giant cells in *Dictyostelium discoideum* by microtubule inhibitors has emphasized the significance of the tight linkage between the centrosome equivalent and the nucleus (Kitanishi-Yamura et al. 1985). The authors conclude that the centrosome/microtubule complex, in defining the cellular locomotory unit, plays a crucial role during cytokinesis, the nucleus being passively drawn by the complex. A structure study of the link between the nucleus and the centrosome equivalent in *Dictyostelium discoideum* has been carried out by Omura and Fukui (1985). The link was shown to resist KI treatment. Such a nucleus-associated body does not possess centrioles, but instead, a central paracrystalline core with a matchbox shape.

K. Conclusion

Isolation of functional centrosomes has revealed the great chemical complexity of this structurally highly conserved organelle. Such a complexity hinders a precise knowledge of the critical centrosomal components. Isolation of centrosomes from various sources is needed to advance in the elucidation of the basic principles of assembly. As more immunological probes become available, the studies should rapidly benefit from the powerful tools of molecular biology. Isolated centrosomes may also provide a useful substrate for studying diverse aspects of microtubule nucleation including centrosome assembly. This should lead to the biochemical or structural identification of the nucleation sites and of their interactions with the other parts of the centrosome. The search for associated enzymatic activities (kinases, phosphatases, ATPases) will also be of importance for centrosome functions. We already know that the structure and the nucleation capacity of the centrosome vary according to the cell cycle. The modification of the cytoplasmic state at the transition interphase-mitosis seems to be governed by kinases that modulate the phosphorylation state of a great number of membrane and cytoskeletal proteins leading to a complete reorganization of the cell. The presence of several kinases (c-AMP dependent kinase, $p34^{cdc2}$ protein kinase) and of calcium binding proteins at the centrosome, raises the question of the role of the microtubule nucleating centre in cell regulation. Knowledge of the target proteins of these kinases at the centrosome and of their role in the duplication cycle should lead to a renewed approach to the morphogenesis of the centrosome and to its possible functions in the cell cycle control.

Acknowledgements. The electron microscopy presented in Figs. 1 and 4 was done by M. Paintrand, Centre de Biologie Cellulaire du CNRS, Ivry sur Seine, France.

We thank J. Berges, N. Bordes, C. Celati, C. Klotz, M. Moudjou and F. Tournier for helpful discussions. This work was supported by C.N.R.S., by a grant M.R.E.S. n°87-C-0555 to MB, by a grant ARC to GK. EB has received a fellowship from La Ligue Nationalle Franciase Contre le Cancer

References

Andersen B, Osborn M, Weber R (1978) Specific visualization of the calcium dependent regulatory protein of cyclic nucleotide phosphodiesterase (modulator protein) in tissue culture cells by immunofluorescence microscopy: mitosis and intercellular bridges. Cytobiologie 17:354–364

Arion D, Meijer L, Brizuela L, Beach D (1988) cdc2 is a component of the M phase-specific histone H1 kinase: evidence for identity with MPF. Cell 55:371–378

Aubin JE, Osborn M, Franke WW, Weber K (1980) Intermediate filaments of the vimentin-type and the cytokeratin-type are distributed differently during mitosis. Exp Cell Res 129:149–165

Bailly E, Dorée M, Nurse P, Bornens M (1989) $h34^{cdc2}$ is located in both nucleus and cytoplasm; part is centrosomally associated at G2/M transition and enters vesicles at anaphase in human cells. The EMBO Journal, 8(13), in press

Bastmeyer M, Russell DG (1987) Characterization of pales spermatocyte spindles, with reference to an MTOC-associated protein. J Cell Sci 87:431–438

Bastmeyer M, Steffen W, Fuge H (1986) Immunostaining of spindle components in tipulid spermatocytes using a serum against pericentriolar material. Eur J Cell Biol 42:305–310

Bataillon E (1911) Les deux facteurs de la pharthenogénése traumatique chez les amphibiens CR Acad Sci (Paris) 152:920–922

Baum P, Furlong C, Byers B (1986) Yeast gene required for spindle pole body duplication: homology of its product with Ca^{2+}-binding proteins. Proc Natl Acad Sci USA 83:5512–5516

Baum P, Yin C, Goetsch L, Byers B (1988) A yeast gene essential for regulation of spindle pole duplication. Mol Cell Biol 8:5386–5397

Bessis M, De Boisfleury A (1976) A catalogue of white blood cell movements (normal and pathologic). Blood Cells 2:365–410

Blackburn GR, Barreau MD, Dewey WC (1978) Partial purification of centrosomes from chinese hamster ovary cells. Exp Cell Res 113:183–187

Blose SH, Bushnell A (1982) Observations on the vimentin 10 nm filaments during mitosis in BHK 21 cells. Exp Cell Res 142:57–62

Bonifacino JS, Klausner RD, Sandoval IV (1985) A widely distributed nuclear protein immunologically related to the microtubule-associated protein MAP-1 is associated with the mitotic spindle. Proc Natl Acad Sci USA 82:1146–1150

Bornens M (1977) Is the centriole bound to the nuclear membrane? Nature 270:80–82

Bornens M, Karsenti E (1984) The centrosome. In: Bittar EE (eds) Membrane, structure and functions. Vol 6. John Wiley, New York pp 100–171

Bornens MM, Paintrand M, Berges J, Marty MC, Karsenti E (1987) Structural and chemical characterization of isolated centrosomes. Cell Motil Cytoskeleton 8:238–249

Boveri T (1901) Uber die Natur der Centrosomen. Jena Z Med Naturwiss 28:1–220

Bre MH, Kreis TE, Karsenti E (1987) Control of microtubule nucleation and stability in Madin-Darby canine kidney cells: occurence of non centrosomal, stable detyrosinated microtubules. J Cell Biol 105:1283–1296

Brinkley BR (1985) Microtubule organizing centers. Annu Rev Cell Biol 1:145–172

Brooks RF, Bennett DC, Smith JA (1980) Mammalian cell cycles need two random transitions. Cell 19:493–504

Brown DL, Schweitzer I, Sunga PS (1982) The site specificity of microtubule initiation by microtubule organizing centers. In: Cappuccinelli P, Morris NR (eds) Microtubules in microorganisms. Marcel Dekker, New York (Microbiological series, vol 8, pp 31–49)

Byers B, Goetsch L (1975) Behavior of spindles and spindle plaques in the cell cycle and conjugation of *Saccharomyces cerevisiae*. J Bacteriol 124:511–523

Byers HR, Fujiwara K, Porter KR (1980) Visualization of microtubules of cells in situ by indirect immunofluorescence, Proc Natl Acad Sci USA 77:6657–6661

Calarco-Gillam PD, Siebert MC, Hubble R, Mitchison T, Kirschner MW (1983) Centrosome development in early mouse embryos as defined by autoantibody against pericentriolar material. Cell 35:621–623

Clayton L, Black CM, Lloyd CW (1985) Microtubule nucleating sites in higher plant cells identified by an autoantibody against pericentriolar material. J Cell Biol 101:319–324

Courvalin JC, Hernandez-Verdun D, Gosti-Testu F, Marty MC, Maunoury R, Bornens M (1986) A protein of Mr 80,000 is associated with the nucleolus organizer of human cell lines. Chromosoma (Berl) 94:353–361

Crozet N (1988) Ultrastructural aspects of in vitro fertilization in sheep. J Ultrastruct Mol Struct Res 98:1–10

Dane PJ, Tucker JB (1986) Supracellular microtubule alignment in cell layers associated with the secretion of certain fish scales. J Cell Sci Suppl 273–291

Davis FM, Tsao TY, Fowler SK, Rao PN (1983) Monoclonal antibodies to mitotic cells. Proc Natl Acad Sci USA 80:2926–2930

Debec A, Szollosi A, Szollosi D (1982) A *Drosophila melanogaster* cell line lacking centrioles. Biol Cell 44:133–138

De Camilli P, Moretti M, Denis Donini S, Lohman SM (1986) Heterogeneous distribution of the c-AMP receptor protein kinase R-II in the nervous system: evidence for its intracelluar accumulation on microtubules, microtubule organizing centres and the the area of the golgi complex. J Cell Biol 103:189–203

Draetta G, Beach D (1988) Acitivation of cdc2 protein kinase during mitosis in human cells: cell-cycle dependent phosphorylation and subunit rearrangement. Cell 54:17–26

Draetta G, Brizuela L, Potashkin J, Beach D (1987) Identification of p34 and p13, human homologs of cell cycle regulators of fission yeast encoded by cdc2 + and suc1 +. Cells 50:319–325

Dunphy WG, Brizuela L, Beach D, Newport J (1988) The *Xenopus* cdc2 protein is a component of MPF, a cytoplasmic regulator of mitosis. Cell 54:423–431

Euteneuer U, Schliwa M (1984) Persistent, directional motility of cells and cytoplasmic fragments in the absence of microtubules. Nature (London) 310:58–61

Evans L, Mitchison TJ, Kirschner WM (1985) Influence of the centrosome on the structure of nucleated microtubules. J Cell Biol 100:1185–1191

Fais D, Nadezhdina, Chentsov YS (1984) Evidence for the nucleus-centriole association in bovine cells obtained by ultracentrifugation. Eur J Cell Biol 133:190–196

Frasch M, Glover DM, Saumweber H (1986) Nuclear antigens follow different pathways into daughter nuclei during mitosis in early *Drosophila* embryos. J Cell Sci 82:155–172

Freeman M, Nüsslein-Volhard C, Glover DM (1986) The dissociation of nuclear and centrosomal division in gnu, a mutation causing giant nuclei in *Drosophila*. Cell 46:457–468

Gauthier J, Norbury C, Lohka M, Nurse P, Maller J (1988) Purified maturation-promoting factor contains the product of a *Xenopus* homolog of the fission yeast cell control gene cdc2. Cell 54:433–439

Gonzalez C, Casal J, Ripoll P (1988) Functional monopolar spindles caused by mutation in mgr, a cell division gene of *Drosophila melanogaster*. J Cell Sci 89:39–48

Gosti F, Marty MC, Courvalin JC, Maunoury R, Bornens M (1987) Centrosomal proteins and lactate dehydrogenase possess a common epitope in human cell lines. Proc Natl Acad Sci 84:1000–1004

Gosti-Testu F, Marty MC, Berges J, Maunoury R, Bornens M (1986) Identification of centrosomal proteins in a human lymphoblastic cell line. EMBO J 5:2545–2550

Gounon P, Lainé MC, Sandoz D (1987) Cytokeratine filament organization in the ciliated cells of the quail oviduct. Eur J Cell Biol 44:229–237

Grafen A (1988) A centrosomal theory of the short term evolutionary maintenance of sexual reproduction. J Theor Biol 131:163–173

Harper JDI, Mitchison JM, Williamson RE, John PCL (1989) Does the autoimmune serum 5051 specifically recognise microtubule organising centres in plant cells? Cell Biol Intern Reports, 13:471–475

Hauser M (1986) Taxol affects both the microtubular arrays of heliozoan axonemes and their microtubule-organizing centers. Eur J Cell Biol 42:295–304

Heidemann SR, Kirschner MW (1975) Aster formation in eggs of *Xenopus laevis*. Induction by isolated basal bodies. J Cell Biol 67:105–117

Heidemann SR, Sanders G, Kirschner M (1977) Evidence for a functional role of RNA in centrioles. Cell 10:337–350

Huang B, Watterson DM, Lee VD, Schibler MJ (1988a) Purification and characterization of a basal body-associated Ca^{2+}-binding protein. J Cell Biol 107:121–131
Huang B, Mangersen A, Lee VD (1988b) Molecular cloning of cDNA for caltractin, a basal body-associated Ca^{2+}-binding protein: homology in its protein sequence with Calmodulin and the yeast cdc31 gene product. J Cell Biol 107:133–140
Hurt E (1988) A novel nucleoskeletal-like protein located at the nuclear periphery, required for the life cycle of *S. cerevisiae*. EMBO J 7:4323–4334
Jasmin BJ, Cartaud J, Bornens M, Changeux JP (1989) The Golgi apparatus in chick skeletal muscle-changes in its distribution during endplate development and after denervation. Proc Natl Acad Sci US (in press)
Kallenbach RJ (1985) Ultrastructural analysis of the initiation and development of cytasters in sea urchin eggs. J Cell Sci 73:261–278
Karsenti E, Maro B (1986) Centrosomes and the spatial distribution of microtubules in animal cells. TIBS 11:460–463
Karsenti E, Bravo R, Kirschner M (1987) Phosphorylation changes associated with the early cell cycle in *Xenopus* eggs. Dev Biol 119:442–453
Karsenti E, Newport J, Hubble R, Kirschner MW (1984) Interconversion of metaphase and interphase microtubule arrays as studied by the injection of centrosomes and nuclei into *Xenopus* eggs. J Cell Biol 98:1730–1745
Katsuma Y, Swierenga SHH, Marceau N, French SW (1987) Connections of intermediate filaments with the nuclear lamina and the cell periphery. Biol Cell 59:193–204
Keryer G, Davis FM, Rao PN, Beisson J (1987) Protein phosphorylation and dynamics of cytoskeletal structures associated with basal bodies in *Paramecium*. Cell Motil Cytoskeleton 8:44–54
Keryer G, Garreau de Loubresse N, Bordes N, Bornens M (1989) Identification of a spindle-associated protein in ciliate micronuclei. J Cell Sci 93:287–298
Kirschner MW, Mitchison T (1986) Beyond self-assembly: from microtubules to morphogenesis. Cell 45:329–342
Kitanishi-Yamura, Blose SH, Fukui Y (1985) Role of the MT-MTOC complex in determination of the cellular locomotory unit in Dictyostelium. Protoplasma 127:133–146
Kleve MG, Clark WH (1980) Association of actin with sperm centrioles: isolation of centriolar complexes and immunofluorescent localisation of actin. J Cell Biol 86:87–95
Klotz C, Bordes N, Laine MC, Sandoz D, Bornens M (1986) A protein of 175,000 daltons associated with striated rootlets in ciliated epithelia as revealed by a monoclonal antibody. Cell Motil Cytoskeleton 6:56–67
Klotz C, Dabauvalle MC, Paintrand M, Bornens M, Karsenti E (1988) Study of the structure-activity relationship of isolated centrosomes. In: Rousset 3AF (ed) Structure and functions of the cytoskeleton. Colloque INSERM/John Libbey. Eurotex Ltd. 171:341–347
Klotz C, Dabauvalle MC, Paintrand M, Weber H, Bornens M, Karsenti E (1990) Parthenogenesis in Xenopus eggs requires centrosomal integrity. J Cell Biol (in press)
Komesli S, Tournier F, Paintrand M, Margolis R, Job D, Bornens M (1989) Mass isolation of calf thymus centrosomes: the identification of a specific configuration. J Cell Biol (in press)
Koonce MP, Cloney RA, Berns MW (1984) Laser irradiation of centrosomes in newt eosinophils: evidence of a centriole role in motility. J Cell Biol 98:1999–2010
Kuriyama R (1984) Activity and stability of centrosomes of chinese hamster ovary cells in nucleation of microtubules in vitro. J Cell Sci 66:277–295
Kuriyama R, Borisy GG (1981) Microtubule-nucleating activity of centrosomes in chinese hamster ovary cells is independent of the centriole cycle but coupled to the mitotic cycle. J Cell Biol 91:822–826
Kuriyama R, Borisy GG (1983) Cytasters induced within unfertilized sea urchin eggs. J Cell Sci 61:175–189
Kuriyama R, Borisy GG (1985) Identification of molecular components of the centrosphere in the mitotic spindle of sea urchin eggs. J Cell Biol 101:524–530
Labbe JC, Lee MG, Nurse P, Picard A, Dorée M (1988) Activation at M phase of a protein kinase encoded by a starfish homologue of the cell cycle control gene cdc2+. Nature 335:251–254

Lee MG, Nurse P (1987) Complementation used to clone a human homologue of the fission yeast cell cycle control gene cdc2+. Nature 327:31–35
Lee MG, Norbury C, Spurr NK, Nurse P (1988) Regulated expression and phosphorylation of a possible mammalian cell cycle control protein. Nature 333:676–679
Le Guen P, Crozet N (1989) Microtubules and centrosome distribution during sheep fertilization. Eur J Cell Biol 98:239–245
Lohka MJ, Hayes MK, Maller JL (1988) Purification of maturation-promoting factor, an intracellular regulator of early mitotic events. Proc Natl Acad Sci USA 85:3009–3013
Malawista SE, Chevance de Boisfleury A (1982) The cytokinetoplast: purified stable and functional motile machinery from human blood polymorphonuclear leukocytes. J Cell Biol 95:960–973
Maller J (1985) Regulation of amphibian oocyte maturation. Cell Differ 16:211–221
Maller J, Poccia D, Nishioka D, Kido P, Gerhart J, Hartman H (1976) Spindle formation and cleavage in *Xenopus* eggs injected with centriole containing fractions from sperm. Exp Cell Res 99:285–294
Marchisio PC, Cirillo D, Naldini G, Primavera MV, Teti A, Zambonin-Zallone, A (1984) Cell substratum interaction of culture avian osteoclasts is mediated by specific adhesion structures. J Cell Biol 99:1696–1705
Maro B, Bornens M (1980) The centriole-nucleus association: effects of cytochalasin B and nocodazole. Biol Cell 39:287–290
Maro B, Paintrand M, Sauron ME, Paulin D Bornens M (1984) Vimentin filaments and centrosomes are they associated? Exp Cell Res 150:452–458
Maro B, Howlett SK, Webb M (1985) Non-spindle microtubule organizing centers in metaphase II arrested mouse oocytes. J Cell Biol 101:1665–1672
Maunoury R (1978) Localization immunocytochimique de la centrosphere de cellules tumorales humaines par utilisation d'anticorps naturels de lapin. CR Acad Sci (Paris) Ser 3, 286:503–506
Mazia D (1961) Mitosis and physiology of cell division. In: Brachet J, Mirsky A (eds) The Cell: biochemistry, physiology, morphology. Academic Press, New York, pp 77–394
Mazia D (1987) The chromosome cycle and the centrosome cycle in the mitotic cycle. Int Rev Cytol 100:49–92
Mazia D, Harris PJ, Bibring T (1960) The multiplicity of the mitotic centers and the time course of their duplication and separation. J Biophys Chem Cytol 7:1–20
McIntosh JR (1983) The centrosome as an organizer of the cytoskeleton. Mol Cell Biol 2:115–142
Meyerhof PG, Masui Y (1979) Properties of a cytostatic factor from *Xenopus laevis* eggs. Dev Bil 72:1982–1987
Mitchison T, Krischner MW (1984) Microtubule assembly nucleated by isolated centrosomes. Nature 312:232–237
Mitchison TJ, Kirschner MW (1986) Isolation of mammalian centrosomes. Methods Enzymol 134:261–268
Mogensen MM, Tucker JB (1987) Evidence for microtubule nucleation at plasma membrane-associated sites in *Drosophila*. J Cell Sci 88:95–107
Moudjou M, Lanotte M, Bornens M (1989) The fate of the centrosome-microtubule network in monocyte-derived giant cells. J Cell Sci 94:237–244
Nadezhdina ES, Fais D, Chentsov YuS (1978) Partial purification of centrioles from spleen cells. Cell Biol Int Rep 2:601–606
Nagano H, Hirai S, Okana K, Ikegami S (1981) A chromosomal cleavage of fertilized starfish eggs in the presence of Aphidicolin. Dev Biol 85:409–415
Neighbors BW, Williams RC, McIntosh JR (1988) Localization of kinesin in cultured cells. J Cell Biol 106:1193–1204
Nelson WJ, Traub P (1982) Is the perinulcear position of the centriole maintained by the intermediate filament network? Cell Biol Int Rep 6:215–223
Nigg EA, Schafer G, Hiltz H, Eppenberger HM (1985) Cyclic-AMP-dependent protein kinase type II is associated with the Golgi complex and with centrosomes. Cell 41:1039–1051
Oliver JM, Osborn WRA, Pfeiffer RJ, Child FM, Berlin RD (1981) Purine nucleoside phosphorylase is associated with centrioles and basal bodies. J Cell Biol 91:837–847

Omura F, Fukui Y (1985) Dictyostelium MTOC: structure and linkage to the nucleus. Protoplasma 127:212–221

Peterson SP, Berns MW (1980) The centriolar complex. Int Rev Cytol 64:81–106

Picard A, Karsenti E, Dabauvalle MC, Doree M (1987) Release of mature starfish ovocytes from interphase arrest by microinjection of human centrosomes. Nature 327:170–172

Picard A, Harricane MC, Labbe JC, Doree M (1988) Germinal vesicle components are not required for the cell cycle oscillator of the early starfish embryo. Dev Biol 128:121–128

Pickett-Heaps JD (1969) The evolution of the mitotic apparatus: an attempt at comparative ultrastructural cytology in dividing plant cells. Cytobios 3:257–280

Piperno G, Huang B, Luck JL (1977) Two-dimensional analysis of flagellar proteins from wild type and paralysed mutants of *Chlamydomonas reinhardtii*. Proc Natl Acad Sci USA 74:1600–1604

Raff JW, Glover DM (1988) Nuclear and cytoplasmic mitotic cycles continue in *Drosophila* embryos in which DNA synthesis is inhibited with Aphidicolin. J Cell Biol 107:2009–2019

Rieder CR, Borisy GG (1982) The centrosome cycle in PtK2 cells: asymetric distribution and structural changes in the pericentriolar material. Biol Cell 44:117–132

Robbins E, Gonatas NK (1964) The ultrastructure of a mammalian cell during the mitotic cycle. J Cell Biol 21:429–458

Rogers KA, McKee NC, Kalnins UI (1985) Preferential orientation of centrioles towards the heart in endothelial cells of major blood vessels is restablished after reversal of a segment. Proc Natl Acad Sci USA 82:3272–3276

Roth KE, Rieder CL, Bowser SS (1988) Flexible-substratum technique for viewing cells from the side: some in vivo properties of primary (9 + O) cilia in cultured kidney epithelia. J Cell Sci 89:457–466

Ruiz F, Garreau de Loubresse N, Beisson J (1987) A mutation affecting basal body duplication and cell shape in *Paramecium*. J Cell Biol 104:417–430

Salisbury JL, Floyd GL (1978) Calcium induced contraction of the rhizoplast of a quadriflagellate green alga. Science (Wash. DC) 202:975–978

Salisbury JL, Baron AT, Coliny BEE, Marlindale VE, Sanders MA (1986) Calcium modulated contractile proteins associated with the eucaryotic centrosome. Cell Motil Cytoskeleton 6:193–197

Salisbury JL, Sanders MA, Hzarpst L (1987) Flagellar root contraction and nuclear movement during flagellar regeneration in *Chlamydomonas reinhardtii*. J Cell Biol 105:1799–1805

Schatten H, Schatten G (1986) Motility and centrosomal organization during sea urchin and mouse fertilization. Cell Motil Cytoskeleton 6:163–175

Schatten H, Walter M, Mazia D, Biesmann H, Paweletz N, Coffe G, Schatten G (1987) Centrosome detection in sea urchin eggs with a monoclonal antibody against *Drosophila* intermediate filament proteins. Characterization of stages of the division cycle of centrosomes. Proc Natl Acad Sci USA 84:8488–8492

Schliwa M, Euteneuer U (1985) Evidence for an involvement of actin in the positioning and motility of centrosomes. J Cell Biol 101:96–103

Schliwa M, Pryzwansky KB, Euteneuer U (1982) Centrosome splitting in neutrophils: an unusual phenomenon related to cell activation and motility. Cell 81:705–717

Schulze E, Kirschner MW (1986) Microtubule dynamics in interphase cells. J Cell Biol 102:1020–1031

Sellitto C, Kuriyama R (1988) Distribution of pericentriolar in multipolar spindles induced by colcemid treatment in chinese hamster ovary cells. J Cell Sci 89:57–65

Sherline P, Mascardo RJ (1982) EGF induced centrosomal separation: mechanism and relationship to mitogenesis. J. Cell Biol 95:316–322

Sluder G, Begg DA (1985) Experimental analysis of the reproduction of spindle poles. J Cell Sci 76:35–51

Sluder G, Rieder CL (1985) Centriole number and the reproductive capacity of spindle poles. J Cell Biol 100:887–896

Sluder G, Miller FJ, Rieder CL (1986) The reproduction of centrosomes. Nuclear versus cytoplasmic controls. J Cell Biol 103:1873–1881

Snyder JA, McIntosh JR (1975) Initiation and growth of microtubules from mitotic centers in lysed mammalian cells. J Cell Biol 67:744–760

Snyder JA, Hamilton BT, Mullins JM (1982) Loss of mitotic centrosomal microtubule initiation capacity at the metaphase-anaphase transition. Eur J Cell Biol 27:191–199

Soltys BJ, Borisy GG (1985) Polymerization of tubulin in vivo Direct evidence for assembly onto microtubules ends and from centrosomes. J Cell Biol 100:1682–1689

Steffen W, Linck R (1988) Evidence for tektins in centrioles and axonemal microtubules. Proc Natl Acad Sci USA 85:2643–2647

Sunkel CE, Glover DM (1988) Polo, a mitotic mutant of *Drosophila* displaying abnormal spindle poles. J Cell Sci 89:25–3

Szollosi D, Callarco P, Dlonahue RP (1972) Absence of centrioles in the first and second meiotic spindles of mouse ovocytes. J Cell Biol 11:521–541

Tamm SL, Tamm S (1988) Development of macrociliary cells in Beroë. I. Actin bundles and centriole migration. J Cell Sci 89:67–80

Tassin AM, Maro B, Bornens M (1985a) Fate of microtubule-organizing centers during myogenesis in vitro. J Cell Biol 100:35–46

Tassin AM, Paintrand M, Berger EG, Bornens M (1985b) The Golgi apparatus remains associated with microtubule organizing centers during myogenesis. J Cell Biol 101:630–638

Testa NG, Allen TD, Lajtha LG, Onions D, Jarrett O (1981) Generation of osteoclasts in vitro. J Cell Sci 47:127–137

Tournier F, Karsenti E, Bornens M (1989) Parthenogenesis in *Xenopus* eggs injected with centrosomes from synchronized human lymphoid cells. Dev Biol (in press)

Tucker R, Pardec A, Fujiwara K (1979) Centriole ciliation is related to quiescence and DNA synthesis in 3T3 cells. Cell 17:527–535

Tucker JB, Milner MJ, Currie DA, Muir JW, Forrest DA, Spencer MJ (1986) Centrosomal microtubule organizing centres and a switch in the control of the protofilament number for cell surface-associated microtubules during *Drosophila* wing morphogenesis. Eur J Cell Biol 41:279–289

Vandre DD, Davis FM, Rao PN, Borisy GG (1986) Distribution of cytoskeletal proteins sharing a conserved phosphorylated epitope. Eur J Cell Biol 41:72–81

Vorobjev IA, Nadehzdina ES (1987) The centrosome and its role in the organization of microtubules. Int Rev Cytol 106:227–284

Welsh MJ, Dedman JR, Brinkley BR Means AR (1979) Tubulin and calmodulin. Effects of microtubule and microfilament inhibitors and localization in the mitotic apparatus. J Cell Biol 81:624–634

Wheatley DN (1982) The centriole: a central enigma of cell biology. Elsevier Biomedical Press, New York

Whitfield WGF, Millar SE, Saumweber H, Frasch M, Glover DM (1988) Cloning of a gene encoding an antigen associated with the centrosome in *Drosophila.* J Cell Sci 89:467–480

Wick SM (1985) Immunofluorescence microscopy of tubulin and microtubule arrays in plant cells. III. Transition between mitotic/cytokenetic and interphase microtubules arrays. Cell Biol Int Rep 9:357–371

Wilsman NJ, Farnum CE (1983) Arrange of C. tubule protofilaments in Mammalian Basal Bodies. J Ultrastruct Res 84:205–212

Wilson EB (1925) The cell and development heredity. McMillan, NY

Wright RL, Salisbury J, Jarvik JW (1985) A nucleus-basal body connector in *Chlamydomonas reinhardfii* that may function in basal body localization or segregation. J Cell Biol 101:1903–1912

Role of Nonsense, Frameshift, and Missense Suppressor tRNAs in Mammalian Cells

D. Hatfield[1], B. J. Lee[1], D. W. E. Smith[2], and S. Oroszlan[3]

A. Introduction

Three classes of point mutations occur in nature: (1) missense; (2) nonsense; and (3) frameshift. Aminoacyl-tRNAs, which suppress mutations within each class, have been characterized in microorganisms; excellent reviews covering these studies have been published (Eggertsson and Söll 1988; Hill 1975; Körner et al. 1978; Murgola 1985, 1989; Sherman 1982; Smith 1979; Steege and Söll 1979). The aminoacyl-tRNAs involved in suppression of point mutations are called missense, nonsense, and frameshift suppressors. Nonsense suppressors are further classified as amber, ochre, and opal when they suppress UAG, UAA, and UGA codons, respectively. Even though our understanding of the occurrence, structure, and function of suppressor tRNAs in mammalian cells is largely just beginning to emerge, it would seem that our interpretation of the role of suppressor tRNAs in mammalian cells may have to be altered from the classical viewpoint. That is, in microorganisms, suppressor tRNAs have largely been thought of as providing a mechanism of correcting or reversing deleterious mutations. It appears that suppressor tRNAs, when they occur in mammalian cells, have specialized functions and are not present in order to reverse the effect of deleterious mutations.

Since our knowledge is most advanced about nonsense suppression in mammalian cells (Celis and Piper 1981; Hatfield 1985; Valle and Morch 1988; Hatfield et al. 1989), the review begins with this group of suppressors. It then focuses on ribosomal frameshifting, and subsequently, on missense suppression.

[1] Laboratory of Experimental Carcinogenesis, National Cancer Institute, National Institutes of Health, Bethesda, MD 20892, USA
[2] Department of Pathology, Northwestern University Medical School, Chicago, IL 60611, USA
[3] Laboratory of Molecular Virology and Carcinogenesis, Bionetics Research Inc., Basic Research Program, National Cancer Institute-Frederick Center Research Facility, Frederick, MD 21701, USA

B. Suppression of Nonsense Codons

I. Naturally Occurring Nonsense Suppressor tRNAs

A naturally occurring nonsense suppressor tRNA is defined as any isoacceptor which exists naturally in a tRNA population and is capable of suppressing a stop codon in protein synthesis. Seven tRNAs have been shown to serve as suppressor tRNAs in mammalian cells. Four of these tRNAs are amber suppressors, which occur in three different amino acid families, and three are opal suppressors, which occur in two different amino acid families. One of the amber suppressors is tyrosine tRNA (Shindo-Okada et al. 1985), another is glutamine tRNA (Feng et al. 1989a; Kuchino et al. 1987; Yoshinaka et al. 1985a, b) and the third and fourth are leucine tRNAs (Valle et al. 1987). The opal suppressors are tryptophan tRNA (Geller and Rich 1980) and two serine tRNAs (Diamond et al. 1981; Hatfield et al. 1982a). The serine tRNAs have recently been shown to form selenocysteyl-$tRNA^{Ser}$ (Lee et al. 1989b). The $tRNA^{Gln}$ occurs in both an undermodified and fully modified form (Kuchino et al. 1987), while the leucine tRNAs are major isoacceptors found in calf liver (Valle et al. 1987). The primary role of each of the amber suppressors and of the tryptophan suppressor is to translate codons within the corresponding amino acid families. The opal suppressor serine tRNAs apparently have two major functions (Lee et al. 1989b); (1) to serve as a carrier molecule for the biosynthesis of selenocysteine; and (2) to donate selenocysteine directly to protein in response to a specific UGA codon. The latter proposal for a function of the opal suppressor serine tRNAs is based on the observation that the glutathione peroxidase gene from a variety of mammalian sources contains a TGA codon in an open-reading frame, which corresponds to a selenocysteine moiety at the active site of the protein product (Chambers et al. 1986; Mullenbach et al. 1987, 1988; Reddy et al. 1988; Sukenaka et al. 1987). A naturally occurring ochre suppressor has not been described thus far in higher eukaryotes, although there is recent evidence that ochre suppressors may occur naturally in mammalian cells (see Sect. B.I.2). Additional characteristics of each of the nonsense suppressors identified in mammalian cells are given below.

1. Amber Suppressor tRNAs

Tyrosine tRNA. Tyrosine tRNA is mammalian cells normally contains a hypermodified nucleotide in the wobble or 5′ position of its anticodon designated as Queuine, or Q base. Lack of Q base in the anticodon of $tRNA^{Tyr}$ results in the undermodified tRNA misreading the termination codon, UAG, in protein synthesis, whereas the Q containing tyrosine tRNA does not serve as a suppressor. This very important observation was first reported for a *Drosophila* $tRNA^{Tyr}$ which lacked Q base (Bienz and Kubli 1981). Tyrosine tRNA Q^- from mammalian cells is also capable of suppressing UAG in protein synthesis. Shindo-Okada et al. (1985) isolated $tRNA^{Tyr}$ Q^- from mouse tumor cells in culture and have coinjected this tRNA and tobacco mosiac viral (TMV) RNA into *Xenopus* oocytes. TMV–RNA contains a UAG termination codon which results in expression of a 180 K readthrough protein when the stop codon is suppressed (Pelham 1978). The mouse $tRNA^{Tyr}$ supported synthesis of the viral 180 K readthrough protein (Shindo-Okada et al. 1985). It should be noted that tyrosine tRNA containing 6-thioqueuine was a more efficient suppressor of the TMV–RNA UAG termination codon than the tyrosine tRNA lacking Q base (Shindo-Okada et al. 1985).

The structures of tyrosine tRNAs which suppress UAG codons have been determined from several higher eucaryotes, including *Drosophila* (Bienz and Kubli 1981; Suter et al. 1986), *A. pernyi* (Feng et al. 1986), tobacco plant (Beier et al. 1984a), wheat germ (Beier et al. 1984b), wheat leaves (Beier et al. 1984b), and lupin seeds (Barciszewski et al. 1985). The only difference in the sequence of the suppressor and nonsuppressor species is in the presence or absence of Q base in the wobble position of the anticodon. Each suppressor species lacks Q base. These studies show that the molecular basis for suppressor activity of tyrosine tRNA is the substitution of G for Q in the wobble position of the anticodon. *Studies involving the role of undermodified tRNAs in the expression of certain proteins demonstrate unequivocally that the extent of base modification on tRNA regulates the expression of specific proteins at the level of translation.*

The nature of the interaction between the GψA anticodon in $tRNA^{Tyr}$ and the UAG termination codon is not understood. G:G base pairings are not permitted in the wobble hypothesis (Crick 1966). The G in the anticodon must participate, however, in the recognition process, since the GψA anticodon does not translate UAA codons (Beier et al. 1984b). Beier et al. (1984b) suggested that the G in the anticodon may interact with the G in UAG in the syn conformation (Jank et al. 1977; Topal and Fresco 1976). Further discussion of the possible interaction of G in the 5′ position of the tyrosine tRNA anticodon and the 3′ position of the UAG termination codon may be found in a review by Valle and Morch (1988). The ψ in the middle position of the anticodon, which is unique to $tRNA^{Tyr}$ of eucaryotes (Sprinzl et al. 1987), apparently also participates in the ability of the Q-deficient isoacceptor to read UAG codons. Johnson and Abelson (1983) have shown that changing the ψ to U in yeast $tRNA^{Tyr}$ results in a loss of suppressor activity. Thus, the ψ:A base pairing in the middle position probably forms a more stable anticodon: codon complex than the U:A base pairing (Ward and Reich 1968) which may be required for suppression of the UAG termination codon (Barciszewski et al. 1985; Beier et al. 1984a, b; Bienz and Kubli 1981; Feng et al. 1986). The coding properties of Q-containing and Q-lacking Asn-, Asp-, and His-tRNAs which, unlike Tyr-tRNA, contain U in the middle position of their anticodon, are discussed in the section on missense suppression.

Glutamine tRNA. Mammalian type-C viruses translate their *gag* and *pol* genes in the same reading frame (Shinnick et al. 1981). The *gag-pol* fusion protein arises, therefore, from suppression of the UAG termination codon at the 3′ end of the *gag* gene, as first demonstrated by Philipson et al. (1978). These investigators added a yeast amber suppressor to reticulocyte lysates programmed with murine Moloney leukemia viral mRNA, which demonstrated an enhancement in the expression of the fusion protein (Philipson et al. 1978). The amino acid which occurs at the readthrough site in vivo was identified by isolating the protease from murine Moloney leukemia virus (MuLV) and determining its amino-terminal sequence (Yoshinaka et al. 1985a). Alignment of these amino acid sequences with the viral DNA sequence (Shinnick et al. 1981) demonstrated that the first four amino acids are encoded at the 3′ end of the *gag* gene. The amino acid at the fifth position is glutamine, which is coded by the *gag* termination codon. Similarly, feline leukemia virus contains a glutamine residue at position five in its protease, which corresponds to the *gag* termination codon (Yoshinake et al. 1985b). These results demonstrate that a glutamine isoacceptor serves as a naturally occurring amber suppressor in mammalian cells.

The glutamine tRNA involved in expression of the *gag-pol* fusion protein in MuLV has been examined by Kuchino et al. (1987) and by Feng et al. (1989a). Kuchino and collaborators reported that a minor CAA glutamine isoacceptor representing 1–2% of the total glutamine tRNA population was induced many fold in MuLV-infected NIH-3T3 cells, and that this isoacceptor is able to suppress the UAG codon in TMV RNA in vitro. In addition, these investigators observed that treatment of both MuLV- (Kuchino et al. 1988) and HIV-infected (Müller et al. 1988) cells with avarol, which is a sesquiterpernoid hydroquinone, results in a substantial reduction in the level of the glutamine suppressor tRNA, which parallels inhibition of viral expression. In contrast, Feng et al. (1989a) found that the levels of glutamine tRNA are the same in MuLV infected and uninfected cells and that the distribution of the glutamine CAG and CAA decoding isoacceptors is unchanged following virus infection. At present, the reason for the discrepancy in the results obtained by the two laboratories is not clear. Using a rabbit reticulocyte lysate programmed with a MuLV-mRNA containing sequences from the *gag* and *pol* regions, Feng et al. (1989a) also found that equivalent amounts of tRNA from MuLV-infected and uninfected NIH-3T3 cells stimulate readthrough suppression to the same extent. Similarly, Panganiban (1988) has shown that transfection of a construct, containing a portion of the MuLV *gag-pol* region (including the UAG codon) fused to lacZ into several vertebrate cell types, leads to an amount of β-galactosidase production which represents about 10% suppression; use of MuLV-infected cells did not enhance enzyme synthesis. Thus, the in vitro and in vivo results demonstrate that suppression of the MuLV amber codon is not dependent on potential virus-induced qualitative or quantitative modification of suppressor tRNA.

Kuchino et al. (1987) also isolated and sequenced two glutamine tRNAs from mouse liver. The anticodon of the major isoacceptor was CUG and that of the minor isoacceptor was UmUG. The primary sequence of these tRNAs differed from each other in the wobble position of the anticodon and at positions 4 and 68 of the acceptor stem. Mouse liver contained two additional glutamine tRNAs which differed from those described above by a single hypomodification at position 18. Both the $tRNA_{UmUG}$ isoacceptor and its hypomodified counterpart promoted suppression of the UAG codon involved in the expression of the 180 kDa readthrough protein in TMV RNA while the $tRNA_{CUG}$ did not (Kuchino et al. 1987). The sequence of the proposed glutamine suppressor is shown in Fig. 1A.

It should be noted that interaction of glutamine UmUG anticodon and the UAG codon requires a wobble in the first and third position of the anticodon. Wobble of the G in the third position of the anticodon with U in the first position of the codon is not unique to the mouse glutamine tRNA. Pure et al. (1985) have reported that the yeast glutamine tRNA which reads CAA is also capable, when

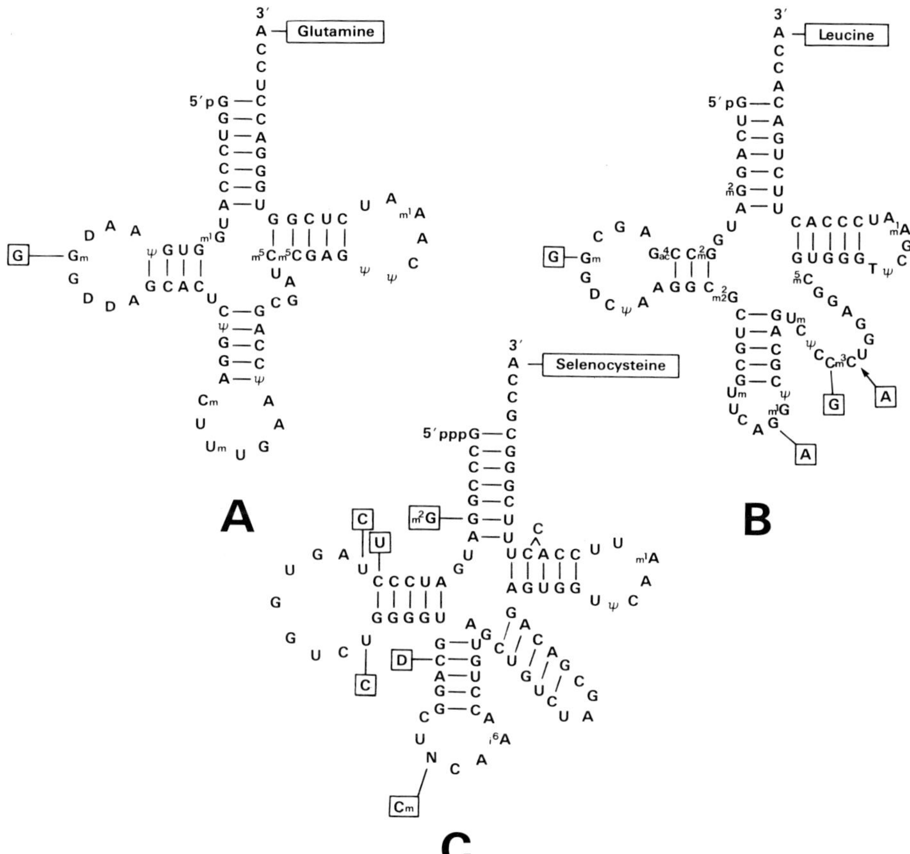

Fig. 1. Primary sequences of nonsense suppressor tRNAs isolated from mammalian sources. The sequence of the amber suppressor glutamine $tRNA_{UmUG}$ and its hypomodified counterpart from mouse liver (Kuchino et al. 1987) are shown in *A*, of the amber suppressor leucine $tRNA_{CAA}$ and $tRNA_{CAG}$ (Valle et al. 1987) in *B* and of the opal suppressor selenocysteine $tRNA_{CmCA}$ and $tRNA_{NCA}$ (Diamond et al. 1981; Hatfield et al. 1982a and see text) in *C*. *Boxed* nucleotides with a *line* show base differences and the *arrow* in the leucine tRNA shows the presence of an extra nucleotide

present in high copy number, of weakly suppressing UAA. In addition, the yeast glutamine tRNA which reads CAG is also capable, in normal concentrations and under normal physiological conditions, of suppressing UAG (Lin et al. 1986; Weiss and Friedberg 1986; Weiss et al. 1987b). Valle et al. (1987) have shown that a calf liver leucine tRNA with the anticodon CAG can suppress UAG codons (see below). Hence, the latter three tRNAs must also include a wobble of the G in the third position of the anticodon to recognize U in the first position of the codon. The unique feature, however, in the mouse glutamine suppressor tRNA is that a wobble is required in the first and third position of the anticodon in order to translate the UAG codon. As noted below, the interaction between a calf liver leucine anticodon and the UAG codon provide an even more intriguing example of codon: anticodon mismatching.

Leucine tRNAs. Valle et al. (1987) observed the presence of two novel amber suppressor leucine tRNAs in mammalian cells. These investigators fractionated total calf liver tRNA on a BD-cellulose column and observed that some of the eluted fractions were capable of suppressing the UAG termination codon in TMV RNA and in beet necrotic yellow vein virus (BNYVV) RNA in a cell-free protein synthesis system. They carefully monitored the suppressor activity through subsequent purification steps which included one-dimensional and then two-dimensional polyacrylamide gel electrophoresis. To rule out the possibility that $tRNA^{Tyr}$ was responsible for the observed suppressor activity as had been demonstrated in numerous other higher eukaryotic systems (see above), two $tRNA^{Tyr}$ species were purified and partially sequenced. Both isoacceptors contained Q base in their anticodon and neither promoted synthesis of the TMV readthrough protein. The two species which suppressed UAG were sequenced and found to be leucine isoacceptors; they are, therefore, novel amber suppressors. Valle et al. (1987) also showed that leucine $tRNA_{IAG}$ from bovine mammary tissue (Vasilieva et al. 1984) did not suppress the UAG codon in TMV RNA and in BNYVV RNA, but that leucine $tRNA_{CAG}$ from bovine mammary tissue, which differs in its primary structure$_x$ from the calf liver suppressor (Tukalo et al. 1980), did promote readthrough. The structures of the leucine suppressors (Valle et al. 1987) are shown in Fig. 1B.

The anticodons in the leucine suppressor tRNAs are CAG and CAA. Neither anticodon can, according to the wobble hypothesis (Crick 1966), base pair with the middle position of UAG. The G in the 3′ position of the CAG anticodon must wobble to read U. As noted above in the section on the glutamine amber suppressor, wobble in the third position of the anticodon has been reported for other suppressor tRNAs. The CAA anticodon can base pair with UAG in the first and third positions. A more detailed discussion of the possible anticodon: codon interactions between these leucine amber suppressor tRNAs and UAG is given by Valle et al. (1987). It is interesting to note that each of the suppressor tRNAs which are dependent on wobble in the 3′ position of the anticodon for recognition of the nonsense codon lack a highly modified base in the 3′ position adjacent to the anticodon. Numerous tRNAs contain a highly modified base in this position

(Sprinzl et al. 1987) and its role may therefore be, at least in part, to restrict wobble. An excellent review on modified bases in tRNA, including those within the anticodon loop, and on the role of modified bases in tRNA has been recently published (Björk et al. 1987).

2. *Ochre Suppressor tRNAs*

The naturally occurring UAG termination codon at the end of the gag gene in MuLV (Feng et al. 1989b) and at the end of the 130 K protein in TMV (Ishikawa et al. 1986), as well as the naturally occurring UGA termination codon in an open reading frame in Sinbis virus (Lin and Rice 1989), have been altered to a UAA termination codon. Introduction of each mutated virus into the corresponding host cell results in formation of mature virus. Furthermore, in vitro examination of TMV expression (Ishikawa et al. 1986) and of MuLV expression (Feng et al. 1989) shows that readthrough of the mutated virus occurs without supplementation of rabbit reticulocyte lysates with exogenous tRNA. These studies demonstrate that mammalian cells (as well as tobacco cells) contain a tRNA or tRNAs capable of reading an ochre termination codon. It is of considerable significance to identify the isoacceptor or isoacceptors which suppress UAA termination codons in higher eukaryotes.

It should also be noted that the yeast glutamine tRNA which reads CAA has been shown in high copy number to suppress UAA termination codons (Pure et al. 1985).

3. *Opal Suppressor tRNAs*

Tryptophan tRNA. A tryptophan tRNA which was isolated from rabbit reticulocytes has been shown to suppress the UGA termination codon in rabbit β-globin mRNA by Geller and Rich (1980). Evidence was presented that the readthrough protein of β-globin occurs naturally in rabbit reticulocytes and that Trp-tRNA is a likely candidate to carry out this suppression. The rabbit reticulocyte $tRNA^{Trp}$ suppressor has not been sequenced to date. It should be noted that a minor serine tRNA which reads UGA in protein synthesis also occurs in rabbit reticulocytes (Hatfield 1985; Hatfield et al. 1979, 1982b; Hatfield and Rice 1986) and this tRNA must also be considered as a potential candidate to account for the presence of β-globin readthrough protein. Antibodies have been generated specifically against the readthrough portion of this protein and the readthrough protein has been purified from rabbit reticulocytes in order to determine the amino acid at the readthrough site (Hatfield et al. 1988).

Serine tRNAs (Selenocysteine $tRNA^{Ser}$). Two minor serine tRNAs have been shown to suppress UGA in protein synthesis (Diamond et al. 1981; Hatfield et al. 1982a). The primary sequences of these tRNAs from bovine liver (Dimond et al. 1981; Hatfield et al. 1982a) are shown in Fig. 1C. They are designated NCA and CmCA on the basis of their anticodon sequences. N is an unknown base but is probably a modified U (Kato et al. 1983). The corresponding serine tRNAs from mouse and human tissues have also been sequenced (Kato et al. 1983) and are very similar to those shown in the figure. The genes encoding these serine tRNAs have been isolated and sequenced from human (O'Neill et al. 1985), rabbit (Pratt et al. 1985), chicken (Hatfield et al. 1983), and *Xenopus* (Lee et al. 1989a) genomes. The genes are identical in sequence, with the exception that the human and rabbit genes contain a T at position 11, while those of chicken and *Xenopus* contain a C at this position. These genes contain a TCA sequence corresponding to the anticodon of the gene product, demonstrating unequivocally that higher eukaryotes contain tRNAs capable of reading a termination codon in their genomes. Interestingly, these isoacceptors also occur as phosphoseryl-tRNA (Hatfield et al. 1982a; Mizutani and Hoshimoto 1984) and as selenocysteyl-$tRNA^{Ser}$ (Lee et al. 1989b) as is further discussed below.

It is interesting to note that the gene for these tRNAs occurs in single copy in the genomes of higher vertebrates (Hatfield 1985; Hatfield et al. 1983; O'Neill et al. 1985; Pratt et al. 1985) and that the two gene products contain several pyrimidine transitions in the 5′ half of their molecules, including one in their anticodons (Diamond et al. 1981; Hatfield et al. 1982a). These pyrimidine transitions, therefore, must arise posttranscriptionally. The human (O'Neill et al. 1985) and rabbit genomes (Pratt et al. 1985) also contain a pseudogene corresponding to the serine tRNA gene. The gene and pseudogene have been mapped to human chromosomes 19 and 22, respectively (McBride et al. 1987). Restriction analysis of DNAs isolated from the white blood cells of ten different humans revealed that the opal suppressor tRNA gene contains a *SalI* restriction fragment-length polymorphism (McBride et al. 1987).

The minor opal suppressor serine tRNAs are aminoacylated with serine by seryl-tRNA synthetase (Mizutani et al. 1984) and then phosphorylated on their serine moiety to form phosphoseryl-tRNA (Hatfield et al. 1982a; Mizutani and Hashimoto 1984). They have an unique pathway of biosynthesis (Lee et al. 1987) in that they are transcribed, unlike other tRNAs, beginning at the first nucleotide inside their coding sequence, and thus they do not have a 5′ leader sequence. The 3′ trailer sequence, on the other hand, is cleaved by the 3′ processing enzyme (Lee et al. 1987). The 5′ triphosphate on the initial nucleotide of the mature tRNA is transported from the nucleus to the cytoplasm of *Xenopus* oocytes and remains intact in the cytoplasm, suggesting that the triphosphate may have a role in the function of these tRNAs. Their kinetics of transport are very similar to those of other tRNAs (Lee et al. 1987). In vivo transcription of the *Xenopus* gene is regulated by several upstream sites, including a TATA box and a GC-rich region at about −30 (Lee et al. 1989a).

The observation that a minor seryl-tRNA from chicken liver was phosphorylated on its serine moeity in the presence of ATP and a kinase preparation from estrogen-induced rooster liver was first described by Mäenpää and Bernfield (1970). At the same time, a minor serine isoacceptor from bovine liver and brain, and from chicken liver, was found to specifically recognize the nonsense codon, UGA (Hatfield and Portugal 1970) in a ribosomal binding assay (Nirenberg and Leder 1964). Subsequently, Sharp and Stewart (1977) demonstrated that a minor seryl-tRNA from bovine mammary tissue formed phosphoseryl-tRNA in the presence of ATP and a kinase preparation from the homologous tissue. It was not until 1982, however, that the minor seryl-tRNA which recognized UGA in a ribosomal binding assay and the minor seryl-tRNA which was phosphorylated on its serine moiety were demonstrated to be the same molecule (Hatfield et al. 1982a). The report that the minor seryl-tRNA from rooster liver did not recognize UGA in a ribosomal binding assay (Mäenpää 1972) was not substantiated by earlier (Hatfield and Portugal 1970) and subsequent studies (Hatfield 1985; Hatfield et al. 1982a). The kinase which phosphorylates these isoacceptors has been purified from bovine liver (Mizutani and Hashimoto 1984). Its molecular weight is approximately 140 kDa; the K_m values for ATP and the opal suppressor tRNA are 2 mM and 21 nM, respectively. The association constants between the opal suppressor serine tRNA and an oligonucleotide consisting of UGA_x (where x designates an unknown number of A residues) and between the mammlian release factor and UGA_x have been examined (Mizutani and Hitaka 1988). A K_a value of $8 \times 10^3\,M^{-1}$ was observed for the tRNA and UGA and of 1.26 $\times 10^6\,M^{-1}$ for the release factor and UGA which led Mizutani and Hitaka (1988) to conclude that the opal suppressor tRNA does not function to suppress UGA termination codons, but functions to suppress UGA codons which may favor readthrough.

Phosphoseryl-tRNA can donate its phosphate to rabbit globin in protein synthesis (Mizutani and Tachibana 1986), but the amount of incorporation was low and the site of incorporation was not established. The possibility that phosphoseryl-tRNA is an intermediate in the metabolic pathway from 3-phosphoglycerate to glycine (Mäenpää and Bernfield 1970) has been ruled out by Mizutani et al. (1988). Other possible roles of phosphoseryl-$tRNA^{Ser}$ have been suggested by Stewart and Sharp (1984). However, the major role of phosphoseryl-tRNA may be to serve as a intermediate in the biosynthesis of selenocysteyl-$tRNA^{Ser}$ (see below).

The recent observation that the minor serine tRNA which reads UGA in protein synthesis and is phosphorylated on its serine moiety to form phosphoseryl-tRNA also exists as selenocysteyl-tRNA (Lee et al. 1989b) strongly suggests that this tRNA has at least two important cellular functions: (1) to serve as a carrier molecule for the biosynthesis of selenocysteine; and (2) to donate selenocysteine directly to protein in response to specialized UGA codons which code for selenocysteine (Lee et al. 1989b). It should be noted in this connection that a TGA codon occurs in mouse (Chambers et al. 1986; Mullenbach et al. 1988), human (Mullenbach 1987, 1988; Sukenaka et al. 1987), bovine (Mullenbach et al. 1988), and rat glutathione peroxidase genes (Reddy et al. 1988) at the position corresponding to the active site of the protein product, and that selenocysteine occurs at this site in the protein. Furthermore, the selenocysteine moiety arises from serine and selenium (Sundee and Evenson 1987). Interestingly, the glutathione peroxidase gene maps to human chromosomes 3, 21, and X; the mapping data confirm that chromosome 3 is the active gene and suggest that the other loci are pseudogenes (McBride et al. 1989).

It is important to note that selenocysteine occurs at the active site of formate dehydrogenase in *E. coli* which is coded by UGA (Zinoni et al. 1987). The occurrence of the selenocysteine moiety in formate dehydrogenase is correlated with a specific tRNA which is aminoacylated with serine (Leinfelder et al. 1988) and also forms selenocysteyl-tRNA (Leinfelder et al. 1989). Thus, the pathway of selenocysteine biosynthesis, and subsequent incorporation of selenocysteine into protein appears to be similar in mammalian (Lee et al. 1989b) and in *E. coli* cells (Böck and Stadtman 1988; Leinfelder et al. 1989).

The means by which UGA may code on the one hand for selenocysteine and on the other hand as a termination codon has been discussed recently by several investigators (Chambers and Harrison 1987; Engelberg-Kula and Schoulaker-Schwarz 1988a, b; Valle and Morch 1988).

An opal suppressor tRNA gene has been isolated and sequenced from *Drosophila* and from a nematode, *C. elegans* (B.J. Lee, M. Rajagopalan, Y.S. Kim, and D. Hatfield, unpublished data). The gene differs from that of vertebrates at a number of nucleotides, demonstrating that this gene has undergone substantial evolutionary change. The vertebrate (Hatfield 1985) and nematode genes have little homology to the corresponding selenocysteyl-tRNA gene in *E. coli* (Böck and Stadtman 1988). These observations provide evidence that the tRNA responsible for the presence of selenocysteine in protein which is coded by UGA is widespread in nature, but has undergone substantial change.

II. Assays for Nonsense Suppressor tRNAs and Nonsense Mutations

In Vitro. Nuclease-treated rabbit reticulocyte lysates (Jackson and Hunt 1983) and wheat germ extracts (Roberts and Paterson 1973), which are then programmed with mRNA and to which is added a suppressor tRNA, have provided a relatively simple means of identifying nonsense suppressors and of identifying nonsense mutations. Assays were devised for identifying opal and ochre suppressor tRNAs by adding rabbit globin mRNA and a suppressor tRNA to the nuclease-treated lysates, and examining the globin products on a polyacrylamide gel (Gesteland and Wills 1979). Rabbit β-globin mRNA terminates in UGA and the next termination signal is followed 22 amino acids downstream by two tandem UAA codons (Efstratiadis et al. 1977). Rabbit α-globin mRNA terminates in UAA, and the next termination signal is 21 amino acids downstrem (Marotta et al. 1977). Since α- and β-globins are 141 and 146 amino acids in length, respectively, then the readthrough protein of β-globin would be expected to migrate more slowly on a polyacrylamide gel than the corresponding α-globin readthrough protein. However, the reverse is found and the reason appears to be due to the large number of proline residues coded within the readthrough region of α-globin mRNA (Gesteland and Wills 1979). Rabbit reticulocyte lysates are also used as an assay for amber suppressors by programming the nuclease-treated lysates with TMV RNA (Pelham 1978) or BNYVV RNA (Ziegler et al. 1985) and examining the products of protein synthesis on a polyacrylamide gel. Wheat germ extracts programmed with the same set of mRNAs as used in reticulocyte lysates have also been used as an assay for nonsense suppressors (Kohli et al. 1979). However, the lysate system has been more widely used.

Nonsense mutations and termination codons have been identified in viruses by assaying viral mutant or normal mRNAs in vitro in the presence of the purified suppressors from microorganisms. A series of human adenoviral mutants which synthesized a polypeptide shorter than the 30 kDa ND1 protein were assayed for restoration of the protein in the presence of an amber and an ochre suppressor from yeast (Gesteland et al. 1977). Two amber and one ochre adenoviral ND1 mutations were identified amongst a series of suspected nonsense mutations. Similarly, an amber and on opal mutation were identified in the thymidine kinase gene of herpes simplex virus by assaying a series of mutant mRNAs for restoration of viral kinase activity (Cremer et al. 1979). In addition, the termination codon in several murine leukemia and sarcoma viral RNAs, which is at the end of the *gag* region, were identified as UAG by utilizing an amber suppressor tRNA from yeast (Murphy et al. 1980).

The specific response of a minor seryl-tRNA^{Ser} to UGA (Hatfield et al 1982a) in a ribosomal binding assay (Nirenberg and Leder 1964) has provided a simple and rapid means of identifying the occurrence of this isoacceptor in tissues and cells of higher vertebrates (Diamond et al. 1981; Hatfield and Portugal 1970; Hatfield et al. 1982a). The occurrence of potential opal suppressor tRNAs within the tRNA population of bovine liver were detected by fractionating the tRNA and then determining which fractions stimulated attachment of ^{3}H-UGA to ribosomes (Hatfield 1972). The assay is based on a previous observation that the binding of a labeled trinucleotide diphosphate to ribosomes is significantly enhanced in the presence of the corresponding isoacceptor which recognizes that codon (Hatfield and Nirenberg 1971). It is interesting to note that the only tRNAs which recognized UGA specifically were the minor opal suppressor seryl-tRNAs. All other tRNAs which stimulated the attachment of ^{3}-H-UGA to ribosomes also recognized their assigned codons.

In Intact Cells. Purified suppressor tRNAs from microorganisms have been injected into cells in culture (Capeschi et al. 1977) and into *Xenopus* oocytes (Bienz et al. 1980, 1981) in order to identify nonsense mutations and to examine their effects on readthrough. For example, *E. coli* and yeast suppressors were injected into mouse L cells which were suspected of carrying a nonsense mutation in the HGPRT gene (Capecchi et al. 1977). the ochre tRNAs, but not the amber or opal, restored HGPRT activity. Thus, the mutation was identified as UAA.

An assay has been developed for quantifying suppressor activity in intact cells (Young et al. 1983). The assay is based on suppression of a natural UAG termination codon in the NSI protein of the influenza virus which extends the protein length by 20 amino acids. An amber suppressor tRNA gene (see Laski et al. 1982 and below) and the influenza virus were introduced into mammalian cells and the cells were then pulse-labeled with ^{35}S-methionine. The resulting labeled NSI protein and readthrough protein were isolated from a cell extract by immunoprecipitation, electrophoresed on a polyacrylamide gel, and the percent readthrough determined. The level of suppression was high (ca. 25%) in cells in which the suppressor gene was transiently introduced, but was low (ca. 2.5%) in cells in which the suppressor was stably integrated into the host's genome. It is not known whether the low level of suppression observed thus far in mammalian systems in which suppressors are permanently integrated is established by the cell because a higher level of readthrough would be lethal, or if higher levels can actually be tolerated. The fact that the level of suppression is ca. 3% in a number of studies involving different mammalian cell lines (Ho et al. 1986; Hudziak et al. 1982; Young et al. 1983) suggests that the host can tolerate only a low level of suppressor activity.

An in vivo assay for measuring the levels of aminoacylation of suppressor tRNA following their amplification has been developed (Ho and Kan 1987). The assay is based on the aminoacylation of the amplified suppressor tRNA in intact cells, extraction of the tRNA at low pH, and the subsequent separation of acylated from unacylated tRNA on a polyacrylamide gel. Amber $tRNA^{Gln}$, $tRNA^{Lys}$ and $tRNA^{Tyr}$ suppressors, which were expressed from the corresponding amplified genes, were aminoacylated 80, 40–50, and 100%, respectively. The lower levels of aminoacylation observed with $tRNA^{Gln}$ and $tRNA^{Lys}$ may be due to the effect of the altered base in the anticodon on the aminoacylation process (Ho and Kan 1987).

III. Introduction of Nonsense Suppressor tRNA Genes into Intact Cells

Nonsense suppressor tRNA genes which have been constructed by site specific mutagenesis, and introduced into cells of higher eukaryotes to yield active suppressors, have provided new approaches for studying nonsense suppression (Capone et al. 1985, 1986; Ho and Kan 1987; Ho et al. 1986; Hudziak et al. 1982; Laski et al. 1982, 1984; Sedivy et al. 1987; Summers et al. 1983; Temple et al. 1982; Young et al. 1983). These studies provide a means of: (1) identifying and characterizing nonsense mutations; (2) quantifying suppression of nonsense codons; (3) analyzing and characterizing viral genomes through classical genetic techniques; (4) determining the long range effects of suppressor tRNAs on cells follwing the permanent insertion of the corresponding genes into the genomes of the host cell; and (5) determining whether the introduction of suppressor tRNAs into cells may provide a basis for gene therapy experiments involving diseases which result from nonsense mutations. Kan and collaborators have designed experiments specifically addressing the use of nonsense suppressor tRNAs in gene therapy (Ho and Kan 1987; Ho et al. 1986; Temple et al. 1982). An amber-suppressor $tRNA^{Lys}$ gene (Temple et al. 1982), and subsequently, an amber-suppressor $tRNA^{Gln}$ gene (Ho et al. 1986), and mRNA from a patient with thalassemia carrying a UAG mutation (AAG → UAG) were coinjected into *Xenopus* oocytes. Functional suppressors were produced which translated the amber mutation. Although these studies provide a model for gene therapy, much greater insight into the ability of suppressors to function in cells is required before such experiments can be undertaken. Further characterization of the $tRNA^{Lys}$ suppressor has shown that it functioned inefficiently as a suppressor in cells in which it has been permanently inserted, even though the gene and gene product were amplified many fold. The suppressor was poorly aminoacylated in cell lines in which it was stably introduced, which accounted for its low suppressor activity. Other concerns must also be addressed before tRNA suppressors can be used in experiments correcting nonsense mutations in human globin. It must be established whether suppressor tRNAs are efficiently expressed in erythroid cells, and if the levels of production and subsequent aminoacylation of suppressor tRNAs are adequate to suppress nonsense codons providing sufficient amounts of globin, but yet the suppressor activity is not at a level which is deleterious to the cell. Furthermore, the level of β-globin mRNA varies in thalassemia patients and often is quite low (see Bunn and Forget 1986, and references therein). Introduction of a suppressor tRNA gene into cells containing a nonsense mutation in globin mRNA has shown an enrichment in the level of the mutated mRNA (see Bunn and Forget 1986, and references therein). This observation may provide a means of increasing the level of β-globin mRNA in thalassemic patients containing a nonsense mutation.

Much of our understanding of the role and effect of suppressor tRNAs in mammalian cells is due to the studies of RajBhandary, Sharp and their collaborators (Capone et al. 1985, 1986; Hudziak et al. 1982; Laski et al. 1982, 1984; Sedivy et al. 1987; Summers et al. 1983; Young et al. 1983). A number of tRNA suppressor genes were generated by site specific mutagenesis in the anticodon of the corresponding normal gene. These suppressors include an amber (Laski et al. 1982) and an ochre (Hudziak et al. 1982) which were derived from a *Xenopus laevis* tyrosine tRNA gene, and an amber, ochre, and opal which were derived from a human serine tRNA gene (Capone et al. 1985). Each suppressor gene was cloned into an appropriate vector for introduction into a given mammalian cell line. A complementary set of nonsense codons was also introduced into mammalian cells to test the biological activity of the corresponding suppressor tRNAs. The nonsense codons included naturally occurring amber and ochre termination codons, encoded in different viral strains (Capone et al. 1985; Laski et al. 1982, 1984) and amber, ochre, and/or opal mutations generated in viral (Hudziak et al. 1982; Laski et al. 1984; Sedivy et al. 1987) and *E. coli* genes (Capone et al. 1986; Hudziak et al. 1982) and in the kanamycin resistance gene (Hudziak et al. 1982; Laski et al. 1984). An extremely useful set of mutations was prepared in an *E. coli* CAT gene in which the serine codon at position 27 was changed to either an amber, ochre, or opal codon (Capone et al. 1986). Cointroduction of the mutant CAT genes, other mutant *E. coli* genes, mutant viral genes, or a virus containing a naturally occurring termination codon and the corresponding suppressor tRNA has shown that the level of suppression was efficient (ranging from ca. 20–50%) in transient systems (Capone et al. 1986; Young et al. 1983), but inefficient (ca. 3%) in cell types in which the suppressor tRNA gene was stably integrated into the host's genome (Ho et al. 1986; Hudziak et al. 1982; Young et al. 1983). Ineffective aminoacylation of suppressor tRNAs may account for the poor suppressor activity in cells in which the suppressor tRNA genes are permanently inserted (Ho et al. 1986). However, whether a secondary mutation may have occurred in the suppressor tRNA gene, in the corresponding synthetase gene, or perhaps whether the low suppressor activity is due to some other reason is not known. Furthermore, it is not known if efficient suppression can be tolerated in cells in which the suppressor is stably integrated. As noted above, the observation that different suppressor tRNA genes which are stably introduced into different mammalian cell lines result thus far in suppression levels of only about 3% suggests that higher levels may be lethal to the cell.

A means of inducing high levels of suppressor activity in mammalian cells has been reported recently (Sedivy et al. 1987). An amber suppressor $tRNA^{Ser}$ gene was cloned into SV40 near its origin of replication. This plasmid was cotransfected into mammalian cells with a SV40 plasmid carrying a temperature sensitive mutation in the large T-antigen gene and cells which stably integrated both DNAs were selected. The suppressor gene was amplified by changing the cells from a nonpermissive to a permissive temperature and suppression levels of an amber codon as high as 70% were observed. This technique was used to suppress an amber mutation in the replicase gene of poliovirus which resulted in an efficient production of virus (Sedivy et al. 1987).

IV. Other Considerations

Several termination codons have been shown to be readthrough in mammalian cells. These include the UAG stop codon in Moloney leukemia virus (Feng et al. 1989a; Kuchino et al. 1987; Philipson et al. 1978; Yoshinaka et al. 1985a) and in feline leukemia virus (Yoshinaka et al. 1985b) and the UGA stop codon in Middelburg and Sindbis viruses (Strauss et al. 1983, 1984), in rabbit β-globin mRNA (Geller and Rich 1980; Hatfield et al. 1988) and in glutathione peroxidase (Chambers et al. 1986; Mullenbach et al. 1987, 1988; Reddy et al. 1988; Sukenaka et al. 1987).

The level of suppression at a stop codon is presumably determined by the competition between the suppressor tRNA, which promotes readthrough, and the release factor, which promotes termination, for the nonsense codon. In microorganisms, the nucleotides surrounding stop codons (i.e., the nucleotide context) also play a role in the efficiency of suppression (Bossi 1983; Miller and Albertini 1983). In higher eukaryotes, the available evidence suggests that nucleotide context is not a determining factor in whether a termination codon will be suppressed, nor how efficiently it will be suppressed (Kohli and Grosjean 1981; Kubli et al. 1982; Mullenbach et al. 1988). Some stop codons occur in an open reading frame (Chambers et al. 1986; Mullenbach et al. 1987, 1988; Reddy et al. 1988; Strauss et al. 1983, 1984; Sukenaka et al. 1987) and they must be translated efficiently for expression of the resulting protein product. For, example, glutathione peroxidase activity is dependent upon efficient readthrough of a UGA codon, which corresponds to an amino acid that is translated within the first 30% of the protein. Mullenbach and collaborators (1988) have compared the sequences surrounding the opal codon in human, bovine, and mouse glutathione peroxidase mRNAs to those surrounding natural opal termination codons in a number of eukaryotic mRNAs. The translated UGA codon has 5′ sequences and 3′ sequences, which are identical to those surrounding natural UGA termination codons. Thus, the nucleotide context of the UGA codon in glutathione peroxidase does not appear to be related to the efficient translation of this codon. These investigators also compared the secondary structure of glutathione peroxidase and 12 other eucaryotic mRNAs which utilize UGA as a termination codon (Mullenbach et al. 1988). This study revealed that glutathione peroxidase mRNA may have a unique conformation in which UGA occurs in a stem that may favor readthrough. Studies from other higher eukaryotic systems also suggest that the nucleotide contexts of termination codons may not play a major role in the level of suppression in mammalian cells (Kohli and Grosjean 1981; Kubli et al. 1982; Mullenbach et al. 1988). However, more information must be obtained about the nature of the suppression process of nonsense codons in mammalian cells before we can definitively assess the effect of the codon context. The reader is also referred to an excellent review on the termination process by Valle and Morch (1988) and to additional considerations of UGA as a codon for selenocysteine and as a termination codon (Chambers and Harrison 1987; Engelberg-Kula and Schoulaker-Schwarz 1988a, b).

Nonsense mutations have also been characterized in mammals. In humans, the occurrence of nonsense mutations in α- and β-globin mRNA genes have been known for some time (see Baserga and Benz 1988; Bunn and Forget 1986 and references therein). Recently, a series of nonsense mutations were prepared in the human β-globin gene to study the effects of nonsense mutations on cellular accumulation of mRNA (Baserga anmd Benz 1988). Each nonsense mutation resulted in a decreased accumulation of β-globin mRNA, whereas missense mutations had no effect on the level of accumulation. Other examples of nonsense mutations identified in humans are a Trp TGG → TGA mutation in the gene for the receptors for plasma low density lipoprotein (Lenman et al. 1985), an Arg CGA → TGA mutation at codon 306 in the gene for protein C which is an anticoagulant serine protease (Romeo et al. 1987), a Lys AAG → TAG mutation at codon 217 in the I-antitrypsin gene (Satoh et al. 1988) and an Arg CGA → TGA mutation in the C1q B-chain (McAdam et al. 1988).

Post transcriptional generation of a stop codon in mRNA which results in the occurrence of a molecular distinct protein has been observed in mammalian cells (Chen et al. 1987; Davidson et al. 1988; Hardman et al. 1987; Higuchi et al. 1988; Powell et al. 1987). In humans, a single gene encodes apolipoprotein (apo) B-100 and apoB-48, where apoB-48 is ca. 48% of the molecular weight of apoB-100. A glutamine codon (CAA) at position 2153 in human apoB-100 is converted to a termination codon by a single pyrimidine transition (Powell et al. 1987). This reaction is tissue specific (Chen et al. 1987; Hardman et al. 1987; Higuchi et al. 1988; Powell et al. 1987) and is hormonally modulated in rat liver (Davidson et al. 1988).

C. Ribosomal Frameshifting

Ribosomal frameshifting or frameshift suppression may operate in one of two directions to alter the reading frame. It may occur by a variety of mechanisms (Craigan and Caskey 1987; Dayhuff et al. 1986; Murgola 1989; Weiss et al. 1987a, 1988) such that the reading frame is altered in the 5′ direction or in the 3′ direction. Ribosomal frameshifting in both directions has been described in bacteria and yeast (see above references and in addition Valle and Morch 1988, and references therein). In mammalian cells, many retroviruses utilize ribosomal frameshifting in the −1 direction to align their *gag* and *pol* reading frames (Craigan and Caskey 1987; Hizi et al. 1987; Jacks and Varmus 1985; Jacks et al. 1987, 1988a, 1988b; Valle and Morch 1988). Since ribosomal frameshifting is best understood in retroviruses, we will examine this means of altering reading frames and then consider the possible involvement of tRNA.

I. Ribosomal Frameshifting in Retroviruses

The *gag* and *pol* genes of many retroviruses occur in different reading frames (see references in legend to Table 1 and in addition Valle and Morch 1988). Some of these retroviruses require a single frameshift event in the −1 direction, while others require two such events, one between *gag-pro* and one between *pro-pol*, both of which are in the −1 direction, to align the different reading frames for expression of the *gag-pro-pol* fusion protein. The ribosomal frameshift sites or suspected sites and signals in a number of vertebrate retroviruses are shown in Table 1. In additon, suspected frameshift sites and signals in the mouse intracisternal A-particle (Mietz et al. 1987), in the nonretrovirus avian coronavirus (designated IBV; Brierley et al. 1987) and in the transposable elements in *Drosophila* designated *gypsy* (Marlor et al. 1986) and 17.6 (Saigo et al. 1984) are also shown. The number of bases in each overlap window and the number of bases from the 3′ end of each window are also shown. The boundaries of the frameshift windows are determined (e.g. in a retrovirus requiring a single frameshift event) by the termination codon which is read in the zero frame (at the end of the *gag* gene) and the first upstream termination codon in the -1 frame. Each overlap window contains one of three common consensus sequences (Jacks et al. 1988b): either A AAC, U UUA or U UUU where asparagine (AAC), leucine (UUA), or phenylalanine (UUU) are read in the zero frame.

The ribosomal frameshift sites of three of the retroviruses shown in Table 1 have been examined in detail. One occurs within the *gag-pro* ribosomal frameshift site in MMTV and involves the A AAC sequence (Hizi et al. 1987). The other two occur within the *gag-pol* ribosomal frameshift site of HIV (Jacks et al. 1988b; Wilson et al. 1988) and RSV (Jacks et al. 1988a) and both involve the U UUA sequence. The polypeptide which is expressed in vivo at the *gag-pro* junction in MMTV (Hizi et al. 1987) and in vitro at the *gag-pol* junction in HIV (Jacks et al. 1988b) and RSV (Jacks et al. 1988a) has been sequenced at the site corresponding

Table 1. Ribosomal frameshift sites and signals in vertebrate viruses and in transposable elements of higher eukaryotes[a]

Source	Overlap window	Bases in overlap	Bases from 3′ end of overlap	Bases at and around the frameshift site			
MMTV	*gag-pro*	16	3	UC*A*	*AAA*	*AAC*	UUG
BLV	*gag-pro*	49	0	UC*A*	*AAA*	*AAC*	UAA
HTLV-1, STLV-1	*gag-pro*	37	18	CC*A*	*AAA*	*AAC*	UCC
HTLV-2	*gag-pro*	28	18	GA*A*	*AAA*	*AAC*	UCC
EIAV	*gag-pol*	241	195	CC*A*	*AAA*	*AAC*	GGG
HTLV-1	*pro-pol*	178	156	CC*U*	*UUA*	*AAC*	CAG
STLV-1	*pro-pol*	121	99	CC*U*	*UUA*	*AAC*	CGG
HTLV-2	*pro-pol*	373	18	CC*U*	*UUA*	*AAC*	CUG
BLV	*pro-pol*	22	0	CC*U*	*UUA*	*AAC*	UAG
SRV-1	*gag-pro*	181	147	CAG	*GGA*	*AAC*	GGA
SRV-2, MPMV	*gag-pro*	181	147	CAG	*GGA*	*AAC*	GGG
VISNA	*gag-pol*	124	45	CAG	*GGA*	*AAC*	AAC
RSV	*gag-pol*	58	0	AC*A*	*AAU*	*UUA*	UAG
MMTV	*pro-pol*	13	0	CAG	*GAU*	*UUA*	UGA
IBV		40	30		UA*U*	*UUA*	*AAC*
HIV-1	*gag-pol*	241 (205)	234 (198)	AA*U*	*UUU*	*UUA*	GGG
HIV-2	*gag-pol*	283	267	GG*U*	*UUU*	*UUA*	GGA
SIV	*gag-pol*	343	213	GG*U*	*UUU*	*UUA*	GGC
gypsy	*gag-pol*	70	51	AA*U*	*UUU*	*UUA*	GGG
Mouse IAP	*gag-pol*	34	3	CUG	*GGU*	*UUU*	CCU
SRV-1, MPMV	*pro-pol*	22	0	GG*A*	*AAU*	*UUU*	UAA
SRV-2	*pro-pol*	22	0	GG*A*	*AAU*	*UUU*	UAG
17.6	*gag-pol*	46	30	GA*A*	*AAU*	*UUU*	CAG

[a] Bases in italics designate conserved heptanucleotide sequences within the overlaps which are associated with or are suspected of being associated with frameshifting (see Jacks et al. 1988a and the text). Abbreviations and references to published work are: *MMTV*, mouse mammary tumor virus (Hizi et al. 1987; Jacks et al. 1987; Moore et al. 1987); *HTLV-1* and -2, human T-cell leukemia virus-1 (Hiramatsu et al. 1987; Inoue et al. 1986; Seiki et al. 1983) and -2 (Shimotohno et al. 1985); *STLV-1*, simian T-cell leukemia virus (Inoue et al. 1986); *EIAV*, equine infectious anemia virus (Kawakami et al. 1987; Stephens et al. 1986). *BLV* bovine leukemia virus, (Rice et al. 1985; Sagata et al. 1985); *SRV-1*, simian acquired immunodeficiency syndrome ([SAIDS] designated as SRV: Power et al. 1986) and SRV-2 (Thayer et al. 1987); *MPMV*, Mason-Pfizer monkey virus, (Sonigo et al. 1986); *VISNA*, VISNA virus (Sonigo et al. 1985); *RSV*, Rous sarcoma virus (an avian virus) (Jacks and Varmus 1985; Schwartz et al. 1983); *IBV* (coronavirus) infectious bronchitis virus (an avian non-retrovirus, Brierley et al. 1987); *HIV-1* and -2, human immunodeficiency virus-1 (Jacks et al. 1988b; Ratner et al. 1985; Sanchez-Pescador et al. 1985; Wain-Hobson et al. 1985) and -2 (Guyader et al. 1987); *SIV*, simian immunodeficiency virus (Chakrabarti et al. 1987; Franchini et al. 1987); *gypsy*, transposable element in *Drosophila* designated *gypsy* (Marlor et al. 1986); *mouse IAP*, mouse intracisternal A-particle (Mietz et al. 1987); *17.6*, transposable element in *Drosophila* designated 17.6 (Saigo et al. 1984).

to the frameshift. In MMTV, leucine occurs at the frameshift site and is coded either by UUG in the zero frame or by CUU in the -1 frame (where C is the 3′ base of the AAC codon in the zero frame and UU are the 5′ two bases of the UUG codon) (Hizi et al. 1987). In HIV, the shift occurs at a leucine residue corresponding to the UUA codon (Jacks et al. 1988b) shown in Table 1. However, both leucine and phenylalanine occur at the frameshift site in a ratio of 7:3, which also makes the assignment of the precise site uncertain (Jacks et al. 1988b). Arginine, which is coded by the 3′ base in UUA and the first two GG bases in the downstream codon, is translated in the -1 frame in HIV. In RSV, the frameshift also occurs at a leucine codon in response to the U UUA sequence (Jacks et al. 1988a). The next amino acid residue in the peptide generated from the frameshift site is isoleucine, which is read in the -1 frame; it is coded by the 3′ A of the UUA codon and the next two downstream bases which are UA.

Sequence of the polypeptide corresponding to the frameshift site in MMTV (Hizi et al. 1987), HIV (Jacks et al. 1988a) and RSV (Jacks et al. 1988b) and generation of series of mutations within the heptanucleotide frameshift signal in RSV (Jacks et al. 1988b) and HIV (Jacks et al. 1988a; Wilson et al. 1988) and sequence of the peptide generated from the mutant RSV frameshift signal (Jacks et al. 1988b) provide insight into the mechanism by which alignment of the different reading frames occurs. Mutations constructed within the RSV heptanucleotide signal (Jacks et al. 1988b) and at most of the corresponding bases in the HIV signal (Jacks et al 1988a; Wilson et al. 1988) show that the frameshift event is inhibited by changes at each position within this region expect the 3′ terminal base. Changes at the 3′ terminal base do not inhibit frameshifting. The amino acid sequence of the peptide generated from the RSV mutant sequence, AAU UU*U* UA (where *U* represents the altered base at the 3′ end of the frameshift signal), demonstrates that asparagine (AAU) and phenylalanine (UU*U*) are decoded in the zero frame and leucine (*U*UA) in the -1 frame (Jacks et al. 1988a). As noted above, asparagine (AAU) and leucine (UUA) are decoded in the zero frame and isoleucine (AUA) in the -1 frame in the normal RSV frameshift event (Jacks et al. 1988b). Thus, a single base change at the 3′ end of the RSV frameshift signal results in two amino acids in the peptide generated from the mutant sequence. This observations demonstrates that alignment of the different reading frames must occur at this site and the alignment occurs by overlapping reading such that the base at the 3′ end of the heptanucleotide signal is decoded twice; once in the zero frame and once in the -1 frame as originally stated by Hizi et al. (1987) from their studies on sequencing the MMTV transframe protein.

Much insight into retroviral frameshifting has been obtained through the studies described above. These studies demonstrate that the shift to the -1 decoding frame occurs by overlapping reading, and not by two of three base reading, and that the frameshift occurs at the 3′ end of the heptanucleotide signal shown in Table 1, and not upstream of this site. These studies do not demonstrate the mechanism by which frameshifting occurs. Thus, we have learned what occurs in frameshifting (i.e., that the frameshift occurs by overlapping reading), where it occurs, but not how it occurs. In regard to a possible mechanism, Jacks et al.

(1987, 1988a,b) have proposed a "slippage" model to account for frameshifting in which the translational machinery slips to the -1 reading frame within the heptanucleotide sequences shown in Table 1.

Mutation of the A AAA AAC sequence in the *gag-pro* frameshift site of HTLV-1 to A ATA TTC inhibited the frameshift event (Nam et al. 1988). This study provides direct evidence that this region which was suspected to be part of the frameshift site in HTLV-1 (Table 1) is indeed involved in the frameshift event.

The observation by Jacks et al. (1988a) that U UUA, U UUU and A AAC sequences at the end of the RSV frameshift site support effective frameshifting, while A AAA and G GGG sequences are not as effective led these investigators to propose that "only certain, specialized 'shifty' tRNAs" can participate in the frameshift event. The proposal is further supported by the observation that only three codons, UUA, UUU, and AAC, are found at the ribosomal A-site within the frameshift sites of each overlapping reading frame examined (Jacks et al. 1988a; Table 1). The possibility that the "shifty" tRNA may lack a hypermodified base in its anticodon loop is considered below.

A stem-loop region which is immediately downstream of the frameshift site in RSV is also required for efficient frameshifting (Jacks et al. 1988a). Disrupting base pairings within the stem by generating specific stem-destabilizing mutations resulted in a decrease in frameshifting, while restoring these base pairings by generating specific stem-restabilizing mutations rescued frameshifting (Jacks et al. 1988a). In HIV, there is no requirement for a downstream stem-loop effect on frameshifting and the only requirement appears to be a short RNA segment which includes the heptanucleotide frameshift signal (Wilson et al. 1988).

II. tRNAs Involved in Frameshifting

At least one, if not both, of the codons within the frameshift signals shown in Table 1 correspond to tRNAs which normally contain a hypermodified base in their anticodon loop. For example, Q base occurs in Asn-tRNA (which is coded by AAU or AAC in a number of the frameshift signals) and in Asp-tRNA (which is coded by GAU in the *pro-pol* signal of MMTV) and Wye base occurs in Phe-tRNA (which is coded by UUU in a number of the frameshift signals). The coding properties of tRNAs lacking Q (Beier et al. 1984a,b; Bienz and Kubli 1981; Meir et al. 1985) or Wye base (Smith and Hatfield 1986) in their anticodon loop are altered. It seems reasonable that the frameshift event may be facilitated if the involved tRNA does not have a highly modified base in the anticodon loop; i.e., such a tRNA may be more "shifty". It is of interest to note that leucine isoacceptors (leucine is required for translation in many of the signals shown in Table 1) do not contain a hypermodified base in their anticodon loop (see Valle et al. 1987 and references therein).

The chromatographic properties of aminoacyl-tRNAs at and around the frameshift site from HIV-1, BLV and HTLV-1 infected cells and from a corresponding set of uninfected (control) cells were examined (Hatfield et al.

1989). HIV-1 utilizes Phe-tRNA and Leu-tRNA within the *gag-pol* frameshift signal (Jacks et al. 1988b; Ratner et al. 1985; Sanchez-Pescador et al. 1985; Wain-Hobson et al. 1985), while BLV (Rice et al. 1985; Sagata et al. 1985) and HTLV-1 (Hiramatsu et al. 1987; Inoue et al. 1986; Seiki et al. 1983) utilize Asn-tRNA and Lys-tRNA within the *gag-pro* and Asn-tRNA and Leu-tRNA within the *pro-pol* frameshift signals (Table 1). The data showed that virtually all of the Asn-tRNA from each set of infected cells was Q-deficient, while a greater proportion from uninfected cells contained Q base (Hatfield et al. 1989). Furthermore, the data showed that virtually all of the Phe-tRNA from HIV-1 infected cells was Wye-deficient, while most of the Phe-tRNA from uninfected cells contained Wye base. The chromatographic properties of other aminoacyl-tRNAs at and around the frameshift site were not altered. It is tempting to speculate from these observations that the presence of G in place of the hypermodified Q base in the 5′ position of the anticodon of Asn-tRNA (and of Asp-tRNAs) (Beier et al. 1984a, b; Bienz and Kubli 1981; Meir et al. 1985; Suter et al. 1986) or of 1-methylG in place of the hypermodified Wye base in the 3′ position next to the anticodon of Phe-tRNA (Kuchino et al. 1982) would facilitate the frameshift event. Clearly, more space in and around the frameshift site would be created in absence of Q or Wye base. In addition, greater flexibility of movement of the respective tRNA anticodon might be expected in absence of a highly modified base in the anticodon loop such as is found in Leu-tRNA and in hypomodified Asn- or Phe-tRNAs.

D. Missense Suppression and Misrecognition of Genetic Codewords

Most mutations which occur in nature are missense. Neither missense suppressor tRNAs nor suppression of missense mutations, however, have been described thus far in mammalian cells. It is unfortunate that the large number of inborn errors in human metabolism which result from missense mutations do not appear to be approachable, at least not by our present knowledge of the utilization of aminoacyl-tRNA in protein synthesis, through gene therapy experiments involving tRNA. Even in hemoglobinopathies, where it is reasonable that a suppressor tRNA gene may be introduced selectively into red blood cell precursors rather than into the germline of intact organisms, it seems unlikely that a tRNA could be engineered to read more efficiently at a specific site to selectively correct a missense mutation. In designing gene therapy experiments involving missense suppressors in cells in culture, it would seem that several criteria must be met before attempting such experiments. (1) The mutation to be corrected should be one that corresponds to an infrequently used codeword, and hence the missense suppressor would hopefully not effect other proteins and, in addition, there would presumably be only a small amount of natural isoacceptor for the suppressor to compete with in translating the codeword. (2) The protein that is to be restored to an active state should be present in low levels and thus a missense suppressor in elevated levels could presumably completely suppress the mutation. Perhaps candidates to consider for such a possibility are the P21 *ras* proteins which occur in minor levels in mammalian cells and in which amino acid changes at specific positions cause the protein to become oncogenic (see Barbacid 1987 for review). Most certainly, an infrequently used codon could be generated at one of the "sensitive" sites making the protein oncogenic. Then a tRNA could be generated with an appropriate anticodon to insert a "wild-type" amino acid in response to the infrequently used codon.

Misrecognition of genetic codewords also occurs within the same amino acid family. This subtle type of misrecognition has been observed in cases where the preference of a tRNA for a codon within the same amino acid family may be changed by virtue of a base modification in the anticodon loop (Björk et al. 1987; Meir et al. 1985; Smith and Hatfield 1986; Smith et al. 1981); and an example involves a mammalian $tRNA^{Lys}$ with anticodon CUU (Raba et al. 1979). The fully modified lysine isoacceptor normally reads AAG codons, while the hypomodified form which lacks N^6-threonyl-adenosine next to its anticodon in the 3′ position wobbles more freely to read AAA codons (Smith and Hatfield 1986; Smith et al. 1981). This form of "misreading" may favor the expression of mRNAs rich in AAA codons and must therefore be considered among the factors that are important in orchestrating the complex pattern of protein synthesis in gene expression (Smith and Hatfield 1986; Smith et al. 1985).

The effects of other hypermodified bases which occur within the tRNA anticodon loop on the coding properties of the corresponding tRNAs have also been examined. The incorporation of histidine from mammalian His-tRNAs with and without Q base into rabbit globin in response to the His codons, CAU and CAC, was examined in rabbit reticulocyte lysates (Smith and Hatfield 1986; Smith and McNamara 1982). No differences were observed in the preference of either tRNA for CAU or CAC. However, incorporation of histidine from *Drosophila* His-tRNA with and without Q base into turnip yellow mosaic viral coat protein in response to CAU and CAC codons manifested different patterns of incorporation (Meir et al. 1985). His-tRNA without Q base showed a strong preference for CAC codons, while that with Q base showed a slight preference for CAU codons. The latter studies which were examined in *Xenopus* oocytes provide in vivo evidence that modification of the wobble base of tRNA may result in a codon preference during translation.

A question may be raised as to whether asparagine, aspartic acid, and histidine tRNAs which are Q^- can misread the corresponding XAG codewords (where X may be either C, A or G), and thus serve as missense suppressors, since tyrosine tRNA Q^- misreads UAG codons (see Sect. B.I.1). This possibility seems highly unlikely, not only because of the competition that would exist between the Q^- tRNAs and the corresponding isoacceptors which normally read XAG codewords, but also because asparagine, aspartic acid, and histidine tRNAs contain U in the middle position of their anticodon. Tyrosine tRNA contains ψ in this position which is apparently essential for suppression to occur (see Sect. B.I.1).

Misreading of genetic codewords involving the insertion of the wrong amino acid into protein has also been observed in mammalian cells in culture following acute starvation for an essential amino acid (Harley et al. 1981; Parker et al. 1978; Pollard et al. 1982). The types of changes observed are consistent with the misreading of pyrimidines for purines at the 3′ codon position. This technique has provided a means of measuring the fidelity of translation in mammalian cells (Harley et al. 1981) and of examining the levels of mistranslation in cells before and after transformation (Pollard et al. 1982).

E. Conclusion

Our knowledge about suppressor tRNAs in mammalian cells has increased substantially in the last few years. Table 2A summarizes the aminoacyl-tRNAs which suppress termination codons and Table 2B the mRNAs which are readthrough in mammalian cells. Clearly, tRNAs capable of suppressing termination codons occur naturally within the tRNA populations of mammalian cells. However, these isoacceptors apparently have specialized functions which do not include suppressing a nonsense mutation in order to correct a deleterious effect. It also seems that high levels of nonsense suppressor activity cannot be tolerated on a permanent basis by mammalian cells (Ho et al. 1986; Hudziak et al. 1982; Young et al. 1983) and thus the optimism for the use of suppressor tRNAs to correct nonsense mutations resulting in high levels of product must await further

Table 2. Natural suppression of termination codons in mammalian cells[a]

A. Aminoacyl-tRNAs which suppress termination codons

tRNA	Source	Anticodon	Codons read	Comments
Tyrosine	Mouse tumor cells	GψA	UAU, UAC, UAG	Suppresses UAG stop codon in TMV RNA in vitro[b]
Glutamine	Mammalian cells	UmUG	CAA, UAG	Kuchino et al.[c] reported that this tRNA suppresses UAG stop codon in TMV RNA in vitro. Their report that this tRNA is enriched many fold in MuLV infected cells was not substantiated by in vivo[d] or in vitro studies[e]
Leucine	Calf liver Bovine mammary tissue	CAG	CUG, UAG	Suppress UAG stop codon in TMV and BNYVV RNAs in vitro[f]
Leucine	Calf liver	CAA	UUG, UAG	
Tryptophan	Rabbit reticulocytes	?	UGG, UGA	Suppresses UGA stop codon in rabbit β-globin in vitro[g]
Selenocysteine	Mammalian tissues	CmCA	UGA	Suppress UGA codon in rabbit β-globin mRNA in vitro[h,i].
Selenocysteine	Mammalain tissues	NCA	UGA	Form phosphoseryl-tRNA[i,j] and selenocysteyl-tRNA[k]

Table 2. (*Continued*)

B. mRNAs which are suppressed

mRNA	Codon	Aminoacyl-tRNA	Comments
Glutathione Peroxidase	UGA	Selenocysteine (see text)	cDNA from human[l,m,n], mouse[l,o] bovine[l] and rat[p] sources has been sequenced and a UGA codon occurs at the active site of the gene product which corresponds to a selenocysteine moiety
Rabbit β-globin	UGA	?	Readthrough protein occurs in rabbit reticulocytes[g,q]
Sindbis and Middelburg viruses	UGA	?	These viruses contain a UGA codon in an open reading frame[r,s]
Moloney, feline and AKR[v] leukemia viruses	UAG	Glutamine	The amino acid at the stop codon in *gag-pol* fusion protein in MuLV and feline LV is Gln[t,u], but it has not been determined in AKR[v]
Moloney leukemia virus	UAA, UGA	?	The UAG stop codon at the end of the *gag* gene has been changed to UAA and UGA and both codons are suppressed intracellularly as well as in vitro[w]
Sindbis virus	UAA	?	The UGA codon in an open reading frame of this virus has been changed to UAA and it is suppressed intracellularly[x]
TMV	UAA		The UAG codon at the end of the 130 K protein was changed to UAA and it is suppressed in vivo and in vitro[y]

[a]References to original work in the table are indicated by a letter and are as follows: [b]Shindo-Okada et al. 1985; [c]Kuchino et al. 1987; [d]Panganiban 1988; [e]Feng et al. 1989a; [f]Valle et al. 1987; [g]Geller and Rich 1980; [h]Diamond et al. 1981; [i]Hatfield et al. 1982a; [j]Mizutani and Hashimoto 1984; [k]Lee et al. 1989b; [l]Mullenbach et al. 1988; [m]Mullenbach et al. 1987; [n]Sukenaka et al. 1987; [o]Chambers et al. 1986; [p]Reddy et al. 1988; [q]Hatfield et al. 1988; [r,s]Strauss et al. 1983, 1984; [t,u]Yoshinaka et al. 1985a, b; [v]Herr 1984; [w]Feng et al. 1988b; [x]Lin and Rice 1989; and [y]Ishikana et al. 1986.

experimentation. An important area for further study in the field of nonsense suppression is the reason why some termination codons are readthrough, while others are not.

Another area for possible scientific development is in the field of missense suppression, since so little is known about the occurrence and role of missense suppressors in mammalian cells. A summary of the possible ribosomal frameshift sites in several of the retroviruses which have been sequenced are shown in Table 1 (see also Jacks et al. 1988a). A question was raised whether one or more of the isoacceptors utilized at the "slippage site" may lack a hypermodified base in its anticodon loop to facilitate the frameshift event. If alteration of a tRNA is required by some viruses for ribosomal frameshifting, then converting these tRNAs to the fully modified form may provide an avenue for inhibiting viral expression (Hatfield 1985). Suppression of expression of viral replicative enzymes in cells infected with HIVs or HTLVs by these or other means would be of considerable therapeutic value.

Acknowledgements. The authors express their sincere appreciation to Drs. Anne-Lise Haenni, Rosaura P.C. Valle, Marie-Dominique Morch, and Eric Kubli for their critical review and helpful suggestions regarding the sections of the manuscript dealing with nonsense suppression and to the many individuals who so generously provided us with preprints and with other data prior to publication. This work was sponsored in part by NCI, DHHS under contract No. N01-CO-74101 with BRI.

References

Barbacid M (1987) *ras* genes. Annu Rev Biochem 56:779–827

Barciszewski J, Barciszewski M, Suter B, Kubli E (1985) Plant tRNA suppressors: in vivo readthrough properties and nucleotide sequence of yellow lupin seeds $tRNA^{Tyr}$. Plant Sci 40:193–196

Baserga SJ, Benz EJ Jr (1988) Nonsense mutations in the human beta-globin gene affect mRNA metabolism. Proc Natl Acad Sci USA 85:2056–2060

Beier H, Barciszewski M, Krupp G, Mitnacht R, Gross HJ (1984a) UAG readthrough during TMV RNA translation: isolation and sequence of two $tRNAs^{Tyr}$ with suppressor activity from tobacco plants. EMBO J 3:351–356

Beier H, Barciszewski M, Sickinger H-D (1984b) The molecular basis for the differential translation of TMV RNA in tobacco protoplasts and wheat germ extracts. EMBO J 3:1091–1096

Bienz M, Kubli E (1981) Wild-type $tRNA^{Tyr}$/G reads the TMV RNA stop codon, but Q base-modified $tRNA^{Tyr}$/Q does not. Nature 294:188–190

Bienz M, Kubli E, Kohli J, de Henau S, Grosjean H (1980) Nonsense suppression in eukaryotes: the use of the *Xenopus* oocyte as an in vivo assay system. Nucleic Acids Research 8:5169–5178

Bienz M, Kubli E, Kohli J, de Henau S, Huez G, Marbaix G, Grosjean H (1981) Usage of three termination codons in a single eukaryotic cell, the *Xenopus* oocyte, Nucleic Acids Research 9:3835–3850

Björk GR, Erickson JU, Gustafsson CED, Hagervall TG, Jönsson YH, Wilkström PM (1987) Transfer RNA Modification. Annu Rev Biochem 56:263–287

Böck A, Stadtman TC (1988) Selenocysteine, a highly specific component of certain enzymes, is incorporated by a UGA-directed co-translational mechanism. Biofactors 1:245–250

Bossi L (1983) Context effects: translation of UAG codon by suppressor tRNA is affected by the sequence following UAG in the message. J Mol Biol 164:73–87

Brierly I, Boursnell ME, Binns MM, Bilimoria B, Block VC, Brown TDK, Inglis SC (1987) An efficient ribosomal frameshifting signal in the polymerase-encoding region of the corona-virus IBV. EMBO J 6:3779–3785

Bunn HF, Forget BG (1986) Hemoglobin: molecular, genetics and clinical aspects. Sanders, Philadelphia USA

Capecchi MR, Vonder Haar RA, Capecchi NE, Sveda MM (1977) The isolation of a suppressible nonsense mutant in mammalian cells. Cell 12:371–381

Capone JP, Sharp PA, RajBhandary UL (1985) Amber, ochre and opal suppressor tRNA genes derived from a human serine tRNA gene. EMBO J 4:213–221

Capone JP, Sedivy JM, Sharp PA, RajBhandary UL (1986) Introduction of UAG, UAA, and UGA nonsense mutations at a specific site in the *Escherichia coli* chloramphenicol acetyltransferase gene: use in measurement of amber, ochre, and opal suppression in mammalian cells. Mol Cell Biol 6:3059–3067

Celis JE, Piper PW (1981) Nonsense suppressors in eukaryotes. Trends Biochem Sci 6:177–179

Chakrabarti L, Guyader M, Alizon M, Daniel MD, Desrosiers RC, Tiollais P, Sonigo P (1987) Sequence of simian immunodeficiency virus from macaque and its relationship to other human and simian retroviruses. Nature 328:543–547

Chambers I, Harrison PR (1987) A new puzzle in selenoprotein biosynthesis: selenocysteine seems to be encoded by the 'stop' codon, UGA. Trends Biochem Sci 12:255–256

Chambers I, Frampton J, Goldfarb P, Affara N, McBain W, Harrison PR (1986) The structure of the mouse gluthione peroxidase gene: the selenocysteine in the active site is encoded by the 'termination' codon, TGA. EMBO J 5:1221–1227

Chen S-H, Habib G, Yang C-Y, Gu Z-W, Lee BR, Weng S-A, Silberman SS, Cai S-J, Deslypere JP, Rosseneu M, Gotto AM Jr, Li W-H, Chan L (1987) Apolipoprotein B-48 is the product of a messenger RNA with an organ-specific in-frame stop codon. Science 238:363–366

Craigan WJ, Caskey CT (1987) Translational frameshifting: where will it stop? Cell 50:1–2

Cremer KJ, Bodemer M, Summers WP, Summers WC, Gesteland RF (1979) In vitro suppression of UAG and UGA mutants in the thymidine kinase gene of Herpes simplex virus. Proc Natl Acad Sci USA 76:430–434

Crick FHA (1966) Codon-anticodon pairing: the wobble hypothesis. J Mol Biol 19:548–555

Davidson NO, Powell LM, Wallis SC, Scott J (1988) Thyroid hormone modulates the introduction of a stop codon in rat liver apolipoprotein B messenger RNA. J Biol Chem 263:13482–13485

Dayhuff TJ, Atkins JF, Gesteland RF (1986) Characterization of ribosomal frameshift events by protein sequence analysis. J Biol Chem 261:7491–7500

Diamond A, Dudock B, Hatfield D (1981) Structure and properties of a bovine liver UGA suppressor serine tRNA with a tryptophan anticodon. Cell 25:497–506

Efstratiadis A, Kafatos F, Maniatis T (1977) The primary structure of rabbit β-globin mRNA as determined from cloned DNA. Cell 10:571–585

Eggertsson G, Söll D, (1988) Transfer ribonucleic acid-mediated suppression of termination codons. Microbiol Rev 52:354–374

Engelberg-Kulka H, Schoulaker-Schwarz R (1988a) Stop is not the end: physiological implications of translational readthrough. J Theor Biol 131:477–485

Engelberg-Kulka H, Schoulaker-Schwarz R (1988b) A flexible genetic code, or why does selenocysteine have no unique codon? Trends Biochem Sci 13:419–421

Feng Y-X, Dong L, Zhang Y (1986) Homogeneous sequence in the anticodon of natural UAG suppressor $tRNA^{Tyr}$. Acta Biochim Biophys Sinica 18:90–95

Feng Y-X, Hatfield D, Rein A, Levin JG (1989a) Translational readthrough of the murine leukemia virus *gag* gene amber codon does not require virus-induced alteration of tRNA. J Virol 63:2405–2410

Feng Y-X, Levin J, Hatfield D, Schaefer T, Gorelick R, Rein A (1989b) Suppression of UAA and UGA termination codons in mutant murine leukemia virus. J Virol 63:2870–2873

Franchini G, Gurgo C, Guo H-G, Gallo RC, Collalti E, Fragnoli KA, Hall LF, Wong-Stahl F, Reitz MS (1987) Sequence of simian immunodeficiency virus and its relationship to the human immunodeficiency viruses. Nature 328:539–543

Geller AI, Rich A (1980) UGA termination suppression $tRNA^{Trp}$ active in rabbit reticulocytes. Nature 283:41–46

Gesteland R, Wills N (1979) Use of yeast suppressors for identification of adenovirus nonsense mutants. In: Celis JE, Smith JD (eds) Nonsense mutations and tRNA suppressors. Academic Press, London, pp 277–284

Gesteland RF, Wills N, Lewis JB, Grodzicker T (1977) Identification of amber and ochre mutants of the human virus Ad2 + ND1. Proc Natl Acad Sci USA 74:4567–4571

Guyader M, Emerman M, Sonigo P, Clavel F, Montagnier L, Alizon M (1987) Genome organization and transactivation of the human immunodeficiency virus type 2. Nature 326:662–669

Hardman DA, Protter AA, Schilling JW, Kane JP (1987) Carboxyl terminal analysis of human B-48 protein confirms the novel mechanism proposed for chain termination. Biochem Biophys Res Commun 149:1214–1219

Harley CB, Pollard JW, Stanners CP, Goldstein S (1981) Model for messenger RNA translation during amino acid starvation applied to the calculation of protein synthetic error rates. J Biol Chem 156:10786–10794

Hatfield D (1972) Recognition of nonsense codons in mammalian cells. Proc Natl Acad Sci USA 69:3014–3018

Hatfield D (1985) Suppression of termination codons in higher eukaryotes. Trends Biochem Sci 10:201–204

Hatfield D, Nirenberg M (1971) Binding of radioactive oligonucleotides to ribosomes Biochemistry 10:4318–4323

Hatfield D, Portugal FH (1970) Seryl-tRNA in mammalian tissues: chromatographic differences in brain and liver and a specific response to the codon UGA. Proc Natl Acad Sci USA 67:1200–1206

Hatfield D, Rice M (1986) Aminoacyl-tRNA (anticodon): codon adaptation in human and rabbit reticulocytes. Biochem Int 13:835–842

Hatfield D, Matthews CR, Rice M (1979) Aminoacyl-transfer RNA populations in mammalian cells: chromatographic profiles and patterns of codon recognition. Biochim Biophys Acta 564:414–423

Hatfield D, Diamond A, Dudock B (1982a) Opal suppressor serine tRNAs from bovine liver form phosphoseryl-tRNA. Proc Natl Acad USA 79:6215–6219

Hatfield D, Varricchio F, Rice M, Forget BG (1982b) The aminoacyl-tRNA population of human reticulocytes. J Biol Chem 257:3183–3188

Hatfield D, Dudock BS, Eden FC (1983) Characterization and nucleotide sequence of a chicken gene encoding an opal suppressor tRNA and its flanking DNA segments. Proc Natl Acad Sci USA 80: 4940–4944

Hatfield D, Thorgeirsson SS, Copeland TD, Oroszlan S, Bustin M (1988) Immunopurification of the suppressor tRNA dependent rabbit beta-globin readthrough protein. Biochemistry 27:1179–1183

Hatfield D, Feng Y-X, Lee BJ, Rein A, Levin JG, Oroszlan S (1989) Chromatographic analysis of aminoacyl-tRNAs which are required for translation of codons at and around the ribosomal frameshift sites in HIV, HTLV-1, and BLV. Virology 173:736–742

Hatfield D, Smith DWE, Lee BJ, Worland PJ, Oroszlan S (1989) Structure and function of suppressor tRNAs in higher eukaryotes. CRC critical reviews in biochemistry. CRC Press (in press)

Herr W (1984) Nucleotide sequence of AKV murine leukemia virus. J Virol 49:471–478

Higuchi K, Hospattankar AV, Law SW, Meglin N, Cortright J, Brewer HB Jr (1988) Human apolipoprotein B (apoB) mRNA: identification of two distinct apoB mRNAs, an mRNA with the apo-B-100 sequence and an apoB mRNA containing a premature in-frame translational stop codon, in both liver and intestine. Proc Natl Acad Sci USA 85:1772–1776

Hill CW (1975) Informational suppression of missense mutations. Cell 6:419–427

Hiramatsu K, Nishida J, Naito A, Yoshikura H (1987) Molecular cloning of the closed circular provirus of human T cell leukemia virus type I: a new open reading frame in the *gag-pol* region. J Gen Virol 68:213–218

Hizi A, Henderson LE, Copeland TD, Sowder RC, Hixson CV, Oroszlan S (1987) Characterization of mouse tumor virus *gag-pol* gene products and the ribosomal frameshift site by protein sequencing. Proc Natl Acad Sci USA 84:7041–7045

Ho Y-S, Kan YW (1987) In vivo aminoacylation of human and *Xenopus* suppressor tRNAs constructed by site-specific mutagenesis. Proc Natl Acad Sci USA 84:2185–2188

Ho Y-S, Norton GP, Palese P, Dozy AM, Kan YW (1986) Expression and function of suppressor tRNA genes in mammalian cells. Cold Spring Harbor Symposium on Quantitative Biology vol 51, Cold Spring Harbor, New York, pp 1033–1040

Hudziak RM, Laski FA, RajBhandary UL, Sharp PA, Capecchi MR (1982) Establishment of mammalian cell lines containing multiple nonsense mutations and functional suppressor tRNA genes. Cell 31:137–146

Inoue J-I, Watanabe T, Sato M, Oda A, Toyoshima K, Yoshida M, Seiki M (1986) Nucleotide sequence of the protease-coding region in an infectious DNA of simian retrovirus (STLV) of the HTLV-1 family. Virology 150:187–195

Ishikawa M, Meshi T, Motoyoshi F, Takamatsu N, Okada Y (1986) In vitro mutagenesis of the putative replicase genes of tobacco mosaic virus. Nucleic Acids Res 14:8291–8305

Jacks T, Varmus HE (1985) Expression of the Rous sarcoma virus *pol* gene by ribosomal frameshifting. Science 230:1237–1242

Jacks T, Townsley K, Varmus HE, Majors J (1987) Two efficient ribosomal frameshifting events are required for synthesis of mouse mammary tumor virus *gag*-related polyproteins. Proc Natl Acad Sci USA 84:4298–4302

Jacks T, Madhani HD, Masiraz FR, Varmus HE (1988a) Signals for ribosomal frameshifting in the Rous sarcoma virus *gag-pol* region. Cell 55:447–458

Jacks T, Power MD, Masiarz FR, Luciw PA, Barr PJ, Varmus H (1988b) Characterization of ribosomal frameshifting in HIV-1 *gag-pol* expression. Nature 331:280–283

Jackson RJ, Hunt T (1983) Preparation and use of nuclease-treated rabbit reticulocyte lysates for the translation of eukaryotic messenger RNA. Methods Enzymol 96:50–74

Jank P, Shindo-Okada N, Nishimura S, Gross HJ (1977) Rabbit liver $tRNA_1^{Val}$: primary structure and unusual codon recognition. Nucletic Acids Res 4:1999–2008

Johnson PF, Abelson J (1983) The yeast $tRNA^{Tyr}$ gene intron is essential for correct modification of its tRNA product. Nature 302:681–687

Kato N, Hoshino H, Harada F (1983) Minor serine tRNA containing anticodon NCA(C4 RNA) from human and mouse cells. Biochem Int 7:635–645

Kawakami T, Sherman L, Dahlberg J, Gazit A, Yaniv A, Tronick SR, Aaronson SA (1987) Nucleotide sequence analysis of equine infectious anemia virus proviral DNA. Virology 158:300–312

Kohli J, Grosjean H (1981) Usage of the three termination codons: compilation and analysis of known eukaryotic and prokaryotic translation termination sequences. Mol Gen Genet 182:430–439

Kohli J, Kwong T, Altruda F, Söll D (1979) Characterization of a UGA-suppressing serine tRNA from *Schizosaccharomyces pombe* with the help of a new in vitro assay system for eukaryotic suppressor tRNAs. J Biol Chem 254:1546–1551

Körner AM, Freinstein SI, Altman S (1978) Transfer RNA-mediated suppression. In: Altman S (ed) Transfer RNA. MIT Press, Cambridge, pp 105–135

Kubli E, Schmidt T, Martin PF, Sofer W (1982) In vitro suppression of a nonsense mutant of *Drosophila melanogaster*. Nucleic Acids Res 10:7145–7152

Kuchino Y, Borek E, Grunberger D, Mushinski J, Nishimura S (1982) Changes of post-transcriptional modification of Wye base in tumor-specific $tRNA^{Phe}$. Nucleic Acids Res 10:6421–6432

Kuchino Y, Beier H, Akita N, Nishimura S (1987) Natural UAG suppressor glutamine tRNA is elevated in mouse cells infected with Moloney murine leukemia virus. Proc Natl Acad Sci USA 84:2668–2672

Kuchino Y, Nishimura S, Schröder HC, Rottmann M, Müller WEG (1988) Selective inhibition of formation of suppressor glutamine tRNA in Moloney murine leukemia virus-infected NIH-3T3 cells by Avarol. Virology 165:518–526

Laski FA, Belagaje R, RajBhandary UL, Sharp PA (1982) An amber suppressor tRNA gene derived by site-specific mutagenesis: cloning and function in mammalian cells. Proc Natl Acad Sci USA 79:5813–5817

Laski FA, Belagaje R, Hudziak RM, Capecchi MR, Norton GP, Palese P, RajBhandary UL, Sharp PA (1984) Synthesis of an ochre suppressor tRNA gene and expression in mammalian cells. EMBO J 3:2445–2452

Lee BJ, Kang SG, Hatfield D (1989a) Transcription of *Xenopus* selenocysteyl-$tRNA^{Ser}$ (formerly designated opal suppressor phosphoserine tRNA) is directed by mutiple 5′ extragenic regulatory elements. J Biol Chem 264:9696–9702

Lee BJ, de la Peña P, Tobian JA, Zasloff M, Hatfield D (1987) Unique pathway of expression of an opal suppressor phosphoserine tRNA. Proc Natl Acad Sci USA 84:6384–6388

Lee BJ, Worland PJ, Davis J, Stadium TC, Hatfield D (1989b) Identification of a selenocysteyl-tRNA^{Ser} in mammalian cells which recognizes the nonsense codon, UGA. J Biol Chem 264:9724–9727

Lehrman MA, Goldstein JL, Brown MS, Russell DW, Schneider WJ (1985) Internalization-defective LDL receptors produced by genes with nonsense and frameshift mutations that truncate the cytoplasmic domain. Cell 41:735–743

Leinfelder W, Zehelein E, Mandrand-Berthelot M-A, Böck A (1988) Gene for a novel tRNA species that accepts L-serine and cotranslationally inserts selenocysteine. Nature 331:723–725

Leinfelder W, Stadtman TC, Böck A (1989) Occurrence in vivo of selenocysteyl-tRNA^{Ser} in *Escherichia coli*: effect of *sel* mutants. J Biol Chem 264:9720–9723

Li G, Rice CM (1989) Mutagenesis of the in-frame opal termination codon preceeding nsP4 of Sindbis virus: studies of translational readthrough and its effect on virus replication. J Virol 63:1326–1337

Lin JP, Aker M, Sitney KC, Mortimer RL (1986) First position wobble in codon-anticodon pairing: amber suppression by a yeast glutamine tRNA. Gene 49:383–388

Mäenpää PH (1972) Seryl transfer RNA alterations during estrogen-induced phosvitin synthesis: quantitative assay of the hormone-responding species by ribosomal binding. Biochem Biophys Res Commun 47:971–974

Mäenpää PH, Bernfield MR (1970) A specific hepatic transfer RNA for phosphoserine. Proc Natl Acad Sci USA 67:688–695

Marlor RL, Parkhurst SM, Corces VG (1986) The *Drosophila melanogaster* gypsy transposable elements encodes putative gene products homologous to retroviral proteins. Mol Cell Biol 6:1129–1134

Marotta C, Wilson J, Forget BG, Weissman S (1977) Human globin messenger RNA: nucleotide sequences derived from complementary DNA. J Biol Chem 252:5040–5053

McAdam RA, Goundis D, Reid KBM (1988) A homozygous point mutation results in a stop codon in the ClqB-chain of a Clq-deficient individual. Immunogenetics 27:259–264

McBride OW, Rajagopalan M, Hatfield D (1987) Opal suppressor phosphoserine tRNA gene and pseudogene are located on human chromosomes 19 and 22, respectively. J Biol Chem 262:11163–11166

McBride OW, Mitchell A, Lee BJ, Mullenbach G, Hatfield D (1988) Gene for selenium-dependent glutathione peroxidase maps to human chromosomes 3, 21, and X. BioFactors 1:285–292

Meier F, Suter B, Grosjean H, Keith G, Kubli E (1985) Queuosine modification of the wobble base in tRNA^{His} influences in vivo decoding properties. EMBO J 4:823–827

Mietz JA, Grossman Z, Lueders KK, Kuff EL (1987) Nucleotide sequence of a complete mouse intracisternal A-particle genome: relationship to known aspects of particle assembly and function. J Virol 61:3020–3029

Miller JH, Albertini AM (1983) Effects of surrounding sequence on the suppression of nonsense codons. J Mol Biol 164:59–71

Mizutani T, Hashimoto A (1984) Purification and properties of suppressor seryl-tRNA: ATP phosphotransferase from bovine liver. FEBS Lett 169:319–322

Mizutani T, Hitaka T (1988) Stronger affinity of reticulocyte release factor than natural suppressor tRNA^{Ser} for the opal termination codon. FEBS Lett 226:227–231

Mizutani T, Tachibana Y (1986) Possible incorporation of phosphoserine into globin readthrough protein via bovine opal suppressor phosphoseryl-tRNA. FEBS Lett 207:162–166

Mizutani T, Narihara T, Hashimoto A (1984) Purification and properties of bovine liver seryl-tRNA synthetase. Eur J Biochem 143:9–13

Mizutani T, Kanbe K, Kimura Y, Tachibana Y, Hitaka T (1988) Non-partition of opal suppressor phosphoseryl-transfer ribonucleic acid (tRNA) in phosphoserine aminotransferase catalysis. Chem Pharm Bull 36:824–827

Moore R, Dixon M, Smith R, Peters G, Dickson C (1987) Complete nucleotide sequence of a milk-transmitted mouse mammary tumor virus: two frameshift suppression events are required for translation of *gag* and *pol*. J Virol 61:480–490

Mullenback GT, Tabrizi A, Irvine BD, Bell GI, Hallewell RA (1987) Sequence of a cDNA coding for human glutathione peroxidase confirms TGA encodes active site selenocysteine. Nucleic Acids Res 15:5484

Mullenback GT, Tabrizi A, Irvine BD, Bell GI, Tainer JA, Hallewell RA (1988) Selenocysteine's mechanism of incorporation and evolution revealed in cDNAs of three glutathione peroxidases. Protein Engineer 2:239–246

Müller WEG, Schröder HC, Reuter P, Sarin PS, Hess G, Meyer zum Büschenfelde K-H, Kuchino Y, Nishimura S (1988) Inhibition of expression of natural UAG suppressor glutamine tRNA in HIV-infected human H9 cells in vitro by Avarol. AIDS Res Human Retrovir 4:279–286

Murgola EJ (1985) tRNA, suppression, and the code. Annu Rev Genet 19:57–80

Murgola EJ (1989) Mutant glycine tRNAs and other wonders of translation suppression. In: Cherayil JD (ed) Transfer RNAs and other soluble RNAs. CRC Press, Boca Raton, (in press)

Murphy EC Jr, Wills N, Arlinghaus RB (1980) Suppression of murine retrovirus polypeptide termination: effect of amber suppressor tRNA on the cell-free translation of Rauscher murine leukemia virus, Moleney murine leukemia virus, and Moloney murine sarcoma virus 124 RNA. J Virol 34:464–473

Nam SH, Kidokoro M, Shida H, Hatanka M (1988) Processing of *gag* precursor polyprotein of human T-cell leukemia virus type I by virus-encoded protease. J Virol 62:3718–3728

Nirenberg M, Leder P (1964) RNA codewords and protein synthesis: the effect of trinculeotides upon the binding of sRNA to ribosomes. Science 145:1399–1407

O'Neill VA, Eden FC, Pratt K, Hatfield D (1985) A human opal suppressor tRNA gene and pseudogene. J Biol Chem 260:2501–2508

Panganiban AT (1988) Retroviral *gag* gene amber codon suppression is caused by an intrinsic *cis*-acting component of the viral mRNA. J Virol 62:3574–3580

Parker J, Pollard JW, Friesen JD, Stanners CP (1978) Stuttering: high-level mistranslation in animal and bacterial cells. Proc Natl Acad Sci USA 75:1091–1095

Pelham HRB (1978) Leaky UAG termination codon in tobacco mosaic virus RNA. Nature 272:469–471

Philipson L, Andersson P, Olshevsky U, Weinberg R, Baltimore D (1978) Translation of MuLV and MSV RNAs in nuclease-treated reticulocyte extracts: enhancement of the *gag-pol* polypeptide with yeast suppressor tRNA. Cell 13:189–199

Pollard J, Harley CB, Chamberlin JW, Goldstein S, Stanners CP (1982) Is transformation associated with an increased error frequency in mammalian cells? J Biol Chem 257:5977–5979

Powell LM, Wallis SC, Pease RJ, Edwards YH, Knott TJ, Scott J (1987) A novel form of tissue-specific RNA processing produces apolipoprotein-B48 in intestine. Cell 50:831–840

Power MD, Marx PA, Bryant ML, Gardner MB, Barr PJ, Luciw PA (1986) Nucleotide sequence of SRV-1, a type D simian acquired immune deficiency syndrome retrovirus. Science 231:1567–1572

Pratt K, Eden FC, You KH, O'Neill VA, Hatfield D (1985) Conserved sequences in both coding and 5′ flanking regions of mammalian opal suppressor tRNA genes. Nucleic Acids Res 13:4765–4775

Pure GA, Robinson GW, Naumovski L, Friedberg EC (1985) Partial suppression of an ochre mutation in *Saccharomyces cerevisiae* by multicopy plasmids containing a normal yeast $tRNA^{Gln}$ gene. J Mol Biol 183:31–42

Raba M, Limberg K, Burghagen M, Katze JR, Simsek M, Heckman JE, RajBhandary UL, Gross HJ (1979) Nucleotide sequence of three isoaccepting lysine tRNAs from rabbit liver and SV40-transformed mouse fibroblast. Eur J Biochem 97:305–318

Ratner L, Haseltine W, Patarca R, Livak KJ, Starcich B, Josephs SF, Doran ER, Rafalski JA, Whitehorn EA, Baumeister K, Ivanoff J, Petteway SR, Pearson ML, Lautenberger JA, Papas TS, Ghrayeb J, Chang NT, Gallo RC, Wong-Staal F (1985) Complete nucleotide sequence of the AIDS virus, HTLV-III. Nature 313:277–284

Reddy AP, Hsu BL, Reddy PS, Li N-Q, Thyagaraju K, Reddy CC, Tam MF, Tu C-PD (1988) Expression of glutathione peroxidase I gene in selenium-deficient rats. Nucleic Acids Res 16:5557–5568

Rice NR, Stephens R, Burny A, Gilden R (1985) The *gag* and *pol* genes of bovine leukemia virus: nucleotide sequence and analysis. Virology 142:357–377

Roberts BE, Paterson BM (1973) Efficient translation of tobacco mosaic virus RNA and rabbit globin 9S RNA in a cell-free system from commercial wheat germ. Proc Natl Acad Sci USA 70:2330–2334

Romeo G. Hassan HJ, Staempfli S, Roncuzzi L, Cianetti L, Leonardi A, Vicente V, Mannucci PM, Bertina R, Peschle C, Cortese R (1987) Hereditary thrombophilia: identification of nonsense and missense mutations in the protein C gene. Proc Natl Acad Sci USA 84:2829–2832

Sagata N, Yasunaga T, Tsuzuku-Kawamura J, Ohishi K, Ogawa Y, Ikawa Y (1985) Complete nucleotide sequence of the genome of bovine leukemia virus: its evolutionary relationship to other retroviruses. Proc Natl Acad Sci USA 82:677–681

Saigo K, Kugiyama W, Matsuo Y, Inouye S, Yoshioka K, Yuki S (1984) Identification of the coding sequence for a reverse transcriptase-like enzyme in a transposable genetic element in *Drosophila melanogaster*. Nature 312:659–663

Sanchez-Pescador R, Power MD, Barr PJ, Steimer KS, Stempien MM, Brown-Shimer SL, Gee WW, Renard A, Randolph A, Levy JA, Dina D, Luciw PA (1985) Nucleotide sequence and expression of AIDS-associated retrovirus (ARV-2). Science 227:484–492

Satoh K, Nukiwa T, Brantly M, Garver RI Jr, Hofker M, Courtney M, Crystal RG (1988) Emphysema associated with complete absence of αl-antitrypsin of a stop codon in an αl-antitrypsin-coding exon. Am J Human Genet 42:77–83

Schwartz DE, Tizard R, Gilbert W (1983) Nucleotide sequence of Rous sarcoma virus. Cell 32:853–869

Sedivy JM, Capone JP, RajBhandary UL, Sharp PA (1987) An inducible mammalian amber suppressor: propagation of a poliovirus mutant. Cell 50:379–389

Seiki M, Hattori S, Hirayama Y, Yoshida M (1983) Human adult T-cell leukemia virus: complete nucleotide sequence of the provirus genome integrated in leukemia cell DNA. Proc Natl Acad Sci USA 80:3618–3622

Sharp SJ, Stewart TS (1977) The characterization of phosphoseryl tRNA from lactating bovine mammary gland. Nucleic Acids Res 4:2123–2136

Sherman F (1982) Suppression in yeast *Saccharomyces cerevisiae*. In: Strathern JN, Jones EW, Broach JR (eds) Molecular biology of the yeast *Saccharomyces*; metabolism and gene expression. Cold Spring Harbor Laboratories, New York, pp 463–486

Shimotohno K, Takahashi Y, Shimizu N, Gojobori T, Golde DW, Chen IS, Miwa M, Sugimura T (1985) Complete nucleotide sequence of an infectious clone of human T-cell leukemia virus type II: an open reading frame for the protease gene. Proc Natl Acad Sci USA 82:3101–3105

Shindo-Okada N, Akimoto H, Nomura H, Nishmura S (1985) Recognition of UAG termination codon by mammalian tyrosine tRNA containing 6-thioqueuine in the first position of the anticodon. Proc Jpn Acad 61:94–98

Shinnick TM, Lerner RA, Sutclife JG (1981) Nucleotide sequence of Moloney murine leukemia virus. Nature 293:543–548

Smith DWE, Hatfield D (1986) Effects of post-translational base modifications on the site-specific function of transfer RNA in eukaryote translation. J Mol Biol 189:663–671

Smith DWE, McNamara AL (1982) The effect of the Q base modification on the usage of $tRNA^{His}$ in globin synthesis. Biochem Biophys Res Commun 104:1459–1463

Smith DWE, McNamara A, Rice M, Hatfield D (1981) The effects of a post-transcriptional modification on the function of $tRNA^{Lys}$ isoaccepting species in translation. J Biol Chem 256:10033–10036

Smith DWE, McNamara AL, Mushinski JF, Hatfield DL (1985) Tumor-specific, hypomodified phenylalanyl-tRNA is utilized in translation in preference to the fully modified isoacceptor of normal cells. J Biol Chem 260:147–151

Smith JD (1979) Suppressor tRNAs in prokaryotes. In: Celis JE, Smith JD (eds) Nonsense mutations and tRNA suppressors. Academic Press, London pp 109–125

Sonigo P, Alizon M, Staskus K, Klatzmann D, Cole S, Danos O, Retzel E, Tiollais O, Haase A, Wain-Hobson S (1985) Nucleotide sequence of the visna lentivirus: relationship to the AIDS virus. Cell 42:369–382

Sonigo P, Barker C, Hunter E, Wain-Hobson S (1986) Nucleotide sequence of Mason-Pfizer monkey virus: an immunosuppressive D-type retrovirus. Cell 45:375–385

Sprinzl M, Hartmann T, Meissner F, Moll J, Vorderwülbecke T (1987) Compilation of tRNA sequences and tRNA genes. Nucleic Acids Res (Sequences supplement) 15:r53–r188

Steege DA, Söll DG (1979) Suppression. In: Goldberger RF (ed) Biological Regulation and Development (vol 1). Plenum, New York, pp 433–485

Stephens RM, Casey JW, Rice NR (1986) Equine infectious anemia virus *gag* and *pol* genes: relatedness to visna and AIDS virus. Science 231:589–594

Stewart T, Sharp S (1984) Characterizing the function of O^{β}-phosphoseryl-tRNA. Methods Enzymol 106:157–161

Strauss EG, Rice CM, Strauss JH (1983) Sequence coding for the alphavirus nonstructural proteins is interrupted by an opal termination codon. Proc Natl Acad Sci USA 80:5271–5275

Strauss EG, Rice CM, Strauss JH (1984) Complete nucleotide sequence of the genomic RNA of Sindbis virus. Virology 133:92–110

Sukenaga Y, Ishida K, Takeda T, Takagi K (1987) cDNA sequence coding for human glutathione peroxidase. Nucleic Acids Res 15:7178

Summers WP, Summers WC, Laski FA, RajBhandary UL, Sharp PA (1983) Functional suppression in mammalian cells of nonsense mutations in the Herpes simplex virus thymidine kinase gene by suppressor tRNA genes. J Virol 47:376–379

Sundee RA, Evenson JK (1987) Serine incorporation into the selenocysteine moiety of glutathione peroxidase. J Biol Chem 262:933–937

Suter B, Altwegg M, Choffat Y, Kubli E (1986) The nucleotide sequence of two homogeneic *Drosophila melanogaster* $tRNA^{Tyr}$ isoacceptors: application of a rapid tRNA anticodon sequencing method using S-1 nuclease. Arch Biochem Biophys 247:233–237

Temple GF, Dozy AM, Roy KL, Kan YW (1982) Construction of a functional human suppressor tRNA gene: an approach to gene therapy for beta-thalassaemia. Nature 296:537–540

Thayer RM, Power MD, Bryant ML, Gardner MB, Barr PJ, Luciw PA (1987) Sequence relationships of type D retroviruses which cause simian acquired immunodeficiency syndrome. Virology 157:317–329

Topal MD, Fresco JR (1976) Complementary base pairing and the origin of substitution mutations. Nature 263:285–289

Tukalo MA, Vlasov V, Vasil'chenko I, Matsuka G, Knorre D (1980) Dokl Akad Nauk SSSR 253:253–256

Valle RPC, Morch M-D (1988) Stop making sense or regulation at the level of termination in eukaryotic protein synthesis. FEBS Lett 235:1–15

Valle RPC, Morch M-D, Haenni A-L (1987) Novel amber suppressor tRNAs of mammalian origin. EMBO J 6:3049–3055

Vasil'ieva IG, Tukalo MA, Krikliviy IA, Matduka GCH (1984) Mol Biol Akad Nauk SSSR 18:1321–1325

Wain-Hobson S, Sonigo P, Danos O, Cole S, Alizon M (1985) Nucleotide sequence of the AIDS virus, LAV. Cell 40:9–17

Ward DC, Reich E (1968) Conformational properties of polyformycin: a polyribonucleotide with individual residues in the syn conformation. Proc Natl Acad Sci USA 61:1494–1501

Weiss WA, Friedberg EC (1986) Normal yeast $tRNA^{Gln}$/CAG can suppress amber codons and is encoded by an essential gene. J Mol Biol 192:725–735

Weiss RB, Dunn JF, Atkins JF, Gesteland RF (1987a) Slippery runs, shifty stops, backward steps, and forward hops: −2, −1, +1, +2, +5, and +6 ribosomal frameshifting. Cold Spring Harbor Symposia on Quantitative Biology vol II, Gold Spring Harbor, New York, pp 687–696

Weiss WA, Edelman I, Culbertson MR, Friedberg EC (1987b) Physiological levels of normal $tRNA^{Gln}$/CAG can effect partial suppression of amber mutations in the yeast *Saccharomyces cerevisiae*. Proc Natl Acad Sci USA 84:8031–8034

Weiss R, Lindsley D, Falahee B, Gallant J (1988) On the mechanism of ribosomal frameshifting at hungry codons. J Mol Biol 203:403–410

Wilson W, Braddock M, Adams S, Rathjen P, Kingsman S, Kingsman A (1988) HIV expression strategies: ribosomal frameshifting is directed by a short sequence in both mammalian and yeast systems. Cell 55:1159–1169

Yoshinaka Y, Katosh I, Copeland TD, Oroszlan S (1985a) Murine leukemia virus protease is encoded by the *gag-pol* gene and is synthesized through suppression of an amber termination codon. Proc Natl Acad Sci USA 82:1618–1622

Yoshinaka Y, Katoh I, Copeland TD, Oroszlan S (1985b) Translational readthrough of an amber termination codon during synthesis of feline leukemia virus protease. J Virol 55:870–873

Young JF, Capecchi M, Laski FA, RajBhandary UL, Sharp PA, Palese P (1983) Measurement of suppressor transfer RNA activity. Science 221:873–875

Ziegler V, Richards K, Guilley H, Jonard T, Putz C (1985) Cell-free translation of beet necrotic yellow vein virus: readthrough of the coat protein cistron. J Gen Virol 66:2079–2087

Zinoni F, Birkmann A, Leinfelder E, Böck A (1987) Cotranslational insertion of selenocysteine into formate dehydrogenase from *Escherichia coli* directed by a UGA codon. Proc Natl Acad Sci USA 84:3156–3160

UAG Suppressor Glutamine tRNA in Uninfected and Retrovirus-Infected Mammalian Cells

Y. Kuchino[1], S. Nishimura[2], H. C. Schröder[3], and W. E. G. Müller[3]

A. Introduction

Three codons, UAG, UAA, and UGA, in the genetic code are normally signals for termination of translation reaction and for the release of the completed polypeptide chain from its ultimate ribosome-bound tRNA. Recently, it has been reported that eubacterial and eukaryotic mRNAs contain a translatable nonsense codon and its readthrough by suppressor tRNA plays an important role in the synthesis of particular proteins which are necessary for specific cellular functions. For example, in-frame UGA nonsense codons have been found in the mouse glutathione peroxidase and *Escherichia coli* formate dehydrogenase genes (Chambers et al. 1986; Zinoni et al. 1986). The translational insertion of selenocystein at the UGA codon, which is the active site of the enzymes from those genes, is required for the expression of their enzyme activities. The internal nonsense codons have also been detected at the *gag-pol* junction of the retrovirus genomes, such as Moloney murine leukemia virus (Mo-MuLV) and Rous sarcoma virus (RSV) (Shinnick et al. 1981; Phillipson et al. 1978; Yoshinaka et al. 1985; Crawford and Goff 1985; Jacks and Varmus 1985). The readthrough of the nonsense codon produces a viral *gag-pol* precursor fusion protein which is later cleaved by proteases to yield the mature viral proteins, including protease. The translation of the internal nonsense codon of the retrovirus genomes so far reported is performed by nonsense suppression or frameshift suppression, resulting in the regulation of the level of *gag* and *gag-pol* readthrough proteins in the virus-infected cells, which is required for the vegetative virus proliferation. (Yoshinaka et al. 1985; Jacks and Varmus 1985; Jacks et al. 1987, 1988; Carigen and Caskey 1987). In contrast, ciliates diverging from universal genetic codes with respect to the usage of the translation termination codons are likely to read all in-frame UAG and UAA codons as glutamine. We reported previously that

[1] Biophysics Division, National Cancer Center Research Institute, 5-1-1, Tsukiji, Chuo-ku, Tokyo 104, Japan
[2] Biology Division, National Cancer Center Research Institute, 5-1-1, Tsukiji, Chuo-ku, Tokyo 104, Japan
[3] Institut für Physiologische Chemie, Abt. Angewandte Molekularbiologie, Duesbergweg 6, Universität, 6500 Mainz, FRG

Tetrahymena thermophila, which is a ciliate protozoa, contains large amounts of two unique glutamine tRNAs having the CUA and UmUA anticodon sequences Kuchino et al. 1985; Hanyu et al. 1986). These tRNAs, $tRNA^{Gln}_{CUA}$ and $tRNA^{GLN}_{UmUA}$, have actively recognize the UAG, and either UAG or UAA codons, respectively, on translation of natural mRNAs, such as TMV-RNA. These data, as well as data on the nucleotide sequences of several ciliate structural genes, including *Tetrahymena* histone genes, strongly suggested that in ciliates, UAA and UAG nonsense codons are used as glutamine codons, but not as translation termination codons at all (Horowitz and Gorovsky 1985; Helftenbein 1985; Caron and Meyer 1985; Preer et al. 1985; Keine and Spear 1982). (Similar divergence in the genetic code was also found in *Mycoplasma*, in which the nonsense codon UGA is used to specify tryptophan, as in the case of mammalian or yeast mitochondrial genomes; Yamao et al. 1985; Schwegen et al. 1983). The existence of glutamine tRNA, which can translate an in-frame UAG nonsense codon as glutamine, has also been shown to be present in yeast. As reported by Friedberg and his colleagues, yeast glutamine tRNAs produced in vivo by transfection of multiple copies of the corresponding tRNA genes with a TTG or CTG anticodon sequence weakly suppress the UAA orcher or UAG amber termination codon (Pure et al. 1985; Weiss and Friedberg 1986). Recently, Yoshinaka et al. (1985) reported that an in-frame UAG codon located between the *gag* and *pol* genes of Mo-MuLV is read as glutamine resulting in the formation of viral protease protein. These data strongly suggest that glutamine tRNA having UAG or UAA readthrough activity might also be present in mammalian cells. We report here that mammalian cells contain a natural UAG suppressor glutamine tRNA, and the cellular content of the tRNA is regulated by retrovirus infection.

B. Isolation and Sequence Analysis of Glutamine tRNA from Mammalian Cells

The *gag* and *pol* genes of Mo-MuLV are separated by an UAG amber codon. The translational readthrough of the amber termination codon synthesizes a *gag-pol* fusion protein, Pr 180, which is proteolytically cleaved to produce a viral protease. The evidence provided by Philipson et al. (1978) revealed that the UAG codon between the *gag* and *pol* genes of Mo-MuLV is a suppressible termination codon recognized by yeast UAG suppressor tRNA. In addition, the data of Yoshinaka et al. (1985) determined the amino acid sequence of a viral protease from Mo-MuLV, indicating that the UAG termination codon at the *gag-pol* junction is used as a glutamine codon. These data implicated that UAG-suppressor glutamine tRNA might be present in mammalian cells. Therefore, we attempted to isolate natural suppressor tRNA from mouse cells, as well as from Mo-MuLV-infected cells. Unfractionated mouse liver tRNA was first fractionated by BD-cellulose column chromatography. As shown in Fig. 1, glutamine acceptor activities were separated into three fractions, designated as fractions I, II, and III in the order of their elution from the column.

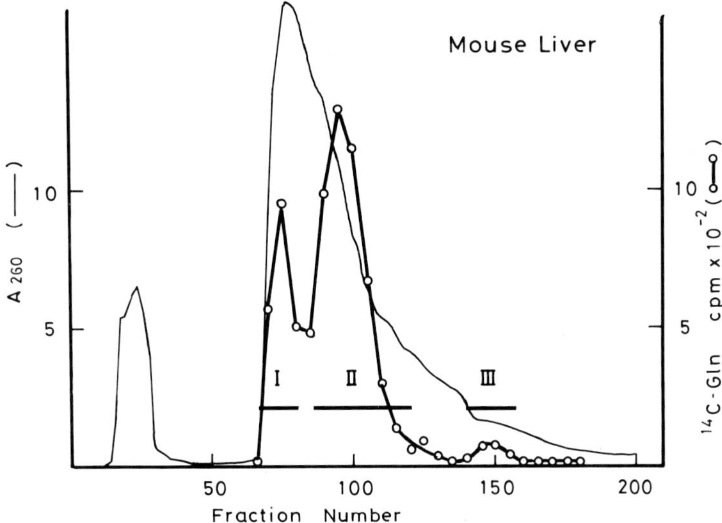

Fig. 1. Fractionation of mouse glutamine tRNA by BD-cellulose column chromatography. Unfractionated BDF-1 mouse liver tRNA (8000 A_{260} units) prepared by phenol extraction was loaded on a BD-cellulose column (100 × 2 cm) and eluted with a 2-liter linear gradient of 0.3 – 1.2 M NaCl in 0.02 M sodium acetate buffer (pH 6.0). The glutamine acceptor activity of each fraction was examined with a crude aminoacyl tRNA synthetase prepared from Ehrlich ascites cells as described previously (Kuchino et al. 1987a). Each of the glutamine acceptor activity-rich fractions, designated as Fractions *I*, *II* and *III*, was used for further purification of glutamine tRNA

Glutamine tRNAs from each fraction were further purified by RPC-5 column chromatography and polyacrylamide gel electrophoresis, and then their nucleotide sequences were determined by post-labeling techniques (Kuchino et al. 1987a, b). Finally, two species of glutamine tRNAs were obtained from mouse liver, and their nucleotide sequences are shown in Fig. 2 with cloverleaf structures. Two species of glutamine tRNA were designated as $\mathrm{tRNA}^{\mathrm{Gln}}_{\mathrm{UmUG}}$ and $\mathrm{tRNA}^{\mathrm{Gln}}_{\mathrm{CUG}}$ according to their anticodon sequences. Glutamine tRNA eluted from fraction I had the same nucleotide sequence as that of major glutamine tRNA, and had the CUG anticodon sequence from fraction II, except for deletion of the adenosine residue at the 3′ terminus of the tRNA, and/or for undermodification at residue 18. Glutamine tRNA eluted from fraction III was a minor species with UmUG anticodon sequence and its hypomodified species, containing unmodified guanosine at residue 18 instead of 2′-0-methylguanosine, was eluted in the later region of fraction II. Glutamine tRNAs having CUG anticodon have been isolated from bovine (Keith 1984) and rat liver (Yang et al. 1983) and the gene corresponding to tRNA has been cloned from human cells (Roy et al. 1982). The nucleotide sequences of glutamine tRNA from bovine and rat liver, and that of $\mathrm{tDNA}^{\mathrm{Gln}}_{\mathrm{CTG}}$ are identical with mouse liver major $\mathrm{tRNA}^{\mathrm{Gln}}_{\mathrm{CUG}}$. The sequence homology between mammalian $\mathrm{tRNA}^{\mathrm{Gln}}_{\mathrm{CUG}}$ and yeast $\mathrm{tRNA}^{\mathrm{Gln}}_{\mathrm{CUG}}$ is 72%. On the

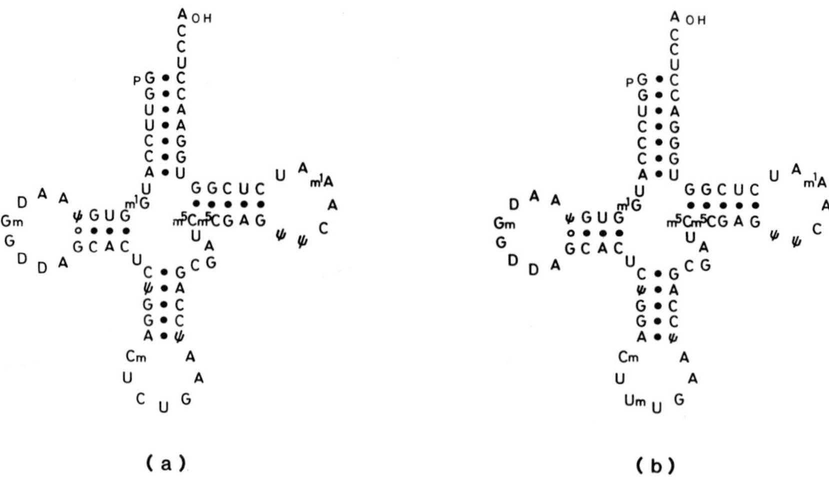

Fig. 2. Cloverleaf structure of two glutamine tRNAs from mouse liver (*a*) $tRNA^{Gln}_{CUG}$; (*b*) $tRNA^{Gln}_{UmUG}$; *Cm*, 2′-0-methylcytidine; *Gm*, 2-methylguanosine; *Um*, 2′-0-methyluridine; ψ, pseudouridine; m^1G, 1-methylguanosine; m^5C, 5-methylcytidine; m^1A, 1-methyladenosine; *D*, dihydrouridine

other hand, the minor species of mouse glutamine tRNA has 71 and 74% sequence homology with yeast $tDNA^{Gln}_{TTG}$ and *Tetrahymena* $tRNA^{Gln}_{UmUG}$, respectively.

C. Analysis of Suppressor Activity of Mammalian Glutamine tRNA

For identification of the tRNA species responsible for UAG suppressor activity, both purified glutamine tRNAs were tested in an in vitro translation assay system with TMV-RNA as a messenger. When TMV-RNA is translated in a cell-free protein biosynthesis system using rabbit reticulocyte lysate, a large polypeptide having 126 kDa mol. wt. is synthesized due to the translation termination at the UAG codon of TMV-RNA. The presence of UAG suppressor tRNA like tobacco $tRNA^{Tyr}_{G\psi A}$ permits to produce a 183 kDa protein at the expense of the 126 kDa protein (Beier et al. 1984). This 183 kDa protein is a readthrough protein of an amber termination codon at the end of the 126 kDa protein. As shown in Fig. 3, a minor species of mouse glutamine tRNA having UmUG anticodon recognized the UAG termination codon, whereas the major mouse glutamine tRNA having CUG anticodon did not. However, the suppressor activity of $tRNA^{Gln}_{UmUG}$ was weaker than that of tobacco $tRNA^{Tyr}_{G\psi A}$, which has the GψA anticodon sequence and is known to be natural UAG-suppressor tRNA in plants.

Recognition of the UAG codon by mouse $tRNA^{Gln}_{UmUG}$ is facilitated by wobble base pairs at the first and third positions of the anti-codon. Wobbling of the first position of the codon in mRNA has been demonstrated in in vivo suppression of the UAG or UAA codon in yeast (Pure et al. 1985; Weiss and Friedberg 1986).

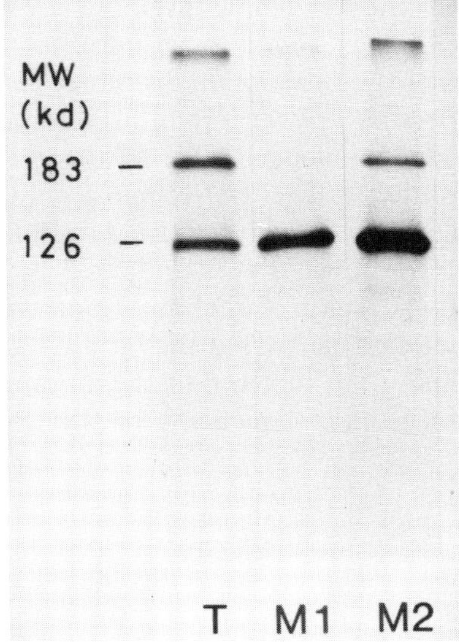

Fig. 3. Detection of UAG readthrough activity of purified mouse glutamine tRNAs in an in vitro translation system. TMV-RNA as a messenger was translated in a rabbit reticulocyte lysate by a reported method except that lysate not supplemented with calf liver tRNA was used. ^{35}S methionine-labeled proteins synthesized in the presence of tobacco $tRNA^{Tyr}_{G\psi A}$ (50 $\mu g\,ml^{-1}$) (*T*), mouse RNA^{Gln}_{CUG} (50 $\mu g\,ml^{-1}$) (*M1*) or mouse $tRNA^{Gln}_{UmUG}$ (50 $\mu g\,ml^{-1}$) (*M2*) were analyzed by polyacrylamide gel electrophoresis using an 8% NaDodSO_4-polyacrylamide slab gel as described

Yeast glutamine tRNA produced in vivo by transfection of multicopies of the corresponding tRNA genes with a TTG or CTG anticodon sequence weakly suppresses the UAA or UAG termination codon. The major mouse glutamine tRNA having CUG anticodon sequence had no UAG readthrough activity, although theoretically it can recognize the UAG codon, if the third position of the anticodon wobbles with U, as in the case of yeast glutamine tRNAs (Fig. 3). In addition, the minor mouse glutamine tRNA having an UmUG anticodon sequence also showed no UAA readthrough activity in an in vitro translation system with rabbit globin mRNA. *Tetrahymena* glutamine tRNA, having UmUG sequence as its anticodon, cannot recognize both UAA and UAG termination codons (data not shown). These data showed that the conformation of glutamine tRNA is an important factor to facilitate the UAG or UAA suppressor activity.

D. Selective Increase of Suppressor Glutamine tRNA in Retrovirus-Infected Cells

We found that mouse liver contains a natural UAG-suppressor glutamine tRNA, $tRNA^{Gln}_{UmUG}$. However, as shown in Fig. 3, the suppressor activity of a minor species of mouse glutamine tRNAs was much weaker than that of tobacco

$tRNA^{Gln}_{UmUG}$. These findings raised the question of how such a small amount of $tRNA^{Gln}_{UmUG}$, with weak suppressor activity, is efficiently used to generate the read-through product that is subsequently cleaved to produce the viral protease. One possible answer is that the amount of suppressor $tRNA^{Gln}_{UmUG}$ is increased in Mo-MuLV infected cells, allowing the synthesis of a sufficient amount of viral proteins. The BD-cellulose column chromatographic profiles of glutamine acceptor activity of tRNA isolated from Mo-MuLV infected and noninfected NIH-3T3 cells were compared. As shown in Fig. 3, the glutamine acceptor activity in the region of fraction M2 was greatly increased in the bulk of tRNA from virus-infected cells. That the increase in glutamine acceptor activity in fraction M2 is due to an increase in the amount of $tRNA^{Gln}_{UmUG}$ was proven by isolation and nucleotide sequencing of the tRNA present in that fraction, and also by its

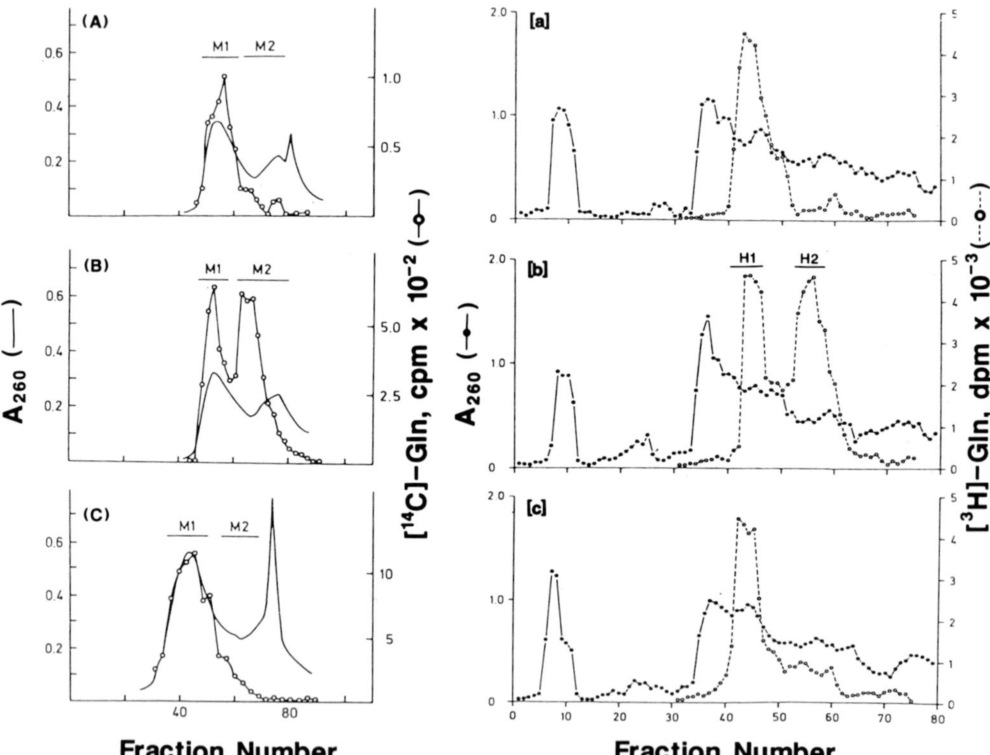

Fig. 4. Comparison of the level of glutamine tRNAs in retrovirus infected and uninfected mammalian cells. (*A*) In uninfected NIH-3T3 cells, (*B*) in Mo-MuLV infected NIH-3T3 cells, (*C*) in Mo-MuLV infected NIH-3T3 cells treated with 1 μg ml^{-1}. Avarol for 4 days. (*a*) In uninfected human H9 cells, (*b*) in HIV infected human H9 cells, (*c*) in HIV infected human H9 cells treated with 1 μg ml^{-1} of Avarol for 4 days[1]. Total tRNAs prepared from each cell mass by phenol extraction were fractionated on a BD-cellulose column using a linear gradient of 0.3–1.2 M NaCl in 0.2 M sodium acetate buffer (pH 6.0). The glutamine acceptor activity of each fraction was analyzed with a crude aminoacyl tRNA synthetase preparation from Ehrlich ascites cells, as described in Fig. 1.

readthrough ability of the UAG codon of TMV-RNA. The increased level of glutamine tRNA having the UAG readthrough activity in in vitro translation of TMV-RNA was also detected in the tRNAs from human H9 cells infected with human T lymphotropic virus (HTLV-IIIB or HIV-1) (Fig. 4). To prove that the increase of suppressor glutamine tRNA was dependent on the virus infection followed by the vegetative proliferation of the virus, the inhibition effects of virus replication on the synthesis of suppressor glutamine tRNA were examined. For the inhibition of virus replication, Avarol from the sea sponge *Dysidea avara* was used (Müller et al. 1987). Avarol at a concentration of 1 $\mu g\,ml^{-1}$ had almost no inhibitory effects on the eukaryotic DNA polymerase α, β, and γ, the eukaryotic RNA polymerase I, II, and III, and the Mo-MuLV reverse transcriptase. However, Avarol added to the cell culture medium at the same concentration almost completely suppressed the release of virus progeny after a 36-hr incubation period, as reported previously. After incubation of Mo-MuLV infected cells with 3 μM (1 $\mu g\,ml^{-1}$) Avarol for 72 h, total tRNA from virus-infected cells was prepared by phenol extraction and fractionated by BD-cellulose column chromatography. As shown in Fig. 4, the amount of suppressor glutamine tRNA in fraction M2 was remarkably and selectively decreased. The cultivation of HIV-infected H9 cells with 3 μM of Avarol also caused a substantial reduction of the amount of suppressor glutamine tRNA (M2) (Fig. 4). Although the relative inhibition of viral RNA synthesis in the presence of 3 μM of Avarol was only 25%, Avarol strongly suppressed the proteolytic cleavage of HIV p53 *gag*-precursor polyprotein. These results clearly indicated that the increased level of suppressor glutamine tRNA is closely coupled with Mo-MuLV or HIV infection, and the subsequent proliferation of those viruses.

E. Influence of Increased Amount of Suppressor tRNA on Translation Reaction of Cellular mRNA

In Mo-MuLV infected mouse cells and HIV infected human cells, proline and lysine tRNA act as a primer of virus DNA synthesis with reverse transcriptase, but glutamine tRNA does not (Shinnick et al. 1981; Ratner et al. 1985). Therefore, the increased amount of suppressor $tRNA^{Gln}_{UmUG}$ may exclusively allow the synthesis of a sufficient amount of a UAG readthrough protein, produced by the insertion of glutamine at the UAG termination codon between the *gag* and *pol* gene of Mo-MuLV. Since suppressor glutamine tRNA having UmUG anticodon normally recognizes the CAA glutamine codon, the high level of this tRNA may also be important in supporting the efficient translation of Mo-MuLV mRNA, where the CAA glutamine codons are used more frequently than those in host-cell mRNA (Shinnick et al. 1981; Maruyama et al. 1986).

Contrary to Mo-MuLV, it has been reported that the production of the *gag-pol* fusion-precursor protein of HIV, yielding the viral protease by later proteolytic cleavage, requires translational frameshifting of viral messenger RNA (Jacks et al. 1988). Therefore, the high level of suppressor glutamine tRNA in HIV infected cells might mainly contribute to the stimulation of the translation of

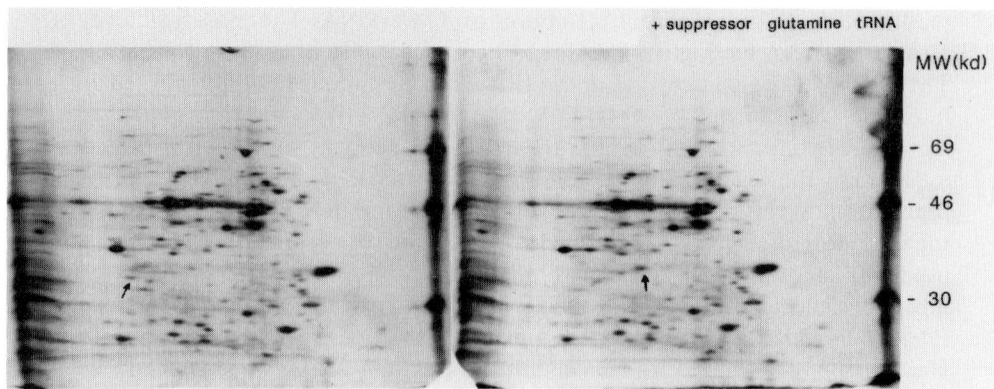

Fig. 5. Effects of suppressor glutamine tRNA on the translation of cellular mRNAs. ^{35}S methionine-labeled proteins synthesized in a rabbit reticulocyte cell free system programed with total poly (A^+) RNA from NIH-3T3 cells were separated by two-dimensional gel electrophoresis. Total poly(A^+)RNA (3 μg) was translated in the presence of 25 $\mu g\ ml^{-1}$ of mouse suppressor glutamine tRNA or without the suppressor tRNA under the conditions defined by the commercial supplier using a rabbit reticulocyte lysate purchased from Amersham

HIV mRNA, which has about two times the amount of CAA codon usage than that of human mRNA (Ratner et al. 1985; Maruyama et al. 1986). The increased amount of suppressor $tRNA^{Gln}_{UmUG}$ makes it possible to enhance production of cellular readthrough proteins by recognition of UAG termination codons residing at the 3′-end of structural genes. To examine the influence of suppressor $tRNA^{Gln}_{UmUG}$ on translation of cellular mRNA, total mRNA from NIH-3T3 cells, purified by oligo dT cellulose column chromatography, was translated in an in vitro protein-synthesis system, using rabbit reticulocyte lysate in the presence of excess amounts of suppressor glutamine tRNA. The ^{35}S methionine-labeled proteins synthesized in vitro were analyzed by the O'Farrel technique, using two-dimensional gel electrophoresis (O'Farrel 1975). As shown in Fig. 5, a number of proteins were synthesized in vitro in response to NIH-3T3 mRNA. When the migration patterns of proteins synthesized under the presence of 25 $\mu g\ ml^{-1}$ of additional suppressor $tRNA^{Gln}_{UmUG}$ were compared with those of proteins synthesized without suppressor $tRNA^{Gln}_{UmUG}$, a small changes of a limited number of proteins were found (Fig. 5), suggesting that suppressor glutamine $tRNA^{Gln}_{UmUG}$ may have an important function in mammalian cells, controlling the expression of genetic information not only of virus mRNA, but also of cellular mRNA.

F. Discussion

In this article, we showed that mouse cells contain two species of glutamine tRNAs, $tRNA^{Gln}_{CUG}$ and $tRNA^{Gln}_{UmUG}$, and the latter minor glutamine tRNAs which have the UmUG anticodon sequence can recognize an UAG termination codon of natural mRNA in an in vitro protein-biosynthesis system. These results clearly indicate that an UAG suppressor glutamine tRNA also exists in mammalian cells, even though the UAG codon is normally used as a translation termination codon. The finding of a common glutamine tRNA which has UAG suppressor activity in yeast, ciliate, and mammalian cells has tempted us to speculate upon how the use of the UAG nonsense codon has evolved in the genetic code. Judging from previous results, it could be assumed that, in the early stage of the evolution of eukaryotes, an ancestral glutamine tRNA which can recognize the UAG codon already existed. During the evolution of eukaryotes, glutamine tRNA remained as the suppressor tRNA at a marginal level, playing a role for the regulation of cellular functions on specific occasions. In ciliates, which branched off from other eukaryotic cells in evolution, the suppressor activity of glutamine tRNA became considerably pronounced by the changes of the anticodon sequence.

Recognition of the UAG nonsense codon by mammalian $tRNA^{Gln}_{UmUG}$ is facilitated by two wobble base-pairs at the first and third positions of the anticodon. Wobbling of the guanine residue at the third position of the anticodon with the uridine residue at the first position of the codon in mRNA has also been demonstrated in yeast (Pure et al. 1985; Weiss and Friedberg 1986). However, such unique codon-anticodon interaction found in the UAG recognition by yeast and mammalian suppressor glutamine tRNA is not in accordance with the wobble hypothesis or the two-out-of-three reading mechanism. Similar unorthodox interaction between the codon and the anticodon has also been shown in the interaction of tobacco $tRNA^{Tyr}_{G\psi A}$ as a natural UAG suppressor tRNA with TMV-RNA (Beier et al. 1984). In this case, tobacco tyrosine tRNA with the $G\psi A$ anticodon recognizes the UAG codon by the formation of U:A and $A{:}\psi$ base pairs between the codon and the anticodon. Recently, leucine tRNA with UAG suppressor activity has been isolated from calf liver by Valle et al. (1987). The codon recognition of this tRNA containing CAG anticodon also involves unusual codon-anticodon interactions, which are an A:A pairing in the second position (so-called wiggle) and a G:U wobble base pairing in the third position of the anticodon. Due to such unique interaction with mRNA, the suppressor activities of these tRNAs might be weaker than those of *Tetrahymena* glutamine tRNA, which have the CUA and UmUA anticodon sequences complementary to the UAG and UAA nonsense codons, respectively (Kuchino et al. 1985; Hanyu et al. 1986).

The interaction of tRNA with mRNA on ribosomes is also affected by the mRNA sequence surrounding the nonsense codon. This has been described as the codon context effect. Those retroviruses so far examined use the readthrough or ribosome frameshifting mechanism to translate the internal nonsense codon for the synthesis of *gag-pol* fusion viral protein. In the cases of Rous sarcoma virus and human immunodeficiency virus (Jacks and Varmus 1985; Jacks et al. 1988), it has been proposed that stem-loop structures adjacent to the 3′ side of the frameshift points are important in the retroviral frameshifting mechanism. Similar mRNA secondary structures flanking the amber nonsense codon that separates the *gag* and *pol* genes have been found in Mo-MuLV and AKV murine leukemia virus (Herr 1984). These structures, which affect the context effect, might also be important to readthrough the in-frame nonsense codon of mRNA. Our preliminary data, using the deletion and site-directed mutational analysis of Mo-MuLV, support this proposal.

Another striking finding of this study is that retrovirus infection, followed by vegetative growth, causes the selective and remarkable increase of the amount of UAG suppressor glutamine tRNA in virus-infected cells. As shown in Fig. 4, the selected increase of minor glutamine tRNA was detected in Mo-MuLV-infected NIH-3T3 cells and in HIV-infected human H9 cells. The increased amount of mammalian $tRNA^{Gln}_{UmUG}$ seems to be important, not only for the sufficient production of a viral protease as an UAG readthrough protein, but also for the efficient translation of the viral mRNAs, since CAA glutamine codons appear frequently in the viral genome, and $tRNA^{Gln}_{UmUG}$ should also read as efficiently the CAA codon. However, at the same time, the increased level of suppressor glutamine tRNA also affects the translation of cellular mRNA, resulting in the formation of additional proteins which might be readthrough proteins of an UAG termination codon at the 3′ end of structural genes (Fig. 5). Although the characteristics of the original proteins are not yet clear, it would be interesting to define the functional changes induced in the readthrough proteins to explain the mechanism of the transformation of virus-infected cells. In addition, it should be noted that the increase of suppressor glutamine tRNA is dependent upon the virus infection and the successive virus growth (Fig. 4). The analysis of viral proteins in Mo-MuLV- or HIV-infected cells treated by Avarol showed that the inhibition of the synthesis of UAG suppressor glutamine tRNA results in the inhibition of the maturation of viral precursor proteins (Kuchino et al. 1988; Müller et al. 1988). These findings strongly suggested that suppressor glutamine tRNA is truly involved in the synthesis of the viral proteins, including viral protease. Therefore, the regulation of suppressor tRNA synthesis seems to be important for the replication of the virus.

The increased level of $tRNA^{Gln}_{UmUG}$ in virus-infected cells may be due to specific transcription activation of the tRNA gene for $tRNA^{Gln}_{UmUG}$, because the sequence homology between $tRNA^{Gln}_{UmUG}$ and $tRNA^{Gln}_{CUG}$ is too high to distinguish the stability of both tRNAs. Since the increase of the level of $tRNA^{Gln}_{UmUG}$ in virus-infected cells is very specific, and the infection has no effect on the level of the major $tRNA^{Gln}_{CUG}$, the factor required for specific activation of the transcription of suppressor tRNA gene may exist in the viral infected cells. This factor, if it is exists, may not be same as the factors IIIB, IIIC, and IIID so far identified. If such a specific transcription factor exists, it would be interesting to characterize it and to elucidate the mechanism by which it is induced by infection with Mo-MuLV or HIV.

Acknowledgements. We are grateful to Drs. H. Beier and N. Hanyu. This study was supported in part by a Grant-in-Aid from the Ministry of Health and Welfare for a comprehensive 10-year strategy for cancer control, by a grant from the Ministry of Education, Science, and Culture, and by a grant from the Bundesgesundheitsamt (AI02II-032–87) and from the Bundesministerium für Forschung and Technologie (No. 0319207A8).

References

Beier H, Barciszewska M, Krupp G, Mitnacht R, Gross HJ (1984) UAG readthrough during TMV RNA translation: isolation and sequence of two tRNAs^{Tyr} with suppressor activity from tobacco plants. EMBO J 3:351–356

Craigen WJ, Caskey CT (1987) Translational frameshifting: where will it stop? Cell 50:1–2

Caron F, Meyer E (1985) Does *Paramecium primaurelia* use a different genetic code in its macronucleus? Nature 314:185–188

Chambers I, Frampton J, Goldfarb P, Affara N, McBain W, Harrison PR (1986) The structure of the mouse glutathione peroxidase gene: the selenocysteine in the active site is encoded by the 'termination' codon, TGA. EMBO J 5:1221–1227

Crawford S, Goff SP (1985) A deletion mutation in the 5′ part of the *pol* gene of Moloney murine leukemia virus blocks proteolytic processing of the *gag* and *pol* polyproteins. J Virol 53:899–907

Hanyu N, Kuchino Y, Nishimura S, Beier H (1986) Dramatic events in ciliate evolution: alteration of UAA and UAG termination codons to glutamine codons due to anticodon mutations in two *Tetrahymena* tRNAs^{Gln}. EMBO J 5:1307–1311

Helftenbein E (1985) Nucleotide sequence of a macronuclear DNA molecule coding for α-tubulin from the ciliate *Stylonychia lemnae*. Special codon usage: TAA is not a translation termination codon. Nucleic Acids Res 13:415–433

Herr W (1984) Nucleotide sequence of AKV murine leukemia virus. J Virol 49:471–478

Horowitz S, Gorovsky MA (1985) An unusual genetic code in nuclear genes of *Tetrahymena*. Proc Natl Acad Sci USA 82:2452–2455

Jacks T, Varmus HE (1985) Expression of the Rous sarcoma virus *pol* gene by ribosomal frameshifting. Science 230:1237–1242

Jacks T, Townsley K, Varmus HE, Majors J (1987) Two efficient ribosomal frameshifting events are required for synthesis of mouse mammary tumor virus *gag*-related polyproteins. Proc Natl Acad Sci USA 84:4298–4302

Jacks T, Power MD, Masiarz FR, Luciw PA, Barr PJ, Varmus HE (1988) Characterization of ribosomal frameshifting in HIV-1 *gag-pol* expression. Nature 331:280–283

Kaine BP, Spear BB (1982) Nucleotide sequence of a macronuclear gene for actin in *Oxytricha fallax*. Nature 295:430–432

Keith G (1984) The primary structures of two arginine tRNAs (anticodons CCU and mcm^{5}a^{2}UCψ) and of glutamine tRNA (anticodon CUG) from bovine liver. Nucleic Acids Res 12:2543–2547

Kuchino Y, Hanyu N, Tashiro F, Nishimura S (1985) *Tetrahymena thermophila* glutamine tRNA and its gene that corresponds to UAA termination codon. Proc Natl Acad Sci USA 82:4758–4762

Kuchino Y, Beier H, Akita N, Nishimura S (1987a) Natural UAG suppressor glutamine tRNA is elevated in mouse cells infected with Moloney murine leukemia virus. Proc Natl Acad Sci USA 84:2668–2672

Kuchino Y, Hanyu N, Nishimura S (1987b) Analysis of modified nucleosides and nucleotide sequence of tRNA. Methods Enzymol 155:379–396

Kuchino Y, Nishimura S, Schröder HC, Rottmann M, Müller WEG (1988) Selective inhibition of formation of suppressor glutamine tRNA in Moloney murine leukemia virus-infected NIH-3T3 cells by Avarol. Virology 165:518–526

Maruyama T, Gojobori T, Aota S, Ikemura T (1986) Codon usage tabulated from the GenBank genetic sequence data. Nucleic Acids Res 14:r151–r197

Müller WEG, Sarin PS, Kuchino Y, Dorn A, Hess G, Meyer zum Büschenfelde K-H, Rottmann M, Schröder HC (1987) Avarol, a novel anti-HIV compound, which modulates posttranscriptional control systems. In: Vettermann W, Schauzu M (eds) AIDS, Bundesministerium für Forschung and Technologie, Bonn, pp. 354–378

Müller WEG, Schröder, HC, Reuter P, Sarin PS, Hess G, Meyer zum Büschenfelde K-H, Kuchino Y, Nishimura S (1988) Inhibition of expression of natural UAG suppressor glutamine tRNA in HIV-infected human H9 cells in vitro by Avarol. AIDS Res & Human Retrovirus 4:279–286

O'Farrell PH (1975) High resolution two-dimensional electrophoresis of proteins. J Biol Chem 250:4007–4021
Phillipson L, Andersson P, Olshevsky U, Weinberg R, Baltimore D, Gesteland R (1978) Translation of MuLV and MSV RNAs in nuclease-treated reticulocyte extracts: enhancements of the *gag-pol* polypeptide with yeast suppressor tRNA. Cell 13:189–199
Preer JR Jr, Preer LB, Rudman BM, Barnett AJ (1985) Deviation from the universal code shown by the gene for surface protein 51A in *Paramecium*. Nature 314:188–190
Pure GA, Robinson GW, Naumovski L, Friedberg EC (1985) Partial suppression of an ochre mutation in *Saccharomyces cerevisiae* by multicopy plasmids containing a normal yeast $tRNA^{Gln}$ gene. J Mol Biol 183:31–42
Ratner L, Haseltine W, Patarca R, Livak KJ, Starcich B, Josephs SF, Doran ER, Rafalski JA, Whitehorn EA, Baumeister K, Ivanoff L, Petteway SRJr, Pearson ML, Lautenberger JA, Papas TS, Ghrayeb J, Chang NT, Gallo RC, Wong-Staal F (1985) Complete nucleotide sequence of the AIDS virus, HTVL-III. Nature 313:277–284
Roy KL, Cooke H, Buckland R (1982) Nucleotide sequence of a segment of human DNA containing the three tRNA genes. Nucleic Acids Res 10:7313–7322
Schweyen RJ, Wolf K, Kaudewita F (1983) Mitochondria 1983, Nucleo-mitochondrial interactions. de Gruyter, Berlin, FRG, pp 1–648
Shinnick TM, Lerner RA, Sutcliffe JG (1981) Nucleotide sequence of Moloney murine leukemia virus. Nature 293:543–548
Valle RPC, Morch M-D, Haenni AL (1987) Novel amber suppressor tRNAs of mammalian origin. EMBO J 6:3049–3055
Weiss WA, Friedberg EC (1986) Normal yeast $tRNA^{Gln}_{CAG}$ can suppress amber codons and is encoded by an essential gene. J Mol Biol 192:725–735
Yamao F, Muto A, Kawauchi Y, Iwami M, Iwagami S, Azumi Y, Osawa S (1985) UGA is read as tryptophan in *Mycoplasma capricolum*. Proc Natl Acad Sci USA 82:2306–2309
Yang JA, Tai LW, Agris PF, Gehrke CW, Wong TW (1983) The nucleotide sequence of a major glutamine tRNA from rat liver. Nucleic Acids Res 11:1991–1996
Yoshinaka Y, Katoh I, Copeland TD, Oroszlan S (1985) Murine leukemia virus protease is encoded by the *gag-pol* gene and is synthesized through suppression of an amber termination codon. Proc Natl Acad Sci USA 82:1618–1622
Zinoni F, Birkmann A, Stadtman TC, Böck A (1986) Nucleotide sequence and expression of the selenocysteine-containing polypeptide of formate dehydrogenase (formate-hydrogenlyase-linked) from *Escherichia coli*. Proc Natl Acad Sci USA 83:4650–4654

Essential Genes for Development of *Dictyostelium*

W. F. Loomis[1]

A. Introduction

A long-term dream of many molecular developmental biologists is to recognize the temporal sequence of gene expression that directs the morphogenetic stages of embryogenesis. In a few species that are amenable to high resolution genetics the pieces are beginning to fall into place. Specific molecular differentiations can now be seen to define the outlines of the physiological changes that direct development. For instance, the combination of classical and molecular genetics in the fruitfuly *Drosophila* has lead to a dramatic increase in understanding the role of well-defined genes in establishing the segmental pattern of embryos and larva. A few dozen maternal genes control the temporal and spatial patterns of expression of another few dozen zygotically expressed genes (Ingham 1988). Structures specific to each segment are then made in the appropriate segments. Exactly how these decisions are made is still poorly understood, but it is a satisfying advance just to be able to name the genes and know their nucleotide sequences. Connecting this primary sequence data to three dimensional differentiations requires other approaches that are hampered in *Drosophila* by the complexity of the embryos. It is difficult to analyze the interaction of gene products that are functioning differently in different compartments, and are present in different ratios at different times. The goal of understanding all of the genes that play major roles in fly embryogenesis will require continued brilliance and stamina for many years to come.

The problems of temporal and cell-type regulation of gene expression are common to many developing organisms. If a process is thought to be conserved among systems, it makes sense to first study it in the simplest system, and only when the details are well established, to proceed to the more complex systems. For these and other reasons, considerable attention has been directed at understanding the molecular basis of development of *Dictyostelium* (Loomis 1975, 1982; Spudich 1987). Recent advances in the ability to isolate, characterize, modify, and reintroduce specific genes into this eukaryotic amoeboid organism has provided the hard facts to support previously inferred causal schemes. It is

[1]Center for Molecular Genetics, University of California San Diego, LaJolla CA 92093, USA

now possible to outline a temporal sequence of essential genes that accounts, at least partially, for the major stages in development of *Dictyostelium*.

The relatively extensive experimental data concerning the mechanisms by which up to 10^5 cells aggregate to form multicellular structures, and then diverge to form two distinct cell types, has been recently reviewed (Gerisch 1987; Janssens and Van Haastert 1987; Williams 1988). A large number of genes and physiological processes have been studied in detail, but a mechanistic synthesis of the data is only now becoming possible. In this review, I will focus on those genes and processes that are well-defined and appear to be essential for development. Since the goal is to analyze the causal connections throughout the complete developmental cycle, observations that cannot yet be incorporated into a coherent picture will not be covered. In several instances, I will argue for interpretations that are not yet part of the consensus view but appear to me to be fruitful lines for future work.

B. Genetic Analysis in *Dictyostelium*

The relative simplicity of development in *Dictyostelium* gives greater impact to each molecular insight that is added to the puzzle, since the total number of genes involved in morphogenesis is less than 500. This number of genes was arrived at by comparing the number of mutations that affect growth to the number of mutations that only affect morphogenesis (Loomis 1977). It was found that mutagenesis of a large population of cells resulted in more than ten times as many mutations in genes that either killed the cells or caused extremely slow growth, than mutations in genes which affected the ability of surviving cells to form the structures normally seen during development of the species. Since the number of genes necessary for growth can be accurately measured by several independent hybridization techniques, the number of genes dispensible for growth but essential for morphogenesis can be estimated. Analysis of the amount of single copy DNA protected by excess vegetative RNA has shown that about 5000 distinct mRNA species are present in growing cells (Firtel 1972). This is about the same number of mRNA species found in a large number of different cell types in species ranging from nematodes to man. Moreover, the number agrees closely with one estimated in *Dictyostelium* from the frequency of lethal mutations relative to the frequency of mutations in specific dispensible genes (Dimond et al. 1973). Therefore, we can be fairly confident that no more than 5000 genes are essential for growth. Since the number of genes specifically required for morphogenesis is no more than one-tenth of the number of vital genes, this analysis indicates that we need not consider more than 500 morphogenetic genes. The number of genes affecting morphogenesis was also estimated by comparing the number of mutations that fell in specific genes to the number of mutations that fell in morphogenetic genes (Loomis 1977). Assuming that each class of genes is equally mutable, the analysis indicated that there are 297 ± 75 genes that are dispensible for growth, but essential for development. While this is not a daunting number of genes, it is still a large number to study in depth, and the analysis of genes involved in the various differentiations that occur during development of *Dictyostelium* is still far from complete.

In some cases, the differentiations of *Dictyostelium* are unique to the life-style of this microorganism, while in other cases the differentiations are similar to those in other multicellular organisms. *Dictyostelium* cells diverge from a totipotent population, much as cells of the trophectoderm and inner cell mass diverge from totipotent morula cells in early mammalian embryogenesis. The regulation of the cell types in *Dictyostelium* following alterations in the morphogenetic field is similar to the regulation of terminally differentiating cells in many metazoan tissues. Since *Dictyostelium* is amenable to high resolution genetic and biochemical analyses, it presents a favorable system to elucidate the general mechanisms that function during cell type divergence and regulation.

Either haploid or diploid cells of *Dictyostelium* can be grown in simple defined meida; they divide by binary fission and have a doubling time of less than 8 h (Loomis 1975; Sussman 1987). Therefore, it is easy and inexpensive to grow large numbers of the desired strains. Development is initiated by collecting the cells and placing them at high cell density, either in suspension or an air-water interface where they will proceed through the stages of development with exceptionally good synchrony. Both haploid strains and diploid strains follow the same exact time couse and form the same structures, i.e., development in this organism is not coupled to obligatory meiotic divisions or sexual recombination. In fact, development proceeds in the absence of exogenous nutrients and so there is no net growth during development. Moreover, there is no obligatory cell division at all.

Genetic analysis in *Dictyostelium* relies on parasexual formation of diploids from independent haploid strains and subsequent haploidization by random chromosome loss (Loomis 1987). Techniques have been developed to select for rare recombinants, allowing mutations to be mapped to one of the six linkage groups. Dominance and recessivity can be assessed in diploid strains carrying wild-type as well as mutant alleles, while lack of complementation by independent recessive mutations shows that they affect the same gene. Most important for genetics of *Dictyostelium*, recessive mutations affecting morphogenesis can be rapidly recognized by visually scoring clones of haploid cells, since single cells grow to populations of several million within a plaque on a bacterial lawn and then proceed to form fruiting bodies several mm high within the confines of the plaque. These techniques have generated a rich store of genes of potential interest. With the advent of molecular genetics, many of these genes have been cloned and are being reintroduced into appropriately constructed strains by DNA transformation. The basic technique is to insert a gene of interest into a vector that can replicate in both *E. coli* and *Dictyostelium*. The vectors carry a bacterial gene that confers resistance to the drug G418, thereby allowing transformed cells to be selected by growth in the presence of the drug (Nellen et al. 1984; Knecht et al. 1986). Both extrachromosomal vectors and integrating vectors have been constructed that result in transformation at a frequency of 10^{-5}–10^{-6}. These vectors can be used to express antisense RNAs or to disrupt specific genes following homologus recombination. Together these techniques have better defined the roles played by several dozen genes and the number of such analyses is increasing rapidly.

The function of individual components in complex processes can often be understood by removing or inactivating them one at a time and then determining the consequences. Cutting a wire in an electrical appliance may have no discernable consequence, may result in faulting functioning, or may completely stop the works. In the latter case, we would conclude that the wire that we had cut plays a critical role, such as turning on the appliance. In the cases where faulty functioning results, we would want to define those processes that still work and those that do not. We might then be able to pin-point the place in the wiring system that had been cut. Of course, this diagnosis is greatly helped by understanding the general purpose of the appliance and how it works. In those cases where cutting a wire has no effect we would conclude that those specific connections are gratuitous. Genetic dissection of developmental pathways follows the same approach by analyzing the consequences of well-defined mutations affecting specific genes. I will review essential, secondary and gratuitous genes that are expressed during development of *Dictyostelium*, and try to show how mutations in these genes define a central dependent sequence that controls the temporal appearance and cell-type specificity of various differentiated functions.

C. Temporal Sequence of Differentiations

When Raper (1935) first reported the isolation of *D. discoideum*, he clearly described the sequence of morphological stages of this species. For the first 6 h, the lawn of cells stays smooth. During the next few hours ripples appear as the cells move chemotactically to aggregation centers. At this stage, cells release pulses of cAMP to which other cells respond by directed cell movement, leading to the aggregation of up to 10^5 cells. This is about the same number of cells as is found in gastrulating embryos of many metazoan species. By 10 h loose aggregates have appeared and become integrated by the deposition of an extracellular matrix that excludes late comers. Synchronous development of up to 10^{11} cells can be induced by collecting growing cells and initiating development at high population densities on filters bathed in buffered salts (Fig. 1; Sussman 1987).

A tip appears at the top of aggregates by 12 h that subsequently leads the aggregate as it converts into a migratory slug; cells in the tip are fated to form the stalk in the final fruiting body. Culmination commences at 18 h when the tip cells start to vacuolize and secrete cellulose along the stalk tube. Cells in the posterior of the slug then rise up to elongating stalk and begin to encapsulate into spores (Fig. 1).

Greater resolution of the sequence of temporal differentiations can be

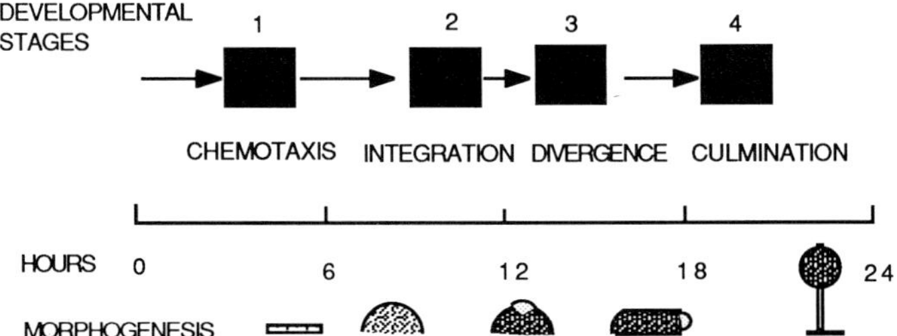

Fig. 1. Stages in development of *Dictyostelium*. When the population density reaches a critical level, the cells express genes necessary for chemotaxis. Within 6 h, cells start to secrete cAMP and migrate toward local concentrations of cAMP. Between 6 and 12 h of development, aggregates containing up to 10^5 cells are formed and covered by an extracellular matrix. During the next few hours, 80% of the cells differentiate into prespore cells and the remainder differentiate into prestalk cells. Terminal differentiation of both spores and stalk cells starts after 18 h of development and is complete by 24 h. During the final 4 h the stalk lifts the ball of spores several mm into the air to form a fruiting body

reached by quantitatively measuring the appearance and disappearance of specific gene products. A series of a dozen developmentally regulated enzymes have been found that appear at specific stages, and their specific activities at any time can be used to define the developmental stage (Loomis 1975). Each marker enzyme has been biochemically and genetically shown to be the product of a single gene; moreover, changes in the specific activity of many of these enzymes has been directly shown to result from accumulation of the specific mRNAs. Therefore, appearance of the enzyme activity can be used as an indication of expression of the stage specific gene. Another 20 or so gene products have been found to accumulate to high levels at various stages by analysis of proteins separated by two-dimensional gel electrophoresis (Coloma and Lodish 1981; Devine et al. 1982; Ratner and Borth 1983; Morrissey et al. 1984; Cardelli et al. 1985; Finney et al. 1985; Loomis 1985). Synthesis of stage specific proteins was measured by pulse labeling with ^{35}S-methionine at various stages of development and by determining the amount of label incorporated into well-defined spots on the 2-D gels. Accumulation of the proteins was measured by silver staining the gels. Different proteins could be recognized that were synthesized and accumulated at various stages. In some cases the proteins were stable and in others they appeared to turn over rapidly. Direct measurement of specific mRNAs using randomly isolated cDNAs has further expanded the number of specific markers that can be used to monitor the developmental progression from one stage to the next (Kimmel and Firtel 1982; Barklis and Lodish 1983; Mehdy et al. 1983; Chisholm et al. 1984). The patterns of accumulation of specific gene products have been used to define four broad stages: (1) chemotaxis; (2) integration; (3) divergence; and (4) culmination.

A large number of mutations that affect development of *D. discoideum* cells have been isolated in a variety of laboratories over the last 40 years (Sussman and Sussman 1953; reviewed in Loomis 1987). Mutations that block chemotaxis were found to also block integration, cell-type divergence, and culmination; likewise, mutations that allowed aggregation to proceed but blocked cell-type divergence and culmination were described and others were found to only block culmination. These mutations define a dependent sequence of morphological stages, although only the most general conclusions can be drawn from these gross phenotypes. It is rather like saying that vertebrate embryos must proceed through the gastrulation and neural plate stages before lens differentaition is induced by the optic vesicles. However, in *Dictyostelium*, the analysis has been taken to the molecular level. By using the molecular markers of temporal differentiation to define progress through development, morphological mutants have been shown to affect the sequence at specific points such that prior markers accumulate normally, but none of those that appear after the block accumulate to significant levels (Loomis et al. 1976; Blumberg et al. 1982). Although it is not known what genes are mutated in the morphological mutants, their phenotypes indicate that there is a set of genes that is required for progression through the stages of development. Attempts are now being made to clone these genes of the central dependent pathway so that their products can be directly analyzed.

D. Initiation of Development

Development of metazoan embryos is initiated when sperm fertilize eggs. In *Dictyostelium* there is no such straight-forward event marking the beginning. In nature, as well as under some conditions in the laboratory, growing cells gradually change their pattern of gene expression as the population density increases and the food source becomes limited. For many experiments this is not a serious drawback, but, for experiments on the early stages of development, it is important to use cells that are still at low titer while growing with bacteria as food stuff. The amoebae are washed free of bacteria and deposited on filter supports. The initial levels of developmentally regulated gene products are low under these conditions and then increase rapidly during the first few hours. It is usually stated that development is initiated by removing exogenous nutrients. However, the signals that induce the early developmental genes may depend more on the sudden increase in population density than on the removal of the food source.

When low titer growing cells are collected and suspended at 10^8 cells ml^{-1} in buffer, the enzymes that serve as markers for early stages of development, including N-acetylglucosaminidase (NAG), increase within the first 6 hours just as they do in filter developed cells. However, if they are suspended at lower population densities (5×10^6 ml^{-1}), the specific activity of NAG fails to increase unless a heat stable molecule secreted by the cells in a high density culture is added to the buffer (Grabel and Loomis 1977, 1978). The molecule appears to serve as a mass effector determining that initial differentiations only occur when there is a sufficient number of cells to produce multicellular structures that will be big enough to be selectively advantageous. Unfortunately the low resolution of the bioassay has precluded determination of the chemical nature of the effector.

All that it known is that it is a molecule of about 1000 daltons that can be inactivated by acid treatment.

Similar requirements for secreted factors were found for expression of several other early genes including I_{42} and discoidin (Mehdy and Firtel 1983; Clarke et al. 1987). Factors found in conditioned medium are required for other genes expressed later in development including CP2 that codes for a cysteine protease, the spore coat genes and an anonymous prespore specific mRNA, 14E6 (Mehdy et al. 1983; Loomis 1985). However, the activity of the mass effector on later genes may be an indirect, secondary consequence of the mass effector triggering the first steps in development that are required for subsequent changes in gene expression.

The presence of nutrients does not block expression of early genes. When cells growing in broth media reach a titer of 5×10^5 cells ml^{-1}, the specific activity of α-mannosidase increases rapidly, followed by that of N-acetylglucosaminidase (Ashworth and Quance 1972; Loomis 1975; Burns et al. 1981). Maximal specific activities are reached at 10^7 cells ml^{-1} although two more cells generations will occur before stationary stage is reached. Other genes expressed during the first 4–6 h of development, such as those coding for the discoidins and gp 24, are also expressed by cells still in the exponential phase of growth (Siu et al. 1976; Loomis et al. 1987). It appears that when cells reach a titer of 5×10^5 ml^{-1}, they secrete sufficient amounts of the effector for it to reach a critical threshold that can induce the genes of early development, even in the presence of excess nutrients. However, genes characteristic of latter stages in development are not expressed while the cells are still growing, perhaps as a consequence of specific repression by nutrients. Moreover, aggregation is greatly delayed by the addition of amino acids to cells incubated at high population densities (Marin 1976, 1977). It appears that the presence of nutrients represses later genes but has little effect on early genes. While it is not presently the consensus view of those working with *Dictyostelium*, these results can be interpreted as indicating that development is initiated when the population density reaches the point where the level of mass effector exceeds a critical threshold necessary for early gene expression, and that nutrients only repress later genes. Once the products of the early genes accumulate, the cells take on new properties and are able to respond chemotactically to gradients of cAMP. Essential genes are activated that initiate the cascade leading to terminal differentiations.

E. Stage 1: Chemotaxis

Three genes expressed during the first 6 h of development, namely, those coding for the cAMP receptor, Gα2, and cAMP phosphodiesterase, have been directly shown to be essential not only for chemotaxis, but also for gene expression at later stages (Klein et al. 1988; Kumagai et al. 1989; Barra et al. 1980; Faure et al. 1989). Cells that are unable to accumulate these proteins due to mutations in their structural genes, or because of the production of antisense RNA from a

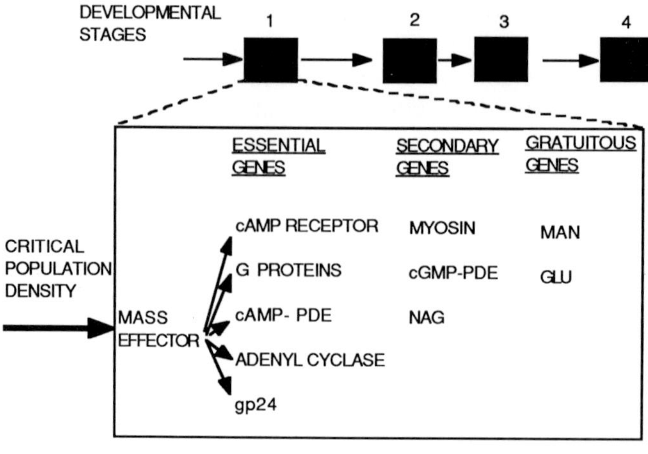

Fig. 2. Stage 1 genes. A secreted mass effector induces the expression of early genes that include at least 5 essential genes, 3 secondary genes, and 2 gratuitous genes. The *cAMP* receptor gene codes for a 44 kd membrane protein that binds external cAMP. Genes for *G* proteins code for the α, β, and γ subunits of the guanosine binding protein that couples the cAMP receptor to internal proteins. The *cAMP-PDE* gene codes for a phosphodiesterase specific to cAMP. Adenyl cyclase synthesizes cAMP. The *gp24* gene codes for the small membrane protein that is involved in cell-cell adhesion.

The *myosin* gene codes for the heavy chain (240 kD) of myosin. The *cGMP-PDE* gene codes for a phosphodiesterase specific to cGMP. The *NAG* gene codes for N-acetylglucosaminidase. The *Man* and *Glu* genes code for α-mannosidase and β-glucosidase, respectively

rearranged copy of the gene, fail to aggregate or proceed through the stages of biochemical differentiation. On this basis they are considered essential genes of the central dependent sequence (Fig. 2). The case for cAMP phosphodiesterase being an essential gene is tempered by the fact that it is secreted and functions outside the cells to keep the cAMP levels in bounds and can be replaced by purified bovine cAMP phosphodiesterase. However, in the absence of experimental assistance, the cells remain as a smooth lawn.

Adenyl cyclase, the enzyme responsible for synthesis of cAMP, accumulates during the first 6 h of development and is undoubtedly essential for subsequent developmental events (Klein 1976; Klein et al. 1977; Roos et al. 1976; Loomis et al. 1978); however, it has not yet been possible to isolate mutants lacking this activity, and so the case for adenyl cyclase is not proven. The same holds true for gp24, a surface glycoprotein implicated in the initial cell-cell adhesion that appears during the first 6 h of development (Loomis et al. 1987; Knecht et al. 1987). While antibodies specific for this protein are able to block cell-cell adhesion as well as aggregation and all subsequent differentiations (Loomis et al. 1987; Loomis 1988), mutations inactivating the structural gene for gp24 have not yet been recovered. However, on the basis of the immunological results, we can be fairly confident that this is an essential gene.

Myosin is considered a secondary gene because cells that lack myosin aggregate, although at a reduced rate (Knecht and Loomis 1987, 1988; Wessels et al. 1988; Peters et al. 1988). In wild-type cells myosin is present in vegetatively growing cells and accumulates about three fold during the first 6 h of development. In antisense or null mutants the cells lack both heavy and light chains of myosin and yet move chemotactically to aggregation centers. They express cell-type specific genes, but fail to differentiate into either spores or stalk cells.

cGMP-phosphodiesterase can also be considered a secondary gene because the phenotype of mutants lacking this activity is not completely blocked at aggregation (Van Haastert et al. 1982); however, chemotatic streaming is dramatically aberrant in mutants lacking this enzyme. The individual cells continue moving after wild-type cells have stopped. Unlike cAMP-phosphodiesterase, the enzyme specific to cGMP is internal and the defect cannot be overcome by adding exogenous activity. It appears that cGMP-phosphodiesterase plays an essential role in the internal signal transduction system leading to chemotaxis.

N-Acetylglucosaminidase is one of the first enzymes to accumulate, yet it only plays a role later during migration of slugs (Dimond et al. 1973). Mutations in the structural gene for this lysosomal enzyme affect the extracellular matrix such that it cannot support normal slug migration. Nevertheless, when migration is not insisted on, subsequent differentiations proceed normally.

Two other lysosomal enzymes also accumulate during the first 6 h of development, namely, α-mannosidase and β-glucosidase; however, cells lacking these enzymes due to structural gene mutations develop normally (Free et al. 1976; Dimond and Loomis 1976). Perhaps these gene products serve selectively advantageous roles in the wild, but in the laboratory, they are gratuitous.

F. cAMP Regulation of Transcription and Chemotaxis

Transcription of many of the genes expressed in the early stages of development of *D. discoideum* is regulated by exogenous cAMP signals. Thus, cAMP functions not only as a chemoattractant but also as a regulator of the genes necessary for chemotaxis (Fig. 3). Accumulation of cAMP receptor mRNA is greatly stimulated by pulses of 10^{-9}M cAMP (Klein et al. 1988). In this way cells that first secrete cAMP stimulate surrounding cells to insert a large number of specific receptors in their surface membranes. cAMP also stimulates transcription of the phosphodiesterase gene (Faure et al. 1989).

cAMP stimulates transcription of a gene, *fdgA*, that codes for a Gα2 protein involved in signal transduction once cAMP is bound to the surface of the cell (Kunagai et al. 1989). Gα2 is essential for the relay response of early developing cells, in which cAMP triggers cells to secrete cAMP and thus pass on the signal. It is also involved in the above mentioned transcriptional regulatory mechanisms. Cells in which the *fdgA* gene is partially deleted fail to respond to cAMP, aggregate, or express genes of later developmental stages.

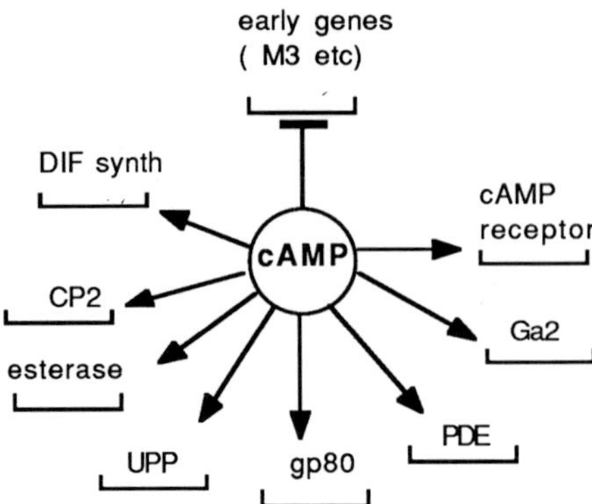

Fig. 3. Transcriptional regulation by cAMP. Pulses of cAMP are generated every 4–6 min during early development when the cells are stimulated by cAMP to synthesize and secrete more cAMP. Cells respond to pulses of cAMP by increasing the transcription of the genes for the cAMP receptor, Gα2, *PDE*, the adhesion glycoprotein gp80, UDP glucose pyrophosphorylase (*UPP*), a serine esterase (D2), a cysteine protease (*CP2*), and by synthesizing the morphogen DIF at an increased rate. Pulses of cyclic AMP also repress a set of early genes such as the one known as *M3*

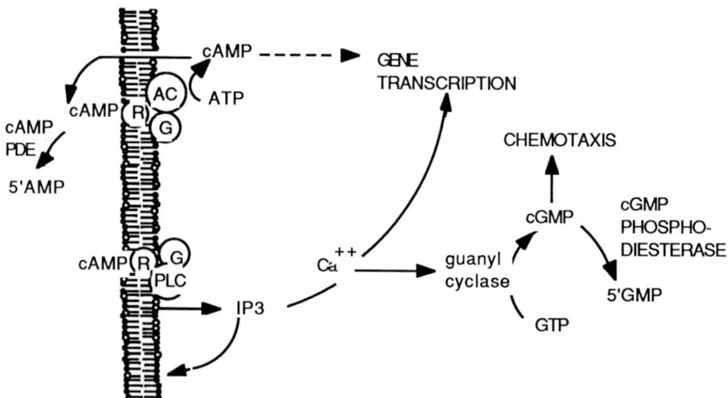

Fig. 4. Transduction of external cAMP signals. Pulses of *cAMP* activate the receptor (*R*) to signal internal events through Gα2 protein (*G*). Adenyl cyclase (*AC*) is activated and synthesizes cAMP at least ten fold more rapidly than in unstimulated cells. Most of the cAMP is secreted where it binds to surface receptors on the same and other cells. Both the external and internal cAMP is degraded to *5'AMP* by a phosphodiesterase (*cAMP-PDE*). Internal cAMP may also activate cAMP-dependent protein kinases along pathways leading to alteration in transcriptional pattern.

The internal levels of inositol phosphates rise rapidly following a pulse of cAMP probably as the result of activation of a phospholipase C (*PLC*). IP_3 triggers release of Ca^{2+} from internal stores. High concentrations of Ca^{2+} further activate PLC and also activate guanyl cyclase such that a spike in the internal concentration of *cGMP* rapidly follows an external pulse of cAMP. Chemotaxis is regulated in part by *cGMP* which is degraded by a specific phophiodiesterase. It is thought that the increase in free calcium may activate proteins involved in transcriptional control

The gene responsible for gp80, the second adhesion protein, is induced by pulses of 10^{-9}M cAMP (Murray et al. 1981, 1983, 1984; Gerisch et al. 1975; Gerisch 1987) as are the genes for UDGP pyrophosphorylase and an esterase (Haribabu et al. 1986; Mann et al. 1988). Expression of these genes is essential for normal development but is not directly involved in the cAMP signaling system.

The mechanisms used by developing cells to respond to cAMP are themselves quite complicated (Fig. 4). Binding of cAMP to the surface receptor activates a G protein coupled to adenyl cyclase such that a burst of cAMP synthesis follows stimulation of the cells. Most of the synthesized cAMP is rapidly secreted to relay the signal, but the transient rise in internal cAMP may be coupled to transcriptional control via cAMP-dependent protein kinases or other pathways. The receptor becomes uncoupled from the G protein shortly after binding cAMP and remains in a desensitized state for about 5 min. Phosphorylation of the receptor followed by slow dephosphorylation parallels the conversion of the receptor to a desensitized form and its return to sensitive state (Janssens and Van Haastert 1987).

The receptor is also coupled to a G protein that activates phospholipase C such that it hydrolyzes phosphatidylinositol in the membrane, releasing phophoinositols and diacylglycerol (DAG). Inositol tris-phosphate, in turn, triggers release of calcium ions from internal stores. Elevated Ca^{2+} stimulates both phospholipase C and guanyl cyclase. The resulting surge in cGMP affects chemotactic movement of the cells. If the cGMP is not broken down by the action of cGMP phosphodiesterase, movement continues for an abnormally long time following stimulation with a pulse of cAMP (Van Haastert et al. 1982).

Pulses of cAMP are also involved in the regulation of several early genes, including M3 and discoidin, that are expressed immediately following the initiation of development (Mann et al. 1988). In this way, the completion of the aggregation stage signals the end of the earliest differentiations. Although the exact pathways to different genes are not yet known, it appears that pulses of exogenous cAMP are transduced along either of two pathways (Fig. 4). The internal concentrations of cAMP, cGMP, DAG, IP_3, and Ca^{++} increase rapidly followng addition of exogenous cAMP, and these internal signals are coupled to the mechanisms that regulate transcription of specific genes (Janssens and Van Haastert 1987).

G. Stage 2: Integration

cAMP pulses generated as the result of differentiations that occurred during the first stage induce genes which are involved in the integration of aggregated cells into multicellular organisms (Fig. 5). An extracellular matrix is secreted that surrounds up to 10^5 cells and excludes late-comers. Synthesis of UDP glucose at this stage is essential to provide the subunits for cellulose and other carbohydrate components of the sheath. Mutations in the structural gene for UDPG pyrophosphorylase (UPP), the enzyme that generates UDPG, block cellulose

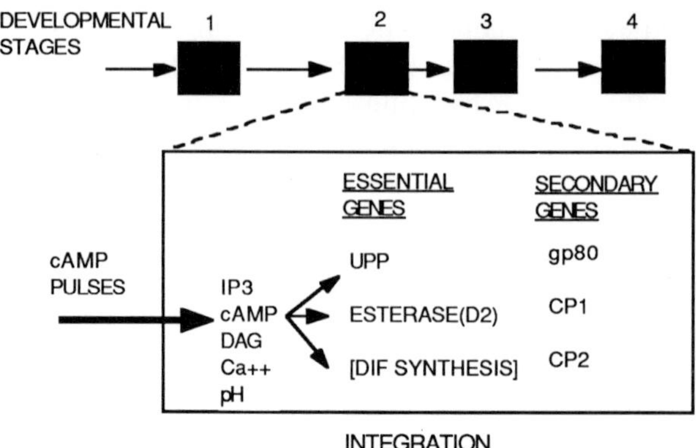

Fig. 5. Stage 2 genes. Changes in the second messages in response to binding of cAMP to the receptors on the surface result in activation of at least 5 genes. The *UPP* gene codes for UDP glucose pyrophosphorylase that generates UDPG. The esterase gene *D2* product is essential for aggregation. Synthesis of the hexanophenone *DIF* is stimulated by cAMP pulses. The *gp80* gene codes for a membrane glycoprotein essential for EDTA-resistant cell-cell adhesion. *CP1* and *CP2* code for related cysteine proteases

synthesis and normal sheath production (Dimond et al. 1976). Strains carrying mutations in UPP are unable to form slugs of the normal size, and the small slugs that do form are unable to migrate. Subsequent biochemical differentiations occur normally but the cells die without forming either spores or stalk cells. UDPG pyrophosphorylase is clearly an essential gene for formation of fruiting bodies, but is not itself an integral part of the central dependent sequence.

Antisense inactivation of another gene, D2, expressed between 6 and 12 h of development has shown that its product is essential for aggregation and integration (Rubino et al. 1989). The gene codes for a serine esterase but its substrate is unknown. Cells in which this gene cannot function aggregate slowly and form loose mounds without integrating into tight aggregates. Although the expression of subsequent genes has not been measured in cells lacking the esterase, the block to morphogenesis resulting from antisense inactivation strongly suggests that this gene plays an essential role in development of *Dictyostelium.*

During this stage, cells first synthesize the hexanophenone, 1-(3,5-dichloro-2,6-dihydroxy-4-methoxyphenyl)-1-hexanone, referred to as DIF due to its role as a *d*ifferentiation *i*nducing *f*actor (Brookman et al. 1982; Morris et al. 1987). It is secreted and is able to induce stalk cell differentiation when present at 10^{-9}M. Although the biosynthethic pathway leading to this compound is not known, mutants have been isolated that do not secrete DIF (Kopachik et al. 1983). These strains are blocked at the aggregation stage unless exogenous DIF is experimentally added. DIF has been directly shown to induce transcription of two prestalk specific genes and to repress several prespore specific genes (Ceccarelli et al. 1987; Williams et al. 1987; Early et al. 1988; Early and Williams 1988). On this basis, synthesis of DIF can be considered an essential process, even though the biosynthetic genes have not been directly measured. By directly assaying DIF production, it has been shown that cAMP and low pH stimulate DIF synthesis (Brookman et al. 1982; Williams et al. 1986; Williams 1988; Kwong and Weeks 1989).

Secondary genes expressed during this stage include the one coding for gp80 and two that code for cysteine proteases, CP1 and CP2. There is direct evidence that gp80 is not essential for subsequent biochemical differentiations or morphogenesis, although it is essential for the formation of full-sized fruiting bodies (Loomis et al. 1985; Gerisch 1987). The cysteine proteases are closely related to each other, and like all the other genes expressed at this stage, are regulated by pulses of cAMP. The signal is transduced from the receptor Gα2 to the pathway that generates IP_3 (Mann et al. 1988). Mutations inactivating CP1 and CP2 have not yet been isolated and, until there is evidence to indicate that they are essential genes, it is best to consider them as secondary genes.

H. Stage 3: Divergence

After 12 h of development, differentiating amoebae start to diverge into prespore and prestalk cells that can be distinguished by differences in the genes they express (Morrissey et al. 1984; Williams 1988). At least 12 gene products have been recognized as newly labelled spots on 2-D gels that are synthesized only in cells destined to become spores, while two gene products, ST430 and ST310, have been found at this stage to be synthesized exclusively in prestalk cells. Three of the prespore proteins, SP96, SP70, and SP60, accumulate in specialized vesicles before being released during culmination to make up the outer layer of spore coats (Orlowski and Loomis 1979; Devine et al. 1983; Erdos and West 1989). Another prespore protein, SP29, is found on the surface of cells and in the extracellular matrix. The genes coding for each of these prespore proteins have been cloned and sequenced (Fosnaugh and Loomis 1989; Early et al. 1988). The prestalk proteins are found in the stalk tube following culmination. The genes coding for these genes have also been cloned and sequenced (Ceccarelli et al. 1987; Williams et al. 1987). Transcription of the genes for these cell-type specific proteins has been shown to be regulated by DIF (Williams et al. 1987; Early and Williams 1988).

Regulation of the prestalk genes coding for ST310, and ST430 (Dd56 and Dd63) could not be shown in wild-type cells, but could be demonstrated in cells of a mutant strain (HM44) in which endogenous production of DIF is blocked (Kopachik et al. 1983; Ceccarelli et al. 1987; Williams et al.1987; Early and Williams 1988). Cells of this strain do not express these genes unless 10^{-9}M DIF is added to the buffer in which they are bathed. The cells were first incubated for 10 h in the presence of 5 mM cAMP and then DIF was added. RNA recognized by the genes coding for ST310 and ST430 accumulated within 4 h under these conditions. Repression of the prespore gene coding for SP29 by DIF was demonstrated by the same techniques. It has been suggested that DIF acts as a morphogen by inducing prestalk specific gene expression and inhibiting prespore differentiation (Williams et al. 1986; Early and Williams 1988). However, the story must be a bit more complicated to account for the observed distribution of DIF in slugs and the regulatory properties of prestalk cells.

Prespore cells are found exclusively in the posterior three-quarters of migrating slugs, while prestalk cells are found predominantly in the anterior quarter. Initially, it was expected that DIF would be found at higher concentrations in the anterior than in the posterior, since that is where prestalk specific differentiations were found. However, extraction of cells taken from various position along the axis of slugs showed that DIF is actually present in two- to threefold higher concentrations in the posterior regions (Fig. 6) (Brookman et al. 1987). Either DIF is not itself the inhibitor of prespore differentiations, or prespore cells are insensitive to it. It is not yet the concensus viewpoint to consider that insensitivity to DIF might be a prespore differentiation, but it can account for the embarassing finding that DIF is present in the

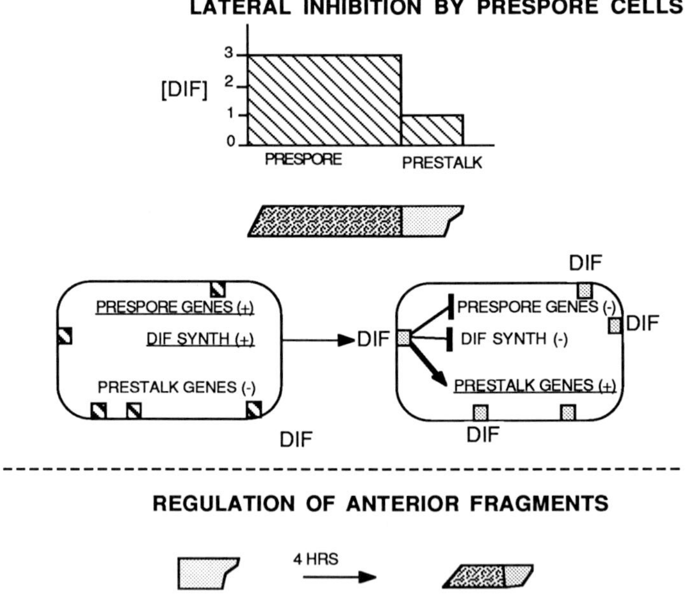

Fig. 6. A model for cell-type proportioning. The measured levels of DIF are two- to threefold higher in posterior fragments of slugs than in anterior fragments, yet cells in the posterior are expressing prespore genes that are repressed by DIF. Moreover, they are not expressing prestalk genes that are induced by DIF. It seems likely that prespore cells are insensitive to DIF. Prestalk cells must be sensitive to DIF and may be kept from becoming insensitive by DIF itself. DIF receptors are indicated by *boxes* that are functional in prestalk cells but inactive in prespore cells (*cross-hatched*). The distribution of DIF along the axis of the slug could be accounted for if only prespore cells produced DIF but all cells participated in the breakdown of DIF. This cell-type specialization for DIF production could also account for the observed regulation of isolated prestalk fragments that give rise to the proper proportion of prespore cells 4 after the original prespore cells are removed

environment of prespore cells at a levels as high or higher than that of prestalk cells (Brookman et al. 1987).

I propose that one of the differentiations that occurs concomitantly with DIF production is loss of sensitivity to DIF. Insensitivity could come about by loss of a surface receptor for DIF, or by uncoupling of the mechanism that transduces the signal from exogenous DIF to the nucleus. Cell type divergence could then be considered as a race between prespore differentiation and the effects of DIF. Cells that had progressed through the first two stages would produce DIF and become insensitive to it, while cells that lagged behind somewhat would be induced by DIF to express prestalk genes and inhibited from expressing the prespore genes. They would also be inhibited from synthesizing DIF or becoming insensitive to it. Under these conditions, DIF will build up to a threshold level when a constant proportion of the cells in the field have differentiated into prespore cells, assuming that all cells participate in its removal. The proportion of prespore cells will be size-invariant as the result of this feedback loop of DIF on DIF production. In fact, the proportion of prespore cells has been found to be invariant in both large and small slugs that differ in total number of cells by a factor of over 100. Size invariance of cell-type proportions is one of the characteristics of regulative developing systems and accepted models must account for it. Another required property of models for regulative systems is that they account for alterations in cell-type proportions following experimental removal of one or more of the original cell-types.

Long ago, Raper (1940) showed that isolated anterior fragments would not form spores if required to undergo terminal differentiation immediately after the posterior cells were removed, but would form spores if anterior fragments were allowed a period of 4–8 h for regulation to occur before being required to undergo terminal differentiation. Conversion of isolated prestalk cells into prespore cells under these conditions has been confirmed using prespore specific antibodies (Sakai 1973). The model in which DIF is produced uniquely by prespore cells and recognized uniquely by prestalk cells not only accounts for the spatial distribution of DIF, but also the regulation of prestalk cells when the source of DIF (prespore cells) is removed. Essentially, the race is started over again following removal of the posterior of a slug, and the number of prespore cells formed among the anterior cells is set at the proper portion for the new smaller slug (Fig 6).

Divergence of cell types in this model is the consequence of a race to DIF insensitivity. Initial inhomogeneities, such as amounts of nutritional stores or position in the cell cycle, could easily affect the running of the race. In fact, it has been found that cells in late G2 of the cell cycle at the start of development preferentially form spores (MacDonald 1984; Weijer et al. 1984; Gomer and Firtel 1987). Likewise, it has been shown that cells with considerable glycogen preferentially form spores when mixed with less well-fed cells (Garrod and Ashworth 1972; Leach et al. 1973). Although these inhomogeneities at the start of development determine to a certain extent which cells will become prespore and which will become prestalk, they are not absolute commitments and the cell types are able to regulate to changes that occur later in development. Nevertheless, we should consider mechanisms that might have give rise to preferential cell-type differentiation as a result of inhomogeneities at the start of development.

McDonald (1984) has shown that cells in early G2 become aggregation competent several hours before cells in late G2. As a consequence, the initial foci of aggregates are preferentially enriched by cells that were in early G2 at the start of development. As an aggregate enlarges, cells of the initial foci will form the central core, which is where the concentration of DIF will first reach threshold levels. Cells that have not yet differentiated along the prespore pathway will be inhibited from becoming insensitive to DIF and will be induced to differentiate into prestalk cells. Thus, we would expect the highest concentration of prestalk cells to be in a central core surrounded by prespore cells. This is exactly what is found when cells high in glycogen and cells low in glycogen are mixed (Tasaka and Takeuchi 1981). The less well fed cells are found preferentially but not exclusively in the middle of aggregates. They are surrounded by cells from the high glycogen population that have accumulated prespore specific antigens. A few hours latter the prestalk cells are found to be grouped at the edge of the aggregate (Tasaka and Takeuchi 1981). If placed on a solid substratum, the prestalk cells will form the anterior of migrating slugs.

The spatial localization of prespore and prestalk cells may be a secondary consequence of cell type divergence. While very few prespore cells are found in the anterior quarter of migrating slugs, prestalk cells are found not only in the anterior quarter but also throughout the posterior of slugs (Sternfeld and David 1982). Prestalk cells found scattered among the prespore cells have been referred to as anterior-like cells, but they appear to be essentially the same as the cells at the anterior (Devine and Loomis 1985). There are about the same number of prestalk cells in the posterior three-quarters of slugs as prestalk cells localized to the anterior quarter. Thus, the spatial separation of cell types is not highly developed in this organism. However, it is striking that the anterior quarter is essentially devoid of prespore cells. Exclusion of prespore cells may result from differential adhesion. If prespore cells adhere to each other more strongly than they do to prestalk cells, they would be expected to sort out. It is also likely that prespore cells adhere to each other more strongly than prestalk cells adhere to each other, since it has been observed that prestalk cells circulate throughout the length of slugs while prespore cells stay in place (Kakutani and Takeuchi 1986; Odell and Bonner 1986; Loomis unpublished results). Perhaps one of the prespore specific differentiations results in a third adhesion mechanism that leads to the observed spatial localization of the cell types.

Prespore specific adhesion could account for sorting out of prestalk cells in spherical aggregates (Tasaka and Takeuchi 1981). Initially, the majority of prestalk cells would be in the interior as the result of inhibitory levels of DIF first appearing there; subsequently, the mass of prestalk cells would be sequeezed to the edge by the surrounding prespore cells that preferentially adhere to each other. Once at an edge, the prestalk mass would migrate to the top of a hemispherical mass supported on a solid substratum as the consequence of greater force being transmitted to the substratum on the side closest to the

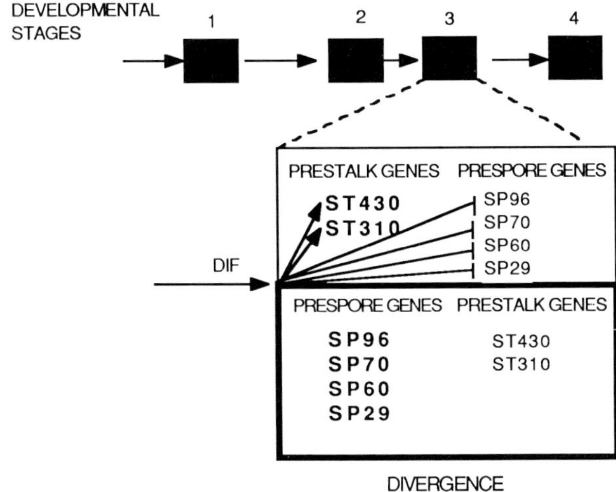

Fig. 7. Stage 3 genes. Prestalk cells that are stimulated by DIF express genes for the stalk tube proteins, *ST430* and *ST310*. Prespore cells express genes for the spore coat proteins, SP96, SP70, SP60, as well as the sheath protein, SP29

substratum. Further movement of the prestalk cells would distend the sheath upwards, generating a tip. In fact, soon after hemispherical aggregates are formed, a tip appears at the top. The tip will lead during slug migration due to its privileged position surrounded by distensible sheath (Loomis 1972).

In molecular terms, differentiations that occur in stage 3 should be considered as the composite of two compartments, the prespore one that is insensitive to DIF, and the prestalk one that is sensitive to DIF (Fig. 7). In the prestalk compartment the genes for ST430 and ST310 are induced and the prespore genes including SP96, SP70, SP60 and SP29 are represented. Cells in the prespore compartment are insensitive to DIF, and so do not express the genes for ST430 or ST310, but do express the spore coat genes. Expression of prespore genes is independent of DIF while expression of prestalk genes is DIF dependent. This is clearly shown in the mutant strain, HM44, that fails to produce DIF itself; prespore genes are expressed but prestalk genes are not (Kopachik et al. 1983). These mutant cells are clearly sensitive to DIF since they respond to exogenous DIF by altering their transcription pattern. It is possible that the mutation in these cells is pleiotropic and not only blocks DIF production, but also blocks the acquisition of DIF insensitivity. It will be interesting to see what gene has been mutated.

I. Stage 4: Culmination

During the last stage, both prepore cells and prestalk cells undergo terminal differentiation and form the final fruiting body. The signal for terminal

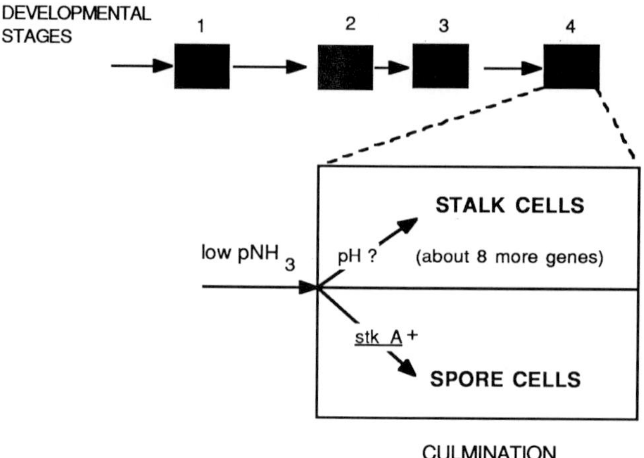

Fig. 8. Stage 4 genes. When the partial pressure of ammonia (pNH_3) decreases, prestalk cells take up water, vacuolize, and secrete cellulose at a high rate. They also express about 8 genes that were not previously expressed. Prespore cells pump out water, encapsulate, and secrete cellulose at a high rate. The *stk*A gene is essential for keeping prespore cells from differentiating into stalk cells

differentiation appears to involve a reduction in the production of ammonia, since culmination can be prematurely induced by removing this gas, while it can be delayed by keeping the pNH_3 high (Schindler and Sussman 1977). Ammonia is given off by the cells as a waste product from the matabolism of amino acids. As development proceeds, the amount of internal stores of proteins used to generate the amino acids decreases, since the cells are not feeding and are burning their reserves. As a consequence, the rate of ammonia production decreases and, when the pNH_3 drops below a threshold level, terminal differentiation is induced (Fig. 8). The decrease in pNH_3 would be expected to result in a decrease in the internal pH, and it may be this that is coupled to gene expression during culmination.

Analysis of newly made proteins separated on 2-D gels has indicated that there are about eight more genes that are expressed exclusively in stalk cells during culmination (Coloma and Lodish 1981; Morrissey et al. 1984). These genes are not expressed in prespore or spore cells. They appear to be repressed in prespore cells by the product of a gene known as stalky, *stk*A. Mutations in this gene, which maps to linkage group II, result in fruiting bodies that are all stalk (Morrissey and Loomis 1981). The prespore cells found in slugs of stalky strains all differentiate into stalk cells, as judged by the massive vacuolization and cellulose deposition characteristic of stalk cells. Moreover, they express the stalk specific genes even though they had previously differentiated as prespose cells (Morrissey et al. 1981). A temperature sensitive mutation in *stk*A has shown that it must function during the last 6 h for normal spore differentiation to proceed (West et al. 1982). It appears that the wild-type product of the *stk*A gene functions during culmination to keep prespore cells from expressing stalk specific genes and undergoing terminal differentiation along the pathway to stalk cells. In formal terms, *stk*A is a homeotic gene since mutations result in the conversion of one tissue type into another. It will be of considerable interest to isolate and determine the primary sequence of this gene.

J. Dependent Sequence

The temporal sequence of differentiations is clocked, gated, and regulated by a cascade of causally related events that include both exogenous signals and internal cellular processes (Fig. 9). The exogenous signals are generated by the cells themselves as they proceed through each development stage. Undifferentiated cells signal their population density by continuously secreting a mass effector(s) that builds up in direct proportion to their density in the environment. There is no prime cause, just exponential growth of the cells. When the mass effector reaches the critical level, all cells respond by initiating development. Similar dependence on mass effectors have been found for development of the bacteria, *Bacillus subtilis* and *Myxococcus xanthus* (Shimkets and Dworkin 1981; Grossman and Losick 1988). Development of metazoan eggs has no such requirement, but terminal differentiation of several mammalian cell types such as that of myoblasts into striated muscle is dependent on population density. Measuring population density by the concentration of secreted molecules appears to be a straightforward way to insure that sufficient cells are in proximity to generate the necessary tissue structures.

During the first stage of development in *Dictyostelium*, genes are activated that are essential for the pulsitile production and secretion of cAMP. Other genes

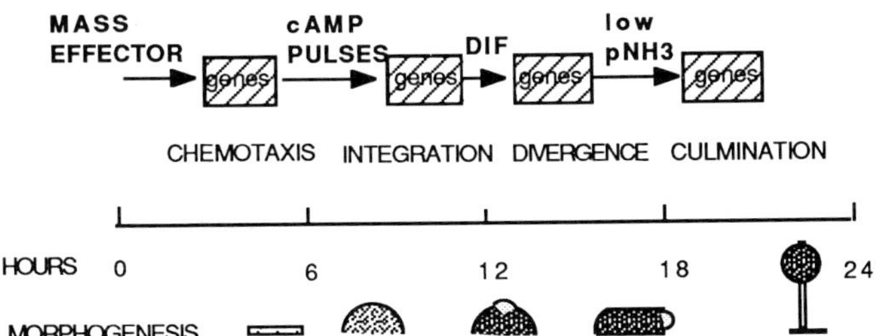

Fig. 9. Dependent sequence of external and internal signals for differentiation. Population density is monitored by the concentration of a mass effector. Above a threshold it induces the genes in stage 1 that are necessary for chemotaxis. Differentiations that occur during stage 1 produce pulses of cAMP that trigger expression of genes in stage 2 that are essential for integration of the cells and subsequent divergence of the cell types. DIF induces prestalk genes and represses prespore genes in 20% of the cells but has no effect on the remaining cells that differentiate into prespore cells. When the ammonia pressure drops, terminal differentiation of the cell types is triggered and culmination results in the formation of fruiting bodies

of the dependent sequence are involved in recognition of cAMP signals and the modulation of cAMP levels. The cAMP receptor is a 44 kd protein with striking similarity of β-adrenergic receptor and bovine rhodopsin (Klein et al. 1988). These proteins all have seven membrane-spanning regions and appear to form a barrel in the membrane. The ability to respond to extracellular signals evolved long before eukaryotes diverged into separate phyla and it is not unexpected that the primary and secondary structures of the receptors should be conserved; it is even possible that components and processes further along the signal transduction pathway may show indications of a common heritage. Antisense inactivation of the cAMP receptor in *Dictyostelium* results in cells that are completely insensitive to exogenous cAMP. Such cells neither aggregate nor express genes characteristic of later stages. However, they do express other genes of the first stage such as the one coding for Gα2 (Devreotes, personnal communication). The product of this gene couples the cAMP receptor to both adenyl cyclase and IP_3 production within the cell. The amino acid sequence of *Dictyostelium* Gα2 protein in 33%, identical to those chickens and mice, indicating not only a common heritage but similarity in function. A mutation that deletes most of the gene results in cells that bind cAMP but do not repond to the signal. Cells lacking Gα2 are also unable to aggregate or express genes characteristic of latter stages. These mutational studies have provided unequivocable evidence that the cAMP receptor and Gα2 genes are essential components of the central dependent pathway of *Dictyostelium* development. The case for other genes expressed during the first stage, such as those for cAMP phosphodiesterase and the early adhesion molecule, gp24, are strong but not quite as fully documented. The evidence that myosin, cGMP phosphodiesterase, and N-acetylglucosaminidase are essential genes is based on the phenotypes of well-characterized null mutations, but the effects of loss of these genes are delayed or surmountable. For these reason they were considered secondary genes of the dependent pathway.

Cells that can respond to pulses of cAMP express genes essential for integration following several rounds of stimulation. Both UDPG pyrophosphorylase and the serine esterase known as D2 are induced by cAMP and play essential roles in the formation of migrating slugs. They are clearly essential genes. The surface glycoprotein, gp80, is essential for the formation of full-sized fruiting bodies, but is not necessary for expression of any later genes (Loomis et al. 1985; Loomis 1988). For this reason it is considered a secondary gene. The production of DIF is stimulated by cAMP pulses and is clearly an essential process for subsequent development, as shown by the phenotype of the strains such as HM44 that cannot produce their own DIF. Cells of these strains aggregate and undergo several of the prespore differentiations, but fail to express prestalk genes unless exogenous DIF is added to the environment. The unusual structure of DIF suggests that specific biosynthetic enzymes accumulate for its production. When the genes coding for these enzymes are recognized, it will be possible to directly show the essential role they play in development.

The mechanism that regulates the proportions of the two cell types that diverge during the third stage is of central interest, since it is likely that similar mechanisms function during divergence of cell types in more complex organisms. DIF clearly plays a role in prestalk differentiations and is a good candidate to also mediate size-invariant proportioning and regulation of proportioning. Since prespore cells are exposed to DIF, yet do not respond to it, they must be insensitive to its repressive effects on prespore differentiations as well as its inductive effects on prestalk genes. In the model I propose, cells still sensitive to DIF are inhibited by threshold levels of DIF from synthesizing DIF themselves, as well as kept from becoming insensitive to it. The two cell types can then be characterized as those that produce DIF, but are insensitive to it (prespore cells) and those that are sensitive to it, but do not produce it (prestalk cells). This is reminiscent of heterothallic yeast in which a given mating type secretes a signal molecule (for example, α factor) but is not sensitive to it because the receptor to that signal is not synthesized; cells of the opposite mating type are sensitive to the signal but do not produce it. The yeast mating factor causes cell cycle arrest and is a specialized case of long-range inhibition. A large number of patterns of differentiation have been interpreted as cases of short-range activation and long-range inhibition (Meinhart 1983). The model I propose for *Dictyostelium* involves long-range inhibition, but insensitivity rather than short-range activation. A similar phenomenon has recently been found in the differentiation of vulval precursor cells in the nematode *Caenorhabditis elegans* (Sternberg 1988). The first cell to differentiate into a vulval precursor in embryos of this species inhibits adjacent cells from following this same fate. However, if the initial cell is killed, adjacent cells take over its function. In *Dictyostelium*, the prespore cells keep prestalk cells from expressing prespore genes. The fact that prestalk cells accumulate preferentially at the anterior may be a secondary consequence of differential adhesion. No matter what the mechanism of cell type divergence and proportioning, the expression of genes during the third stage is undoubtedly essential for fruiting body formation, although this has yet to be shown genetically.

During culmination, stalk cells express a small number of new genes when the pNH_3 decreases to levels where terminal differentiation is induced. Expression of these genes is repressed in prespore cells by the action of the *stk*A gene product. This is an essential gene of the dependent pathway, since mutants lacking is activity die without forming any spores.

If we look at the dependent pathway throughout the development cycle of *Dictyostelium* (Fig. 9), we see that each stage is triggered by a specific signal molecule that reaches threshold at the beginning of the time period. At several positions along the pathway certain genes are essential for production of the molecule that signals progressing to the next stage. Not all the genes within a given stage are expressed at the same time and do not share all regulatory components. Thus, within each stage there are subroutines that control the individual genes. The final result is that the cells follow a temporal program of gene expression that can adapt to a variety of conditions such that the physiology of the cells changes in an orderly and productive manner. Similar sequential inductions appear to determine the stages in terminal differentiation in such vertebrate cells as myoblasts, erthyroblasts, oocytes, and spermatocytes. Perhaps they follow the logic first worked out in *Dictyostelium.*

References

Ashworth J, Quance J (1972) Enzyme synthesis in myxamoebae of the cellular slime mold *Dictyostelium discoideum* during growth in axenic culture. Biochem J 126:601–608

Barklis E, Lodish HF (1983) Regulation of *Dictyostelium discoideum* mRNAs specific for prespore or prestalk cells. Cell 32:1139–1148

Barra J, Barrand P, Blondelet M, Brachet p (1980) *Pds*A, a gene involved in the production of active phosphodiesterase during starvation of *Dictyostelium discoideum* amoebae. Mol Gen Genet 177:607–614

Blumberg D, Margolskee J, Chung S, Barklis E, Cohen N, Lodish H (1982) Specific cell-cell contacts are essential for induction of gene expression during differentiation of *Dictyostelium discoideum.* Proc Natl Acad Sci 79:127–133

Brookman J, Town C, Jermyn K, Kay R (1982) Developmental regulation of a stalk cell differentiation-inducing factor in *Dictyostelium discoideum.* Dev Biol 91:191–196

Brookman J, Jermyn K, Kay R (1987) Nature and distribution of the morphogen DIF in *Dictyostelium* slugs. Development 100:119–124

Burns R, Livi G, Dimond R (1981) Regulation and secretion of early developmentally controlled enzymes during axenic growth in *Dictyostelium discoideum.* Dev Biol 83:407–416

Cardelli JA, Knecht DA, Wunderlich R, Dimond, RL (1985) Major changes in gene expression occur during at least four stages of development of *Dictyostelium discoideum.* Dev Biol 110:147–156

Ceccarelli A, McRobbie S, Jermyn K, Duffy K, Early A, Williams J (1987) Structural and functional characterization of the *Dictyostelium* gene encoding a DIF inducible pre-stalk-enriched mRNA sequence. Nucl Acids Res 15:7463–7476

Chisholm RL, Barklis E, Lodish HF (1984) Mechanism of sequential induction of cell-type specific mRNAs in *Dictyostelium* differentiation. Nature 310:67–69

Clarke M, Kayman S, Riley K (1987) Density-dependent inductor of discoidin-1 synthesis in exponentially growing cells of *Dictyostelium discoideum.* Differentiation 34:79–87

Coloma A, Lodish H (1981) Synthesis of spore-specific and stalk-specific proteins during differentiation of *Dictyostelium discoideum.* Dev Biol 81:238–251

Devine KM, Loomis WF (1985) Molecular characterization of anterior-like cells in *Dictyostelium discoideum.* Dev Biol 109:364–372

Devine KM, Morrissey J, Loomis WF (1982) Differential synthesis of spore coat proteins in prespore and prestalk cells of *Dictyostelium.* Proc Natl Acad Sci USA 79:7361–7365

Devine K, Bergmann J, Loomis WF (1983) The spore coat proteins of *Dictyostelium discoideum* are packaged in prespore vesicles. Dev Biol 99:437–446

Dimond RL, Loomis WF (1976) The structure and function of β-glucosidases in *Dictyostelium discoideum.* J Biol Chem 251:2680–2687

Dimond RL, Brenner M, Loomis WF (1973) Mutations affecting N-acetylglucosaminidase in *Dictyostelium discoideum.* Proc Natl Acad Sci 70:3356–3360

Dimond RL, Farnsworth P, Loomis WF (1976) Isolation and characterization of mutations affecting UDPG pyrophosphorylase in *Dictyostelium discoideum.* Dev Biol 50:169–181

Early A, Williams J (1988) A *Dictyostelium* prespore-specific gene is transcriptionally repressed by DIF in vitro. Development 103:519–524

Early A, Williams J, Meyer H, Por S, Smith E, Williams K, Gooley A (1988) Structural characterization of the *Dictyostelium discoideum* prespore-specific gene D19 and its product, the cell surface glycoprotein PsA. Mol Cell Biol 8:3458–3466

Erdos G, West C (1989) Formation and organization of the spore coat of *Dictyostelium discoideum.* Exp Mycol 13:169–182

Faure M, Podgorski G, Franke J, Kessin R (1989) Rescue of a *Dictyostelium discoideum* mutant defective in cyclic nucleotide phosphodiesterase. Dev Biol 131:366–372

Finney RE, Langtimm CJ, Soll DR (1985) Regulation of protein synthesis during the preaggregative period of *Dictyostelium discoideum* development: involvement of close cell associations and cAMP. Dev Biol 110:171–191

Firtel R (1972) Changes in the expression of single-copy DNA during development of *Dictyostelium discoideum*. J Mol Biol 66:363–377

Fosnaugh C, Loomis WF (1989) The spore coat genes, SP60 and SP70, of *Dictyostelium discoideum*. Mol Cell Biol 9:5215–5218

Free S, Schimke R, Loomis WF (1976) The structural gene for α-mannosidase-1 in *Dictyostelium discoideum*. Genetics 84:159–174

Garrod D, Ashworth J (1972) Effect of growth conditions on development of the cellular slime mould, *Dictyostelium discoideum*. J Embryol Exp Morphol 28:463–479

Gerisch G (1987) Cyclic AMP and other signals controlling cell development and differentiation in *Dictyostelium*. Annu Rev Biochem 56:853–79

Gerisch G, Fromm H, Huesgen A, Wick U (1975) Control of cell contact sites by cyclic AMP pulses in differentiating *Dictyostelium* cells. Nature 255:547–549

Gomer RH, Firtel RA (1987) Cell-autonomous determination of cell-type choice in *Dictyostelium* development by cell-cycle phase. Science 237:758–762

Grabel L, Loomis WF (1977) Cellular interaction regulating early biochemical differentiation in *Dictyostelium*. In: Cappucinelli P (ed) Development and Differentiation in Cellular Slime Molds. Elsevier, Amsterdam, pp 189–199

Grabel L, Loomis WF(1978) Effector controlling accumulation of N-acetylglucosaminidase during development of *Dictyostelium discoideum*. Dev Biol 64:203–209

Grossman A, Losick R (1988) Extracellular control of spore formation in *Bacillus subtilis*. Proc Natl Acad Sci (USA) 85:4369–4375

Haribabu B, Rajkovic A, Dottin R (1986) Cell-cell contact and cAMP regulate the expression of a UDP glucose pyrophosphorylase gene of *Dictyostelium discoideum*. Dev Biol 113:436–442

Ingham P (1988) The molecular genetics of embryonic pattern formation in *Drosophila*. Nature 335:25–34

Janssens P, van Haastert PJM (1987) Molecular basis of transmembrane signal transduction in *Dictyostelium discoideum*. Microbiol Rev 51:396–418

Kakutani T, Takeuchi I (1988) Characterization of anterior-like cells in *Dictyostelium* as analyzed by their movement. Dev Biol 115:439–445

Kimmel A, Firtel R (1982) The organization and expression of the *Dictyostelium* genome. In: Loomis WF (ed) The Development of *Dictyostelium*. Academic Press, San Diego CA.

Klein C (1976) Adenylate cyclase activity in *Dictyostelium discoideum* amoebae and its changes during differentiation, FEBS Lett 68:125–127

Klein C, Brachet P, Darmon M (1977) Periodic changes in adenylate cyclase and cAMP receptors in *Dictyostelium discoideum*. FEBS Lett 76:145–149

Klein P, Sun T, Saxe C, Kimmel A, Johnson R, Devreotes P (1988) A chemoattractant receptor controls development in *Dictyostelium discoideum*. Science 241:1467–1472

Knecht DA, Loomis WF (1987) Antisense RNA inactivation of myosin heavy chain gene expression in *Dictyostelium discoideum*. Science 236:1081–1086

Knecht DA, Loomis WF (1988) Developmental consequences of the lack of myosin heavy chain in *Dictyostelium discoideum*. Dev Biol 128:178–184

Knecht DA, Cohen S, Loomis WF, Lodish HF (1986) Developmental regulation of *Dictyostelium* actin gene fusions carried on low-copy and high copy transformation vectors. Mol Cell Biol 6:3973–3983

Knecht DA, Fuller D, Loomis WF (1987) Surface glycoprotein, gp24, involved in early adhesion of *Dictyostelium discoideum*. Dev Biol 121:277–283

Knecht DA, Fuller D, Loomis WF (1987) Surface glycoprotein, gp24, involved in early adhesion of *Dictyostelium discoideum*. Dev Biol 121:277–283

Kopachik W, Oohata A, Dhokia B, Brookman J, Kay R (1983) *Dictyostelium* mutants lacking DIF, a putative morphogen. Cell 33:397–403

Kumagai A, Pupillo M, Gunderson R, Miake-Lye R, Devreotes P, Firtel R (1989) Regulation and function of $G\alpha$ protein subunits in *Dictyostelium*. Cell 57:265–275

Kwong L, Weeks G (1989) Studies on the accumulation of the Differentiation Inducing Factor (DIF) in high cell density monolayers of *Dictyostelium discoideum*. Dev Biol 132:554–558

Leach C, Ashworth J, Garrod D (1973) Cell sorting out during the differentiation of mixtures of metabolically distinct populations of *Dictyostelium discoideum.* J Embryol Exp Morphol 29:647–661

Loomis WF (1972) Role of surface sheath in the control of morphogenesis in *Dictyostelium discoideum.* Nature 240:6–9

Loomis WF (1975) *Dictyostelium discoideum*: a developmental system. Academic Press, New York

Loomis WF (1977). The number of developmental genes in *Dictyostelium.* Birth Defects 14:497–505

Loomis WF (1982) The Development of *Dictyostelium.* Academic Press, New York

Loomis WF (1985) Regulation of cell-type-specific differentiation in *Dictyostelium.* Cold Spring Harbour Symp Quant Biol 50:769–777

Loomis WF (1987) Genetic tools for *Dictyostelium discoideum.* Methods Cell Biol 28:31–65

Loomis WF (1988) Cell-cell adhesion in *Dictyostelium discoideum.* Dev Gen 9:549–559

Loomis WF, White S, Dimond RL (1976) A sequence of dependent stages in development of *Dictyostelium discoideum.* Dev Biol 53:171–177

Loomis WF, Klein C, Brachet P (1978) The effect of divalent cations on aggregation of *Dictyostelium discoideum.* Differentiation 12:83–89

Loomis WF, Wheeler SA, Springer W, Barondes S (1985) Adhesion mutants of *Dictyostelium discoideum* lacking the saccharide determinant recognized by two adhesion blocking monoclonal antibodies. Dev Biol 109:111–117

Loomis WF, Knecht D, Fuller D (1987) Adhesion mechanisms and multicellular control of cell-type divergence of *Dictyostelium discoideum.* UCLA Symp Mol Cell Biol 51:399–349

Mann S, Pinko C, Firtel R (1988) cAMP regulation of early gene expression in signal transduction mutants of *Dictyostelium.* Dev Biol 130:294–303

Marin F (1976) Regulation of development in *Dictyostelium discoideum.* Part 1 Initiation of the growth to development transition by amino-acid starvation. Dev Biol 48:110–117

Marin F (1977) Regulation of development in *Dictyostelium discoideum.* Part 2 Regulation of early cell differentiation by amino-acid starvation and inter-cellular interaction. Dev Biol 60:389–395

McDonald SA (1984) Cell-cycle regulation of center initiation in *Dictyostelium discoideum.* Dev Biol 117:546–549

Mehdy MC, Firtel RA (1983) A secreted factor and cycle AMP jointly regulate cell-type-specific gene expression in *Dictyostelium discoideum.* Mol Cell Biol 5:705–713

Mehdy MC, Ratner D, Firtel RA (1983) Induction and modulation of cell-type-specific gene expression in *Dictyostelium.* Cell 32:763–771

Meinhardt H (1983) A model for the prestalk/prespore patterning in the slug of the slime mold *Dictyostelium discoideum.* Differentiation 24:191–202

Morris H, Taylor G, Masento M, Jermyn K, Kay R (1987) Chemical structure of the morphogen differentiation inducing factor from *Dictyostelium discoideum.* Nature 328:811–814

Morrissey J, Loomis WF (1981) Parasexual genetic analysis of cell proportioning mutants of *Dictyostelium discoideum.* Genetics 99:183–196

Morrissey J, Farnsworth P, Loomis WF (1981) Pattern formation in *Dictyostelium discoideum*: an analysis of mutants altered in cell proportioning. Dev Biol 83:1–8

Morrissey J, Devine K, Loomis WF (1984) The timing of cell type specific differentiation in *Dictyostelium discoideum.* Dev Biol 103:414–424

Murray B, Yee L, Loomis WF (1981) Immunological analysis of a glycoprotein (contact sites A) involved in intercellular adhesion of *Dictyostelium discoideum.* Supramol Struct Cell Biochem 17:387–401

Murray B, Niman H, Loomis WF (1983) A monoclonal antibody recognizing gp80, a membrane glycoprotein implicated in intercellular adhesion of *Dictyostelium discoideum.* Mol Cell Biol 3:863–870

Murray BA, Wheeler S, Jongens T, Loomis WF (1984). Mutations affecting a surface glycoprotein, gp80, of *Dictyostelium discoideum.* Mol Cell Biol 4:514–519

Nellen W, Silan C, Firtel RA (1984) DNA-mediated transformation in *Dictyostelium discoideum*: regulated expression of an actin fusion. Mol Cell Biol 4:2890–2898

Odell G, Boner J (1986) How the *Dictyostelium discoideum* grex crawls. Philos Trans R Soc Lon Sec B 312:487–525
Orlowski M, Loomis WF (1979) Plasma membrane proteins of *Dictyostelium*: the spore coat proteins. Dev Biol 71:297–307
Peters D, Knecht DA, Loomis WF, DeLozanne A, Spudich J, Van Haasert PJM (1988) Transmembrane signal transduction, chemotaxis and cell aggregation in *Dictyostelium discoideum* cells without myosin heavy chain. Dev Biol 128:158–163
Raper K (1935) *Dictyostelium discoideum*, a new species of slime mold from decaying forest leaves. J Agric Res 50:135–147
Raper K (1940) Pseudoplasmodium formation and organization in *Dictyostelium discoideum*. J Elisha Mitchell Sci Soc 56:241–287
Ratner D, Borth W (1983) Comparison of differentiating *Dictyostelium discoideum* cell types separated by an improved method of density gradient centrifugation. Exp Cell Res 143:1–13
Roos W, Scheidegger C, Gerisch G (1976) Adenylate cyclase activity oscillations as signals for cell aggregation in *Dictyostelium discoideum*. Nature 226:259–261
Rubino S, Mann S, Hori R, Pinko C, Firtel R (1989) Molecular analysis of a developmentally regulated gene required for *Dictyostelium* aggregation. Dev Biol 131:27–36
Sakai Y (1973) Cell type conversion in isolated prestalk and prespore fragments of the cellular slime mold *Dictyostelium discoideum*. Dev Growth Differ 15:11–19
Schindler J, Sussman M (1977) Ammonia determines the choice of morphogenetic pathways in *Dictyostelium discoideum*. J Mol Biol 116:161–170
Shimkets L, Dworkin M (1981) Excreted adenosine is a cell density signal for the initiation of fruiting body formation in *Myxococcus xanthus*. Dev Biol 84:51–60
Siu CH, Lerner R, Ma G, Firtel R, Loomis WF (1976) Developmentally regulated proteins of the plasma membrane of *Dictyostelium discoideum*. The carbohydrate-binding protein. J Mol Biol 100:157–178
Spudich J (1987) *Dictyostelium discoideum*: molecular approaches to call biology. Methods Cell Biol 28:1–516
Sternberg P (1988) Lateral inhibition during vulval induction in *Caenorhabditis elegans*. Nature 335:551–554
Sternfeld J, David CN (1982) Fate and regulation of anterior-like cells in *Dictyostelium* slugs. Dev Biol 93:111–118
Sussman M (1987) Cultivation and synchronous morphogenesis of *Dictyostelium* under controlled experimental conditions. Methods Cell Biol 28:9–29
Sussman R, Sussman M (1953) Cellular differentiation in *Dictyosteliaceae*: heritable modifications of the developmental pattern. Ann NY Acad Sci 56:949–960
Tasaka M, Takeuchi I (1981) Role of cell sorting in pattern formation in *Dictyostelium discoideum*. Differentiation 18:191–196
Van Haastert P, van Lookern Campagne M, Roos F (1982) Altered cGMP-phosphodiesterase activity in chemotactic mutants of *Dictyostelium discoideum*. FEBS Lett 147:149–152
Weijer CJ, Duschl G, David CN (1984) Dependence of cell-type proportioning and sorting on cell cycle phase in *Dictyostelium discoideum*. J Cell Sci 70:133–145
Wessels D, Soll DR, Knecht DA, Loomis WF, DeLozanne A, Spudich J (1988) Cell motility and chemotaxis in *Dictyostelium* amoebae lacking myosin heavy chain. Dev Biol 128:164–177
West C, Lubniewski A, Gregg J, Newton B (1982) A temperature-dependent choice in cell differentiation. Differentiation 23:91–102
Williams J (1988) The role of diffusible molecules in regulating the cellular differentiation of *Dictyostelium discoideum*. Development 103:1–16
Williams J, Pears C, Jermyn K, Driscoll D, Mahbubani H, Kay R (1986) The control of gene expression during cellular differentiation of *Dictyostelium discoideum*. In: Booth I, Higgins C (eds) Symp Soc Microbiol. Cambridge University Press, pp 277–298
Williams J, Ceccarelli A, McRobbie S, Mahbubani H, Kay R, Berks A, Jermyn K (1987) Direct induction of *Dictyostelium* prestalk gene expression by DIF provides evidence that DIF is a morphogen. Cell 49:185–192

Subject Index